TEXTILES

TEXTILES

SECOND EDITION

by Norma Hollen
and Jane Saddler
IOWA STATE UNIVERSITY

drawings by Harriet Allen
IOWA STATE UNIVERSITY

photography by Lou Facto
IOWA STATE UNIVERSITY

THE MACMILLAN COMPANY, NEW YORK
COLLIER-MACMILLAN LIMITED, LONDON

First Printing

Some of section on fabrics © 1952 by Norma Hollen and Jane Saddler in *Modern Textiles.*

Library of Congress catalog card number: 62–8155

The Macmillan Company, New York
Collier-Macmillan Canada, Ltd., Toronto, Ontario

Printed in the United States of America

PREFACE

This book has been written for a first college course in textiles. Concepts, principles, and facts about fibers, yarns, fabric constructions, and finishes are presented in technical terms. An explanation of physical and chemical terminology is given so that chemistry need not be a prerequisite for understanding the text.

The primary objective is to give enough information about fabrics so the student can intelligently select and care for textile products. Illustrations, written and visual, relate to both apparel and household textiles, but the text is not oriented to specific end-uses, since textile principles can be applied to any end-use. We hope both students and teachers will be able to make these applications.

A good overview of the textile industry is included so that students will understand production as well as consumer problems and will have a greater appreciation for past developments as well as a broad concept of future possibilities in the field.

Textiles is a rapidly changing field. It is impossible for one to "keep up-to-date" without reading about, experimenting with, and evaluating new products as they come on the market. So that new developments can be related to or classified with the basic understandings learned in a textile course, much emphasis has been placed on classification of information.

Fibers are organized according to the Textile Fiber Products Identification Act of 1960. Fiber blends are discussed. New yarn developments as well as traditional spinning techniques are included, with emphasis on yarn properties. Basic fabrics are discussed in the unit on fabric constructions; other fabrics are described in the Glossary. New developments in finishing are presented with the emphasis on the effect produced.

There is little repetition in the text, but facts, concepts, and principles are interrelated, so that it is necessary to recall or refer to other sections when studying. The book is cross-indexed for easy reference.

In studying textiles, students must handle and examine fabrics. It is usually the teacher's

v

responsibility to select and prepare the fabrics. We have found that cutting or tearing fabrics into strips, stacking them in units, stapling at intervals, and cutting between staples is an easy way to prepare swatches. (*See* Fig. 1:1.)

We wish to express our appreciation to Mrs. Harriet Lewis for her constructive criti-cism and valuable suggestions and to the students at Iowa State University, for whom the first book was written and by whom we have been guided in testing the effectiveness of this revision.

Norma Hollen
Jane Saddler

Fig. 1:1. An easy way to prepare fabric swatches.

TABLE OF CONTENTS

TEXTILES

Introduction

The study of textiles is concerned with fabrics and the materials from which they are made.

Fabrics include apparel or clothing items; household fabrics such as carpets, upholstery, sheets, etc.; and industrial fabrics such as conveyor belts, tire cord, bagging, and so forth. Apparel fabrics are used for protection from the elements, for beauty, and possibly as status symbols.

Consumers want different properties in fabrics depending on the end-use of the textile. It is desirable for lingerie to have smoothness, softness, elasticity, absorbency, and easy-care as well as beauty; while for a dance dress beauty may be the only important property desired.

Different consumers want different properties for the same end-use. One person may place a high value on easy-care and will only buy blouses that can be washed, dried, and worn without ironing; another person who likes crisp smooth textures will willingly give more time and energy in caring for her blouses.

Everyone should know something about textiles, but the homemaker perhaps should know more since the selection and care of textiles for the family is primarily her responsibility.

One thing is true of all fabrics. The performance and care required are determined by a combination of factors, namely, the fiber content, the yarn structure, the method of construction, and the fabric finish.

Labeling

Labeling is done to help the consumer make satisfactory fabric choices, but no labeling can supply all of the facts about fabrics. Informative labeling is essential to indicate color performance, stability in fabrics, and possibly how to care for textiles. The care required is usually based on the kind of dye used or on the heat-sensitivity of the fiber. The labeling of textiles cannot tell the entire story of the fabric, or of the expected performance, nor will it ever take the place of a body of knowledge about textiles built up over a lifetime of experience and study. The consumer needs to be alert to recent changes in fibers, yarns, fabrics, and finishes, and to relate these developments to the basic information she already has. Above all she must know her own values relative to use and care of textiles.

Apparel and household textiles are labeled to identify the product, to aid the retailer in selling his product, and to aid the consumer in making an intelligent selection from among the many possibilities.

Trademarks, trade names, or brand names identify the goods of a particular manufacturer. These names are registered with the U.S. Patent Office.

Textile legislation has been enacted to protect the consumer from unsafe apparel fabrics and to inform the consumer of the kind of fiber in the fabric. The laws are:

1939 Wool Products Labeling Act.
1951 Fur Products Labeling Act.
1953 Flammable Fabrics Act.
1960 Textile Fiber Products Identi-
    fication Act.

Trade Practice Rules are rules and regulations prepared by representatives of a particular industry under the auspices of the Federal Trade Commission. The F.T.C. may bring complaints against persons violating the Trade Practice Rules.

Standards are important to the manufacturer, to buyers for cutting trades, to the retail market, to institutions, and also to consumers. "A standard for any end-use item should be based on the test and evaluational results which, in the experience of store or commercial technicians, may be expected to indicate a quality that will be relatively free from consumer complaints." [1]

[1] Labarth, Dr. Jules, in Press, J. J., ed., *Man-Made Textiles Encyclopedia* (New York: Textile Book Publishers, 1959), p. 667.

Standards for textiles have been developed in the last forty years. In the early 1920's quality control laboratories were started in the mail order houses and by a few large department stores. The primary purpose of such laboratories is to test merchandise before the store orders it in large quantities. The store will often order to fit its own specifications basic items like sheets, towels, underwear, and work clothes, which are not greatly influenced by fashion. Commercial testing laboratories were also started during the early 1920's.

The manufacturers of man-made fibers realized that some sort of standards were needed for their fibers to achieve acceptability as quality merchandise. The American Viscose Corporation established the Crown Tested Plan in which manufacturers were granted the privilege of using the Crown Tested label on their merchandise if it met certain minimum specifications set up by the American Viscose Corporation. The advantages of this plan were three-fold: to the rayon company, it meant that their fiber would be used as it was intended; to the fabric manufacturer, it meant that he would profit from promotional advertising paid for by the American Viscose Corporation; and to the consumer, it gave assurance that fabrics so labeled would give certain satisfactions. The Crown Tested Plan led to the development of the American Standard Minimum Requirements for Rayon and Acetate Fabrics, L-22, by the American Standards Association in 1952.

American Standards are voluntary standards formulated by a committee made up of representatives of all interested groups. The standard is then voted on by a Standards Board and various Review Boards. The standards are developed slowly because of the number of people involved. In 1960 the American Standards L-22 were revised to include all fiber fabrics in seventy-five end-uses in apparel and home furnishings. The American Standards L-22 provides for identification of textile items relative to care with minimum information on sewn-in labels. Using the American Standards intelligently calls for the education of the consumer. Through purchases, refusal to purchase, or justifiable complaints, the consumer can exercise a decided influence on the retailer, who in turn influences the textile market.

In 1920 the existence of a two-year cycle in the textile industry was first observed.[2] This cycle begins at the retail level and is brought about by alternating waves of retailers' optimism and pessimism. A retailer's experience of short supplies one year will be followed by over-purchasing the following year and vice versa. The effect of the retailer's attitude is said to be great, since an increase or decline in orders will have a magnified effect when transmitted back to the garment cutting and mill levels.

Everyone is a customer of the textile industry. In 1960, each person in the United States used an average of seventy-five yards of cloth, while in other parts of the world as little as six to twelve yards per person were used. Today consumers have a choice of twenty different kinds of fibers used in numerous yarn and fabric constructions which have a variety of finishes.

United States mill consumption of textile fibers for 1959 and 1960 is shown in the chart below.[3]

Fiber	Million Lbs.		%	
	1959	*1960*	*1959*	*1960*
Raw cotton	4,354	4,203.2	64.0%	64.8%
Raw wool	445	404.2	6.5%	6.2%
Raw silk	6.4	6.9	0.1%	0.1%
Man-made	1,996.7	1,877.0	29.4%	28.9%
Total	6,802.1	6,491.3	100.0%	100.0%

Textile fiber consumption, however, cannot be accurately measured in absolute pounds, especially when comparing one fiber with another. The term Utility Poundage was originated by the Textile Economics Bureau to express a more accurate estimate based on:

[2] *Textile Organon*, **30**:56 (Apr. 1959).
[3] Compiled from *Textile Organon*, **31**:50 (Mar. 1960).

(1) Widely differing spinning losses involved in processing the various fibers. The average spinning loss is given below.

Cotton	9%
Wool	5%
Silk	23%
Man-made	
filament	1.5%
staple	4%

(2) The relative weight of fabrics made of different fibers. The average number of square yards of fabric that can be made from one pound of fiber is given below.

Cotton	3.5 sq. yd.
Wool	2 sq. yd.
Silk	5.5 sq. yd.
Rayon and acetate	2 sq. yd.
Non-cellulosic	7 sq. yd.

This indicates that the covering power varies widely.

(3) The wear life of the finished product. This is an important aspect and includes appearance life as well as durability. Changes in style may result in garments being discarded before they are worn out.

The chart below gives the Utility Poundage for 1959.[4]

Fiber	Million Lbs.	%
Cotton	3,962.1	56.0%
Wool	422.7	6.0%
Silk	4.9	0.1%
Man-made	2,674.8	37.9%
Total	7,064.5	100.0%

[4] Compiled from *Textile Organon*, **31**:50 (Mar. 1960).

I. TEXTILE FIBERS

GENERAL DISCUSSION

Fibers are the fundamental units used in the making of textile yarns and fabrics. All fibers have advantages and disadvantages, or good and poor characteristics. There is no perfect fiber. No fiber can possess all the desirable characteristics; for instance, it cannot be soft and stiff at the same time.

Until the twentieth century, all fibers were obtained from natural sources. The commonly used fibers were flax, wool, silk, and cotton. Wool and flax were most widely used prior to the Industrial Revolution, because they were easy to spin and were quite plentiful. Cotton was difficult to spin by hand because of its short length. Silk has always been expensive because of the labor involved in its production. When spinning and weaving became power operations, cotton became the most widely used textile fiber, a position it holds today.

In the last sixty years, more than sixteen different kinds and many types of man-made fibers have been introduced.

A fiber to be spinnable must have sufficient length, pliability, strength, and cohesiveness to form a yarn. Milkweed and kapok are examples of fibers that are too brittle to spin into yarns. Extremely long fibers or filaments need not be cohesive since the fibers are not spun into yarn in the conventional way. Fibers must also be inexpensive, available, and constant in supply to be economically suitable for use.

All fibers are alike in that their length is much greater than their diameter. They are made of long molecule chains called polymers.

Natural fibers are subject to *lack of uniformity* due to weather conditions, nutrition or soil fertility, and disease. They vary in quality for the above reasons and because they are produced in several varieties and breeds. Supima cotton and Merino wool are examples of good quality fibers.

Man-made fibers are more uniform in size

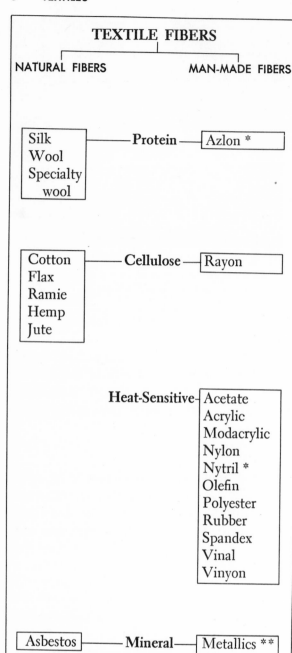

TEXTILE FIBERS

NATURAL FIBERS   MAN-MADE FIBERS

Silk
Wool   **Protein** —— | Azlon * |
Specialty
   wool

Cotton
Flax   **Cellulose** —— | Rayon |
Ramie
Hemp
Jute

Heat-Sensitive — Acetate
Acrylic
Modacrylic
Nylon
Nytril *
Olefin
Polyester
Rubber
Spandex
Vinal
Vinyon

| Asbestos | —— **Mineral** —— | Metallics ** |
Glass

NOTE: The man-made fiber names listed are the *generic* fiber family names established by the Federal Trade Commission. These names are required by the Textile Fiber Products Identification Act to be present on the label.

* These fibers are no longer made in the United States.

** These fibers are discussed in the section on yarns.

and quality because it is possible to control the entire production process. The production process can be varied or modified to make different types of fibers.

Proper yarn and fabric construction can be used to minimize some fiber weaknesses, and finishes can be employed to improve the appearance, texture, and performance of the fibers, yarns, and fabrics.

FIBER STRUCTURE

Fibers differ from one another in physical structure and chemical composition.

Physical Structure

Physical structure includes length, diameter, surface contour, crimp, cross-sectional shape, and molecular arrangement.

FIBER LENGTH

Fibers are obtained from the producer in the following forms.

Filament	*Staple*
Monofilament	Natural
Multifilament	Man-made staple
	Filament tow (made into spun yarns)

Filaments

Filaments are long continuous strands measured in yards. Silk is the only natural filament fiber. All man-made fibers are extruded from the spinneret as filaments, but some are reduced to staple and used in that form only, while others are used as both filament and staple. Yarns made from filaments are of two types: multifilament and monofilament.

Fig. 1:2. Types of filament fiber yarns. A. Multifilament yarn. B. Monofilament yarn. (Courtesy of E. I. du Pont de Nemours & Company.)

Fig. 1:3. Staple from man-made fibers after the uniformly cut lengths have been fluffed. (Courtesy of E. I. du Pont de Nemours & Company.)

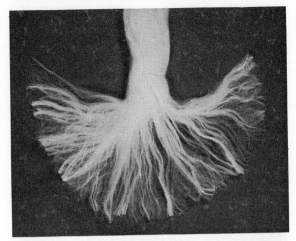

Fig. 1:4. Section of filament tow or rope, showing the thousands of filaments from which it is made. (Courtesy of E. I. du Pont de Nemours & Company.)

Multifilament yarns are made of a number of tiny filaments twisted together. The size and number of the filaments may vary. Yarns of this type give pleasant surface texture, softness, luster, and luxurious drape. They are used in blouses, lingerie, and silk-type dresses. (*See* A, Fig. 1:2.)

Monofilament yarns are composed of a single solid strand of great strength and smoothness. Very sheer hoisery is made from very fine monofilaments. Sheer blouses, veils, and gowns are other examples of monofilament use. Large monofilaments are used in car seat-covers, screenings, webbing for furniture, and similar materials. (*See* B, Fig. 1:2.)

Staple Fibers

All staple fibers, either natural or man-made, are short in length and are measured in inches. They range from three-quarters of an inch to fifteen inches in length. (*See* Fig. 1:3, showing staple fibers.)

The meaning of the word "staple" has changed through the centuries. It was first used in the fourteenth century as a descriptive term for merchandise to which certain towns had exclusive rights. Later it came to mean basic commodities in a particular line of business. Still later, it was used to express the length of wool and cotton fibers. During World War I, Germany began the practice of cutting "artificial silk" into short lengths for use in cotton- and wool-type fabrics as there was a shortage of these fibers. The word "staple" was applied to these cut fibers and is now the standard name for any fiber of a length expressed in inches. All of the natural fibers except silk are staple.

Filament Tow

Filament tow is a collection of many parallel filaments without twist which are grouped together in rope form. (*See* Fig. 1:4.) *Light tow* of 500 to 5000 denier is made into staple fibers for spun yarn by the direct spinner (page 111). *Heavy tow* of 15,000 to 500,000 denier is made into staple fiber by the tow-to-top direct spinning system described on page 112. Filament tow may also be cut as it leaves the spinning machine and baled for shipment to a yarn spinning mill. Several different lengths of cut-staple are shown in Figure 1:5, page 8.

Man-made filament and staple are spun by different equipment, often in different factories, because of the difference in number of holes needed in the spinnerets.

FIBER DIAMETER

The finer the diameter of a fiber, the more pliable it is and the softer it feels. The thicker the fiber, the more body and stiffness it has.

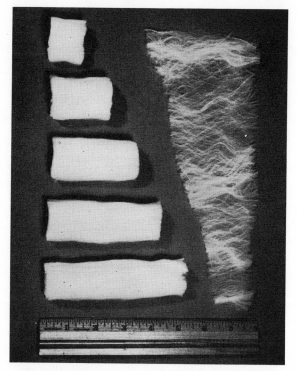

Fig. 1:5. Filament rope or tow cut into uniform lengths as required by the ultimate use in fabrics and garments. (Courtesy of E. I. du Pont de Nemours & Company.)

In natural fibers, fineness is a major factor in determining quality. It is measured in *microns*. (A micron is 1/1000 of a millimeter.)

Diameter Range for Natural Fibers

Cotton	16 to 20 microns
Flax	12 to 16 microns
Wool	10 to 70 microns
Silk	11 to 12 microns

The diameter of man-made fibers is determined according to end-use. It is controlled by the size of the spinneret holes and by stretching during or after spinning. The fineness of man-made fibers is measured in *denier*. For any fiber, the higher the denier or micron number, the coarser the fiber.

SURFACE CONTOUR

Surface contour refers to the surface of the fiber along its shaft.

Natural fibers grow in certain shapes and are *not uniform* throughout their length. Man-made fibers, within certain limitations, can be made in any desired shape. They can be exactly the same diameter throughout, or they can be made thick-and-thin by varying the pressure during spinning, by intermittent drawing of the fibers during or after spinning. Uniform fibers make uniform yarns; thick-and-thin fibers contribute to texture in fabrics.

Fiber shape is determined by end-use. For blending with natural fibers, man-made fibers are made as nearly as possible like the fibers with which they are to be blended.

Wool is the only fiber which has a broken surface caused by overlapping sections like fish scales or shingles. No man-made fiber has yet been produced with anything other than a smooth unbroken surface. The surface of some man-made fibers is serrated, lobed or has indentations caused by the evaporation of the solvent after spinning. When viewed under the microscope, these indentations in the surface cause shadows which are sometimes referred to as "false lumen" because they look like cotton, which has a real lumen. The many shadows from serrated fibers are called "lengthwise striations."

CROSS-SECTIONAL SHAPE

The cross-sectional shape of a fiber is important because it contributes to the surface appearance of the fiber. It helps give properties of luster, bulk, and body to the fibers, yarns, and fabrics. And it helps determine the *hand* or feel of a fabric. Figure 1:6 shows typical cross-sections.

Circular shape is achieved by extruding the spinning solution through circular holes, by melt spinning, or by stretching while wet or plastic. These fibers make compact rather than spongy yarns. Circular cross-sections with serrated edges result from shrinkage of the fiber in the coagulating bath during wet spinning. Many serrations give high luster.

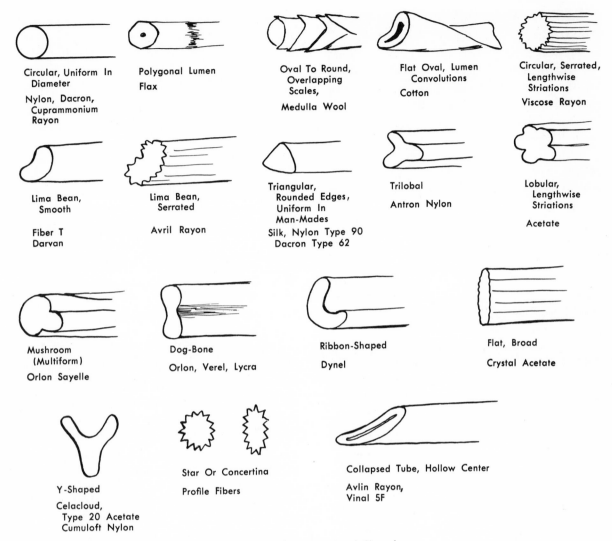

Circular, Uniform In Diameter

Nylon, Dacron, Cuprammonium Rayon

Polygonal Lumen

Flax

Oval To Round, Overlapping Scales,

Medulla Wool

Flat Oval, Lumen Convolutions

Cotton

Circular, Serrated, Lengthwise Striations

Viscose Rayon

Lima Bean, Smooth

Fiber T Darvan

Lima Bean, Serrated

Avril Rayon

Triangular, Rounded Edges, Uniform In Man-Mades

Silk, Nylon Type 90 Dacron Type 62

Trilobal

Antron Nylon

Lobular, Lengthwise Striations

Acetate

Mushroom (Multiform)

Orlon Sayelle

Dog-Bone

Orlon, Verel, Lycra

Ribbon-Shaped

Dynel

Flat, Broad

Crystal Acetate

Y-Shaped

Celacloud, Type 20 Acetate Cumuloft Nylon

Star Or Concertina

Profile Fibers

Collapsed Tube, Hollow Center

Avlin Rayon, Vinal 5F

Fig. 1:6. Typical cross-sectional fiber shapes.

Polygonal shape is found only in flax. It gives luster to the fiber.

Oval shape also gives good cover and a pleasing hand that is neither silky nor harsh.

Triangular shape occurs in silk and has been achieved in some of the new man-made fibers by using a highly viscous solution, melt spinning through triangular holes, but not stretching after spinning. This shape gives better cover, has a soft luster, and a smooth silky feel.

Lobular or multiform shape probably results from evaporation of the solvent during dry spinning. It gives a good hand.

Dog-bone or *dumbbell shape* in staple form makes woolen-like yarns and fabrics.

Flat ribbon-like shape gives good cover and a crisp hand. Wild silk is somewhat this shape. Man-made fibers of this shape are used for crisp lustrous fabrics and imitation straw. The spinning solution is forced out through slits in the spinneret rather than through holes. Cellular rayon, a collapsed tube-like fiber of this shape, is very pliable and when blended with other fibers it entwines around them, restricting their movement and increasing firmness.

Y-shaped cross-section gives excellent cover and bulk. It is used for stuffing where warmth without weight is desired. In a fine denier fiber for clothing, it imparts a sparkling luster.

Hollow center fibers give buoyancy. They are seldom used in clothing but are excellent for life jackets. They are made by emulsifying air in the spinning solution or from gas bubbles formed when in contact with the coagulating bath.

Other fiber shapes are possible and if a new shape will give a plus value to a fiber, it may well be that in the future each man-made fiber will be available in a variety of shapes.

CRIMP

Crimp refers to the waves or bends that occur along the length of a fiber. Fiber crimp should not be confused with weave crimp which results from the interlacing of yarns in a fabric, nor with molecular crimp which results from the way fiber chains are built up.

Fiber crimp increases cohesiveness, resiliency, resistance to abrasion, and gives increased bulk to fabrics. It helps fabrics maintain their loft or thickness, increases absorbency and warmth, but reduces luster.

A fiber may have one of three kinds of crimp, namely, mechanical crimp, natural or inherent crimp, and latent or chemical crimp.

Mechanical Crimp

Mechanical crimp is imparted to fibers by passing them between fluted rollers to produce a two-dimensional wave. The bends in mechanical crimp are usually angular in contrast to the rounded waves of a natural crimp. If heated rollers are used, the crimp will be permanent in all heat-sensitive fibers.

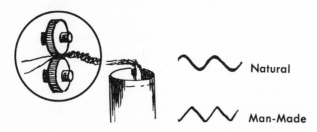

Fig. 1:7. Mechanical crimping gears.

Natural or Inherent Crimp

Natural or inherent crimp occurs in cotton and wool. Cotton has a two-dimensional twist called convolutions. (*See* page 38.) Wool has three-dimensional crimp. (*See* page 27.)

Latent or Chemical Crimp

Latent or chemical crimp exists in the fiber in an undeveloped state until the finished garment is immersed in a suitable solution to develop it. As the fiber becomes wet, it coils and curls. Some of the man-made rayons, acetates, and Orlons possess latent crimp properties. They are discussed in detail in the individual fiber sections.

MOLECULAR ARRANGEMENT

The way the molecules in a fiber are joined together and the length of the molecule chain help determine fiber properties such as strength, absorbency, extensibility or elongation, elasticity, resiliency, pliability, chemical stability, and to some extent, hand and luster.

Fibers are made up of long straight-chain molecules called *linear polymers*. The arrangement of molecules in a fiber resembles the arrangement of fibers in a yarn. The molecules may be parallel to the fiber axis, at right angles to the fiber axis, or spiral as they are in cotton and flax.

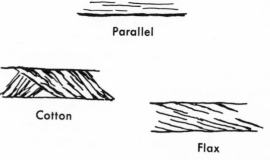

Fig. 1:8. Alignment of molecules relative to the fiber axis.

The alignment of molecules relative to the fiber axis is called *molecular orientation*. If most of the molecules are parallel to the fiber axis, the fiber is highly *crystalline*. If the arrangement is not orderly and regular, the fiber is *amorphous*.

Crystalline   Amorphous   Crystalline

Fig. 1:9. Crystalline and amorphous molecule arrangements.

When man-made fibers are extruded from the spinneret, most of the molecules are in random orientation. The molecules on the surface are somewhat regular due to the frictional resistance of the solution to the sides of the spinneret holes. Stretching or drawing increases the crystallinity of the fiber, reduces the diameter, and packs the molecules closer together.

Unstretched Or Undrawn

Stretched Or Drawn

Fig. 1:10. Before and after drawing the fiber.

When linear molecule chains are packed close together, there is considerable attraction between the hydrogen atoms of the chains. (The attraction is similar to that of a magnet for a piece of iron.) This is called *hydrogen bonding*. These bonds are weak cross-links, but because there are so many of them, they make the fibers stronger. The more closely the molecules are packed, the more effective the hydrogen bonds will be. Fibers which are highly oriented are stronger than unoriented fibers. For example, flax, which is more highly oriented than cotton, has greater strength. (*See* Fig. 1:8.)

Chemical Composition

The chemical composition is the basis on which fibers are classified.

Cellulose fibers are polyhydroxy alcohols.
Protein fibers are composed of various amino acids.
Acetate fibers are polyesters of cellulose.
Nylon fibers are polyamides.
Polyester fibers are esters of dihydric alcohol.
Acrylic fibers are addition polymers of acrylonitrile.
Modacrylic fibers are co-polymers of acryonitrile and other substances.
Nytril fibers are addition polymers of vinylidene dinitrile.
Saran fibers are addition polymers of vinylidene chloride.
Vinyon fibers are addition polymers of vinyl chloride.
Vinal fibers are addition polymers of vinyl alcohol.
Spandex fibers are elastomers composed of polyurethane.
Olefin fibers are addition polymers of ethylene, propylene, or other olefin units.

A knowledge of chemistry is helpful in understanding and interpreting the differences in fibers, but even without this, one can see that there are chemical differences and that these differences must explain the chemical reactivity of the fibers.

FIBER PROPERTIES

Durability

Fiber properties related to durability are those which make the fabric long wearing.

STRENGTH

The strength of a fiber is defined as the ability to resist strains and stresses and is expressed as tensile strength (pounds per square inch) or as tenacity (grams per denier).

Strong fibers have long molecule chains. Degree of polymerization is the term used to describe the length of the molecule chain. The D.P. of cotton is about 10,000, while that of regenerated cellulose is 300 to 500. Strong fibers are highly oriented, while weak fibers contain large sections of amorphous areas. Strong fibers make strong yarns; thus fine strong-fibered yarns may be used in production of sheer fabrics. Extremely sheer nylon hose are possible because of the high strength of the fiber.

The chart below lists the typical strengths of fibers.

Fiber Strength (Tenacity)

	Dry	*Wet*
High Strength		
Fortisan	8.5	5.5
Ramie	6.7	8.7
Flax	6.6	8.4
Glass	6.4	5.8
Nylon	8.8–4.3	7.4–3.6
Dacron	7.5–4.5	7.5–4.5
Vycron	6.3–4.2	same
Medium Strength		
Silk	4.5	3.9
Fortrel	4.7–3.7	same
Cotton	3.8	4.8
Zefran	3.5	3.1
Dynel	3.3–2.5	same
Kodel	3.0–2.5	same
Verel	2.8–2.5	2.7–2.4
Creslan	2.7	same
Acrilan	2.7–2.0	2.0
Orlon	2.5	2.1
Saran	2.5	same
Low Strength		
Rayon	1.7–5.0	1.0
Arnel	1.2–1.4	0.8–1.0
Acetate	1.1–1.5	0.8
Wool	1.3	0.8
Vinyon HH	0.7–1.0	same

ABRASION RESISTANCE

Abrasion resistance is the ability of a fiber to withstand the rubbing or abrasion it gets in everyday use. Inherent toughness, natural pliability, and smooth filament surface are fiber characteristics that contribute to abrasion resistance. The following fibers are ranked in the order of their resistance to abrasion: nylon, polyesters, acrylics, wool, cotton, rayon, acetate.

COHESIVENESS

Cohesiveness is the ability of fibers to cling together during spinning. This is an important property in staple but not in filament. Cohesiveness is due to the crimp and unevenness of the fiber. Cohesive fibers can be shorter in length, since there need not be so many points of contact between individual fibers.

RESILIENCY

Resiliency is the ability of a fiber or fabric to recover over a period of time from deformations of stretching, bending, or twisting. A resilient fabric has good crease recovery, hence requires a minimum of ironing. Resilient fabrics also retain high bulk and do not pack down in use. Resiliency is a property important for beauty and ease of care as well as durability.

ELASTICITY

Elasticity is the ability of a stretched material to return immediately to its original size.

PLIABILITY OR FLEXIBILITY

Pliability or flexibility is the ease of bending or shaping. Pliable fibers are easily twisted to make yarns. They make fabrics that resist splitting when folded or creased many times in the same place.

STIFFNESS OR RIGIDITY

Stiffness or rigidity is the opposite of flexibility. It is the resistance to bending or creasing. Rigidity and weight together make the body of the fabric. Rigidity is important in spinning because it determines the resistance to insertion of twist.

ELONGATION

Elongation is the deformation caused by stretching. It is expressed as the percentage of the original length. For example, if a yarn 100 cm. long can be stretched to 110 cm. before it breaks, it has 10% extension or elongation. For production of yarns and fabrics a minimum of 10% elongation is desirable.

Elongations vary at different temperatures and when wet or dry. The chart below shows the elongation of some fibers under standard conditions, 63% relative humidity at 70°F.

ELONGATION AT BREAK

Fiber (Dry)	% Elongation
Dynel	39
Acrilan	35
Wool	25–35
Vycron	31–35
Zefran	33
Verel	33
Creslan	32
Fortrel	30–45
Nylon (reg.)	26–32
Nylon (staple)	16–42
Dacron (staple)	25–36
Kodel	24–30
Dacron (reg.)	19–25
Orlon (staple)	20–28
Rayon (reg.)	15–30
Nylon (High Tenacity)	16–28
Acetate	25
Silk	20
Dacron (H.T.)	10–14
Corval (cross-linked)	12–15
Zantrel (high wet modulus)	10
Rayon (H.T.)	9–12
Avril (high wet modulus)	5– 9
Cotton	6– 7
Flax	2
Glass	2

Resiliency, elasticity, pliability, and elongation are due partially to fiber crimp and/or molecular crimp. All protein fibers have molecular crimp. Nylon has a folded molecular structure as it comes from the spinneret and even when cold drawn retains some crimp.

Cross-linkages and side chains help to explain these properties. Cross-linkages prevent the molecules from sliding over one another and give them good recovery from strain. Cross-linkages and side chains occur naturally in the protein fiber. Man-made fibers, cotton, and flax can be chemically cross-linked. This is the basis of the wash-and-wear finish. An excess of cross-links and/or the formation of many short cross-links makes a fiber rigid and inflexible.

STABILITY

Stability is important in the easy-care of fabrics and also in making them usable for a long time. Stability is the retention of size, shape, or form. A stable fabric does not stretch, sag, or shrink beyond stated limits with moisture, heat, or strains. Stable fibers make stable fabrics. Wool fibers shrink because of their scale structure; rayon fibers shrink and stretch because they are so easily distorted when wet. Rayon fibers swell greatly when wet, which forces the molecules apart and weakens the bonds. Cross-linked rayons and high wet modulus rayons, discussed on page 58, have greater stability than regular rayon.

PLASTICITY

Plasticity is that property of a fiber which enables the user to shape it semi-permanently or permanently by moisture, heat, and pressure, or by heat and pressure alone. This property relates to the beauty and ease of care as well as to the durability of the fabric. This is important from the consumer standpoint.

Wool has this property because of its scale structure and its lack of stability.

Thermoplastic fibers are those which soften on heating. These fibers can be permanently shaped by heat (heat-set). Thermoplastic fibers are all heat sensitive but vary in the degree of sensitivity. They should be washed in warm not hot water and pressed at temperatures of the lowest ironing range.

When fibers are heated they either decompose or melt. Melting consists of separating the molecules. It is believed that cellulose fibers do not melt because of the large molecule size and because of the strong attractive forces between the hydroxyl groups. Protein fibers do not melt because of the presence of cross-linkages. Heating causes the molecules to vibrate, and if there are few cross-linkages, attractive forces, or reactive groups, the molecules vibrate with such force that they tear themselves apart, or melt. The sections on fibers tell how heat sensitivity affects production and care of fabrics.

The chart below shows differences in heat sensitivity.

Fiber	Melting Point (°F)
Kodel	560
Creslan	554
Arnel	512
Nylon 66	482
Dacron	480
Acetate	474
Acrilan	460
Orlon	456
Nylon 6	428
Verel	302
Vinyon	260
Dynel	250
Olefin	240

Comfort

Fiber properties related to comfort are density, absorbency, hygroscopicity, and conductivity of electricity and heat.

DENSITY AND SPECIFIC GRAVITY

Density and specific gravity are measures of the weight of a fiber. Density is the weight in grams per cubic centimeter, and specific gravity is the ratio of the mass of the fiber to an equal volume of water at 4°C. The mass of the molecule and the elements it contains determine the specific gravity of a fiber. The weight of a fabric is determined by the weight of the fibers in it. For example: Orlon is lighter in weight than wool; thus, an Orlon fabric will weigh less than a wool fabric of the same thickness.

ABSORBENCY

Absorbency is defined as the ability of a fiber to take up moisture and is expressed in terms of moisture regain, which is the percentage of moisture that a bone-dry fiber will absorb from the air under standard conditions of temperature and moisture.

Absorbent fibers make fabrics which are comfortable because they take up perspiration readily. Thus they feel comfortable on hot humid days, or in damp climates. Absorbent fibers do not build up as much static electricity, which also makes them more comfortable in dry, cold weather. Absorbent fibers are hydrophilic, or "water loving," while non-absorbent fibers are hydrophobic, or "water hating." Absorbency is important from the beauty standpoint since it makes easy dyeability possible. Absorbency is also related to resiliency. Fabrics made of hydrophilic fibers tend to wrinkle more when wet or damp.

Absorbency is due to the chemical composition and the molecular structure of the fiber. Cellulose fibers, which have many hydroxyl (OH) groups available, are very absorbent. Protein fibers, which have reactive amino (NH_2) and carboxyl (COOH) groups, are very absorbent; fibers which have few reactive groups are not absorbent. Highly oriented groups are less absorbent than fibers with many

DENSITY AND SPECIFIC GRAVITY			
Fibers	Density (Grams per C.C.)	Fibers	Density (Grams per C.C.)
Glass	2.56	Acetate	1.30
Saran	1.71	Wool	1.30
Viscose	1.52	Silk	1.30
Flax	1.50	Kodel	1.22
Cotton	1.48	Zefran	1.19
Dacron	1.38	Creslan	1.18
Fortrel	1.38	Acrilan	1.17
Vycron	1.38	Orlon	1.16
Verel	1.37	Nylon	1.14
Dynel	1.35	Polypropylene	0.91
Vinyon	1.34		

amorphous areas, since there is no space for water molecules to enter.

TABLE OF MOISTURE REGAIN

Fiber	Per Cent of Moisture Regain
Wool	15–30
Rayon, regular	13
Rayon, high wet modulus	12.2
Flax	12
Mercerized cotton	11
Fortisan	10.7
Silk	10
Cotton	8
Acetate	6
Nylon	4
Verel	3.5
Dynel	3.5
Arnel	3
Nytril	2.6
Zefran	2.5
Creslan	2.2
Orlon	1.5
Acrilan	1.5
Dacron	0.4
Fortrel	0.4
Kodel	0.4
Vycron	0.4
Lycra	0.3
Olefin	0.0

WICKING OR WETTING

Wicking or wetting refers to the conduction of moisture along the fiber or through the fabric, although the fiber itself does not absorb much moisture. This property is related to surface wetting and is not the same as absorbency.

ELECTRICAL CONDUCTIVITY

Electrical conductivity is related to the build-up of static electricity charges on a fabric. A good conductor does not build up static.

HEAT CONDUCTIVITY

Heat conductivity is largely a yarn or fabric property, since fibers themselves are neither warm nor cool. However, because of the physical structure of fibers, they tend to make warm or cool fabrics. Heat comes from the body: if fabrics permit the body heat to escape, they are cool; if they hold body heat close to the body, they are warm. The thicker the fabric and the spongier the yarn, the warmer the fabric will be. Crimped fibers make spongy yarns because they do not pack down. Yarns made from staple fibers have some protruding fiber ends which prevent the fabric from clinging closely to the body; thus staple fibers usually make warmer fabrics than filaments.

Beauty and Hand

Fiber properties related to beauty and hand in fabrics are listed below. Hand is a term used to describe how a fabric feels. The words soft, lofty, lively, warm, silk-like, wool-like, and so forth are descriptive terms used with the word "hand" to describe the texture of the fabric. To say a fabric has an "attractive hand" does not really describe the feel, because attractive means different things to different people. Most of the terms defined below relate to hand.

LOFT

Loft or compressional resiliency refers to the ability of a fiber, yarn, or fabric to spring back to its original thickness after being compressed. In fibers, loft is due to crimp. This property is important in sweaters, blankets, and carpets.

COVER

Cover is the ability to occupy space for the purpose of concealment or protection. Fibers with irregular cross-sections and with crimp, curl, or twist give better cover for protection purposes because they occupy more space and create dead air cells for warmth. They also give better skin contact properties.

BODY

Body is a solid, firm feel which is dependent

on the rigidity and weight of the yarns and fibers in the fabric. In fabrics, body is obtained by use of coarse fibers.

DRAPE

Drape refers to the manner in which cloth hangs. It may be soft and limp, or stiff and bouffant. A draper was originally one who made cloth. The word "draperies" comes from the word "drape." Drapability is not a fiber property, but fibers which are soft and pliable are often said to have good drapability.

LUSTER

Luster is the light reflected from a surface. It differs from shine in that it is more subdued, since the light rays striking the surface are broken up. Smooth flat fibers reflect more light

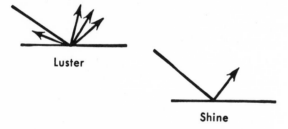

Fig. 1:11. Reflectance of light from fabric surface.

than round or rough fibers. Fibers with many striations have high luster. Yarns of long fibers which are laid together with little or no twist reflect more light than yarns with short fibers which must be twisted together to form a yarn. Manufactured fibers can be delustered by adding oil or pigment to the solution from which the fiber is spun.

COLOR

Color in fabrics contributes to their beauty, and therefore *dye affinity* can be considered a beauty property. Affinity to take and hold dyes is due to the chemical reactivity of the fiber. Absorbent fibers take dye more readily than non-absorbent fibers.

Care

Properties which determine the care of fabrics are related to the chemical composition of the fibers.

CHEMICAL RESISTANCE

The chemical reactivity of each fiber depends on the arrangement of the elements in the molecule and the reactive groups it contains.

Dry-cleaning solvents, perspiration, soap, synthetic detergents, bleaches, atmospheric gas, soot, and sunshine may all cause chemical degradation on some or all of the fibers.

Not all chemicals are harmful. Alkali strengthens cotton, alkali and chlorine may be used to make wool shrink-resistant, and chemicals that under ordinary conditions might be harmful can be used under scientifically controlled conditions to produce designs and beneficial finishes.

RESISTANCE TO MOTHS, MILDEW, AND SILVERFISH

Resistance to moths, mildew, and silverfish is due to the chemical composition of the fiber. These properties are important to the consumer because they indicate the type of care needed during storage as well as during use. Fibers without natural resistance must have protective finishes added or have their chemical composition changed to make them resistant.

FLAMMABILITY

Flammability or inflammability refers to the ease of ignition and the speed and length of burning. Non-flammable fibers will not burn. Flammability depends not only on the chemical composition but on the air incorporated in the yarn or fabric. Combustible finishes or dyes may make a non-flammable fiber burn. Finishes may also be added to make the fibers non-flammable.

REFERENCES

1. Hopff, H., and Greber, G., "Fibers from Addition Polymers," *CIBA Review*, **12**:137 (Apr. 1960).
2. Janner, George, and Campbell, Jerome, "Deskbook of Manmade Fiber Facts," *Modern Textiles Magazine*, **41**:47 (Sept. 1960).
3. Moncrieff, R. W., *Man Made Fibers*, 3rd ed., New York: Wiley, 1957.
4. Ashmore, W. G. S., Jr., and Benton, T., "1962 Man-Made Fiber Chart," *Textile World*, **112**:159 (July 1962).

FIBER IDENTIFICATION

Visual Inspection

Inspection of a fabric for appearance and hand is always the first step in fiber identification. Manufactured fibers can be made into fabrics that resemble natural fiber fabrics, and natural fibers can be changed by finishes. Large, irregular yarns can make a cotton fabric look like a linen fabric, and the use of staple fiber can make rayon fabrics resemble wool.

Experience in using and feeling fabrics develops the ability to do a better job of identification by inspection. This experience can be gained by weaving, hand crafts, sewing, merchandising, or laboratory work with actual fabrics.

Look for the following things when inspecting a fabric:

1. Length of fiber. (Untwist a yarn for this.) Any fiber can be made into staple length, but not all can be filament length.
2. Luster, or the lack of luster.
3. Body, texture, hand—soft to hard, rough to smooth, warm to cool, or stiff to flexible.

The Microscope Test

A knowledge of fiber structure, obtained by seeing the fibers in the microscope and observing some of the differences among fibers in each group, is of help in understanding fiber and fabric behavior.

Directions for using the microscope:

1. Clean the lens, slide, and cover glass.
2. Place a drop of water on the slide.
3. Untwist a yarn and place the loosened fibers on the slide. Cover with the cover glass and press down to eliminate air bubbles.

4. Place the slide on the stage of the microscope, and then focus with low power first. If the fibers have not been well loosened, it will be difficult to focus on a single fiber.
5. If a fabric contains more than one kind of fiber, test each. Be sure to check both the warp and filling yarns.

Some fibers look very similar under the microscope, and a solvent test may be needed to complete the identification.

Photomicrographs of individual fibers are given later.

Solubility Tests

Solubility tests are very useful in fiber identification. These tests may be done on a microscope slide so the results can be watched. The following chart gives a list of fibers and the solvents that will dissolve them. If the analysis is made in the sequence given, it is possible to dissolve out one fiber at a time without damaging those below it on the list. Viscose, cuprammonium, and cotton all dissolve with the same solvent, but they can also be easily identified by the microscope. The same is true of wool and vicara.

Solubility tests [1] can be used to determine the percentage and location of the fibers in a blend by dissolving out each component fiber from separate swatches and then comparing them with the original fabric.

Fiber	Solvent
Cellulose acetate	Glacial acetic acid
Vinyon HH	Chloroform
Dynel and Vinyon N	Dimethylformamide
Nylon	90% phenol
Viscose	Cuprammonium hydroxide
Cuprammonium	Cuprammonium hydroxide
Cotton	Cuprammonium (partially)
Wool	20% bleach (NaOCl)
Orlon	Dimethylformamide 55°C.
Acrilan	Concentrated nitric acid
Dacron	

The alkali test is described on page 30. The acetone test is on page 66.

[1] Wilson, W. R., "The Use of Solvents in Fiber Identification," *Canadian Textile Journal*, **69**:75 (Oct. 1952).

Fig. 1:12. Identifying fibers by the burning test. (Courtesy of Opal Roberson.)

The Burning Test

The burning test can be used to identify the *group*, such as cellulose, protein, thermoplastic, or mineral, to which the fibers belong.

If visual inspection is used with the burning test, individual fiber identification can be carried further.

General directions for the burning test:

1. Ravel out and test several yarns from each side of the fabric to see if they have the same fiber content. Differences in luster, twist, and color will indicate that there might be two or more kinds of fibers in the fabric.
2. Hold the yarn horizontally, as shown in Figure 1:12. Use tweezers if desired. Feed the yarns slowly into the edge of the flame from the alcohol lamp and observe what happens. Repeat this several times to check results.

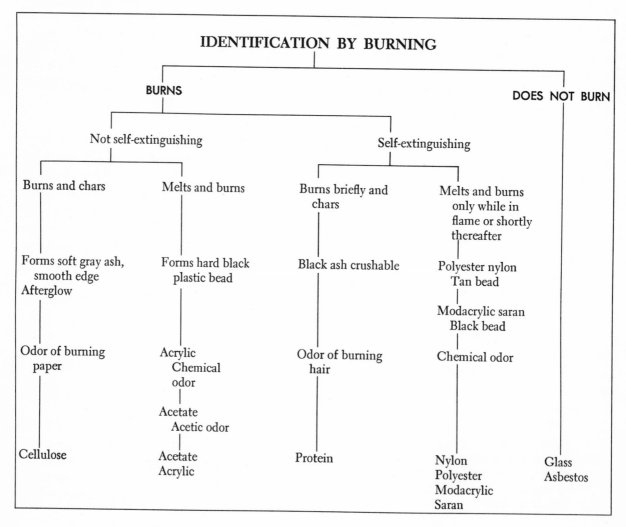

IDENTIFICATION BY BURNING

BURNS — DOES NOT BURN

Not self-extinguishing — Self-extinguishing

Burns and chars — Melts and burns — Burns briefly and chars — Melts and burns only while in flame or shortly thereafter

Forms soft gray ash, smooth edge Afterglow — Forms hard black plastic bead — Black ash crushable — Polyester nylon Tan bead

Modacrylic saran Black bead

Odor of burning paper — Acrylic Chemical odor — Odor of burning hair — Chemical odor

Acetate Acetic odor

Cellulose — Acetate Acrylic — Protein — Nylon Polyester Modacrylic Saran — Glass Asbestos

II. THE
NATURAL
FIBERS

PROTEIN FIBERS

NATURAL PROTEIN	MAN-MADE PROTEIN
Silk	Azlon [1]
Wool	
Specialty wools	

Natural protein fibers are products of animal growth. Man-made protein fibers (regenerated) are made by dissolving and resolidifying protein from plants or animals.

Protein fibers all contain the elements *carbon*, *hydrogen*, *oxygen*, and *nitrogen*. Wool also contains *sulfur*, which gives it some properties which are different from those of silk and azlon.

[1] No longer produced in the U.S.

The basic units of the protein molecule are amino acids which join together by condensation to build up a polypeptide chain. These are linear chains. Although they are shorter than the molecule chains of cellulose, protein fibers have side chains and wool has cross-linkages and a double chain so the molecular weights are similar.

A simple formula for the amino acid unit of the protein fiber is:

$$\begin{array}{c} R \\ | \\ CH \quad O \\ | \quad \parallel \\ NH_2 \quad C\text{-}OH \\ \text{Amino} \quad \text{Carboxyl} \\ \text{group} \quad \text{group} \end{array}$$

These groups provide sites for water molecules to lodge and explain why protein fibers are absorbent and hygroscopic. Another reason for their absorbency is the large spaces within the fiber. Wool will accept a solution with a molecule size of propyl alcohol without having to be swelled to admit the solution.

The amino groups react with acid dyes. The carboxyl groups react with alkalis and oxidizing agents. This explains why wool is harmed by alkalis.

Observe that the molecule chain has a somewhat folded configuration. This contributes to the flexibility, resiliency, and elasticity of the protein fibers.

The chart below lists some properties that are common to all protein fibers, and gives their importance to the consumer. Structure is compared in the chart at lower right.

PROPERTIES COMMON TO ALL PROTEIN FIBERS

Property	*Importance to the Consumer*
Medium density (1.3)	Fabrics of same thickness feel lighter than cellulosics.
Weaker when wet	Wool loses about 40% of its strength when wet; silk 15%. Handle carefully during washing.
Resilient	Wrinkles hang out between wearings.
	Fabrics tend to hold their shape.
Absorbent; moisture regain in wool 15–30%, in silk 10%	Comfortable in skin contact fabrics.
Hygroscopic	Comfortable in cool, damp climates.
Harmed by oxidizing agents	Chlorine bleaches damage fiber. Sunlight causes white fabrics to turn yellowish.
Weakened by alkalis	Use neutral or slightly alkaline soap or detergent. Perspiration weakens the fibers.
Harmed by dry heat	Wool becomes harsh and brittle and scorches easily with dry heat. Silk yellows with heat.
Flame resistance	Protein fibers do not burn readily, are self-extinguishing, have odor of burning hair, and form a black crushable ash.

Silk

**Liveliness, Suppleness
Dry Tactile Hand
Soft Luster
Covering Power**

Silk is often referred to as the "queen of the fibers." Chinese legends tell us that silk was discovered in 2640 B.C. by a Chinese empress. The Chinese carefully guarded their secret of the silk cocoon for 3000 years. They wove beautiful fabrics which were sold to Eastern traders, who carried them back to their own countries where they were prized very highly. The demand silk thus created was very great. In A.D. 300 refugees from China took cocoons to Korea and started raising silkworms. Japan learned about sericulture from the Koreans. The industry spread through central Asia into Europe, and by the twelfth century Italy was the silk center of Europe. This leadership was taken over by France in the seventeenth century. Weaving of silk became important in England when many Huguenot weavers emigrated from France to England in 1685.

Sporadic attempts to cultivate silk have been made in the United States. It was written in the charters of the various colonies that a silk industry must be started. Because of climatic conditions the north was not able to grow mulberry trees, and, in the south, growing cotton, which was also needed by the mother country, was much more profitable. But as late as 1833, some manufacturers of silk fabrics tried raising silkworms.

COMPARISON OF STRUCTURE		
Wool	*Silk*	*Azlon*
Staple	Filament or staple	Staple
Cell structure, overlapping scales	Solid fiber	Solid fiber
Elliptical cross-section	Triangular cross-section	Round cross-section

During World War II the government froze the import and production of silk in this country. The existing fibers were reserved for use by the armed forces. Our supplies from Japan and China were cut off, and for the decade from 1939 to 1949, we were without silk.

Since the introduction of nylon for hosiery, half of Japan's market for silk has been lost. Another threat facing their silk industry today is that of a labor shortage due to technological progress. The industry has relied in the past on women from farm families for its labor force. With agricultural prosperity and industrialization in Japan, it is no longer necessary for women to do this work to maintain minimum survival for their families as it once was. Sericulture has largely been a household operation, and for production to survive, it will be necessary to combine and systematize these small operations—to develop organization similar to the cooperatives in the United States. Unless these changes are made in the industry, it is predicted that silk will be so expensive that it will become a luxury fiber like vicuña.

Silk can be produced in any temperate climate, but it has only been successfully produced where there is a cheap source of labor. Silk is a continuous filament protein fiber produced by the silkworm. (*See* Fig. 2:1.) *Cultivated* silk is obtained by a carefully controlled process in which the silkworm lives a coddled and artificial life especially for the purpose of producing fibers. *Wild* silk production is not controlled; instead, these silkworms feed on oak leaves and spin cocoons under natural conditions.

Sericulture

Sericulture is the name given to the production of cultivated silk. The sericulture process begins with the silk moth which lays eggs on specially prepared paper. (*See* Fig. 2:1.) The eggs are kept in cold storage until they are needed for hatching. Hatching takes place continuously throughout the mulberry growing season, thus making it possible to keep labor and equipment at a minimum. The eggs

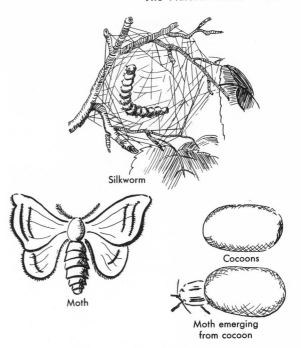

Fig. 2:1. Silkworm, moth, and cocoon.

are hatched into caterpillars which are put on special mats and fed fresh, young mulberry leaves.

When the silkworm is grown, it spins a fiber cocoon around itself. The bulk of the silk moths are killed inside the cocoons by heat, and only those which are needed for reproduction are allowed to emerge. The pierced cocoons are used for staple fiber.

Since it is possible to control the fineness, uniformity, and strength of the silk fiber by selective breeding, better silk is resulting from research in this area.

The silk fiber is a double strand held together by a gum or sericin, a water soluble substance secreted by the silkworm. This sericin is a very important part of the silk fiber. It serves as a warp sizing for the silk yarns as they are threaded on the loom and woven into the "gray goods" cloth. Because of the sericin, the silk yarns can be used without twist (zero-twist). When the sericin is removed from the fiber in the degumming process (about 25% weight loss), the fabric structure becomes more mobile. The low twist and the mobile structure are major factors in the "dry" tactile hand and the liveliness, suppleness, and drape of silk fabrics. Zero twist yarns are important in the good covering power exhibited by silk.

Triangular cross section, longitudinal striations, and fine denier are other factors that contribute to the aesthetic properties of silk fabrics.

Processing Silk—From Fiber to Yarn

Reeling or unwinding the filaments from the cocoon is done in an establishment called a filature. Until fifty years ago reeling was done by hand. The conventional system of reeling described below still requires much hand labor.

CONVENTIONAL REELING

A number of filaments from several cocoons are gathered together onto an aluminum reel. (*See* Fig. 2:2.) One operator can handle a basin of twenty spindles (five to eight cocoons to one spindle). The operator deter-

Fig. 2:2 Winding silk filaments on a reel.

mines the denier of the yarn solely by eyesight. The silk is rewound, twisted into a skein, and packaged for shipping. (*See* Fig. 2:3.) The

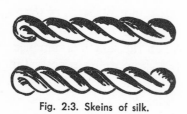

Fig. 2:3. Skeins of silk.

skeins are packaged into books (thirty skeins to a book) weighing four and one half pounds. Twenty to thirty books are formed into bales for shipment. When the silk arrives at the mill, it is opened, bunched, soaked, dried, and wound on bobbins. (*See* Fig. 2:4.)

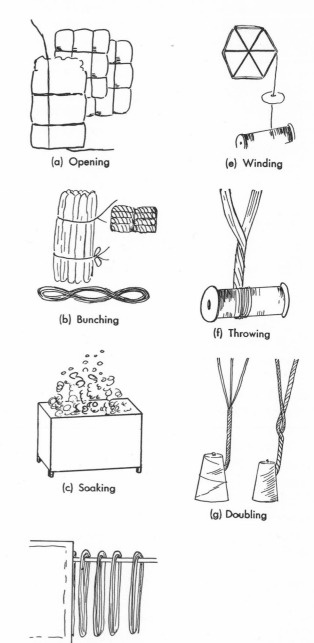

(a) Opening

(e) Winding

(b) Bunching

(f) Throwing

(c) Soaking

(g) Doubling

(d) Drying

Fig. 2:4. Processing silk in the mill.

AUTOMATIC OR DIRECT REELING

In automatic reeling, the silk fibers are laced from the cocoon through a guide to a chemical bath which softens the thread. The filaments go around a revolving horizontal roller, which dries and winds them onto a spool or cone ready for weaving on delivery. Silk in this form has a high import duty. In addition to speeding up the process of winding the filament, the automatic reeler also has a cocoon finding-feeding mechanism which regulates the size and uniformity of the yarn. Uniform yarns are more suitable for weaving on high-speed looms than are hand reeled silk yarns which slow up the weaving process. This machine increases production three or four times and cuts labor by 70 per cent, since one operator can manage 400 to 600 spindles. Reelers who have mechanized account for less than half of the silk production. In 1952, there were four automatic silk reelers in operation in Japan.

Types of Silk

Silk refers to cultivated silk.

Wild or *tussah* silk is a tan-colored fiber from the uncultivated silkworm which feeds on scrub oak. As the cocoons are always pierced, the fibers are shorter than reeled silk. Shantung, pongee, and honan are fabrics made from wild silk.

Doupion silk comes from two silkworms who spin their cocoons together. The yarn is uneven, irregular, and large in diameter.

Raw silk refers to cultivated silk-in-the-gum. Raw silk varies in color from gray-white to canary yellow, but since the color is in the sericin, boiled-off silk is white.

Reeled silk is the long continuous filament, 300 to 1600 yards in length.

Spun silk refers to yarns made from silk from pierced cocoons and waste silk.

Waste silk is comprised of the tangled mass of silk on the outside of the cocoon and the fiber from pierced cocoons.

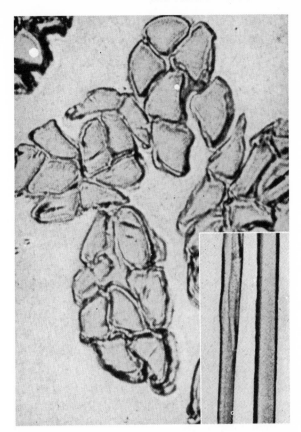

Fig. 2:5. Photomicrograph of silk fiber; longitudinal and cross-sectional view. (From Werner Von Bergen and Walter Krauss, *Textile Fiber Atlas.* Copyright 1949 by Textile Book Publishers, Inc.)

Properties

Silk has a desirable combination of properties which are not found in any of the new fibers; smoothness, soft luster, resiliency, toughness, and adaptability to temperature. Its individual properties have been duplicated and in many cases excelled, but this particular combination is found only in silk. In promotional jargon, "only silk is silk."

Silk is the only natural filament. It is a solid fiber but unlike the man-made fibers is not uniform size. (*See* Fig. 2:5.) The filaments are 300 to 1800 yards long. In cross section the fibers are like triangles with rounded corners. The rod-like, almost circular fibers are responsible for the luster and smoothness of silk.

Silk is a high-medium strength fiber which loses some strength when wet. Filament silk can be made into very sheer fabrics.

Silk takes dyes well, and it seems to have a depth of color or jewel-like tone not found in the man-made fibers which look like silk. Fast colors are available, but many converters need to be educated to use them. Brilliant colors are often not fast to washing.

Following dyeing, silk fabric to be made into taffeta is worked in a formic acid solution which hardens the fibers' surface and lends the fabric a crisp hand commonly known as *scroop*.

Silk is unique among natural fibers in that it makes a filament yarn which, when woven into fabric, produces a spun-like hand referred to as a "dry" tactile hand.

Silk is sold and usually woven "in-the-gum." The sericin makes up about one-fourth the fiber weight and is removed by degumming. This is done by washing it in hot water and soap or synthetic detergent for two to four hours, then rinsing one to three hours in clean hot water. Sericin must be completely removed to develop the inherent fiber properties.

In order to compensate for the loss of gum or sericin, weighting can be added. Iron, tin, or lead salts are used. Silk will absorb up to 400% of its own weight. A small amount of weighting is desirable to give good draping qualities, but an excessive amount weakens the fiber so that it breaks and abrades more easily than unweighted silk.

In 1938, the Federal Trade Commission passed rulings on the labeling of silk fabrics. The term "Pure Dye Silk" refers to silk, other than black, which contains metallic salts up to ten per cent. "Pure Dye Silk" may be used on black silks which have been weighted up to fifteen per cent. These rulings refer to silk in the United States only. The term "Pure Dye" is used because the weighting is done during the dyeing process. Weighted silk does not burn like other protein fibers. It chars and holds its shape; the metal glows like the filament in a light bulb when in contact with the flame. The odor of burning chicken feathers is noticeable. Weighting was prohibited during World War II, and silk fabrics on the market since then contain little or no weighting.

Water spotting, caused by migration of weighting agents to the outer edge of the spot, was one of the early problems of silk. Most manufacturers are now using a water spot-resistant finish.

Wash-and-wear silk, and silk with durable pleats are now made by application of resin finishes.

REFERENCES

1. Takamatsu, Y., "Japan Is Doing Something about Silk," *Modern Textiles Magazine*, **33**:32 (July 1952).
2. Mauersberger, H. R., *Matthews' Textile Fibers*, 6th ed., New York: Wiley, 1954, p. 789.
3. Wesson, Sheldon, "Japan's Prosperity Can Hurt Future Silk Output," *Women's Wear Daily*, December 30, 1960.
4. "Silk-like Fabrics from Man-made Fibers," (Staff Prepared), *Textile Industries*, **124**:93 (Aug. 1960).

Fig. 2:6. Shearing of wool. (Courtesy of the Wool Bureau.)

Wool

Warmth

Resiliency

Felting

Hygroscopic

Flame Resistance

No one knows when man started using wool as a textile fiber. Probably he first used the skins for clothing and later discovered that he could form a cloth of felt by pounding and matting the fibers together. We do know that man knew of wool during the Second Stone Age and that as early as 3000 B.C. the Babylonians were expert in spinning and weaving wool cloth.

During the Dark Ages the wool industry, which had become important in the world, almost disappeared. In the eleventh and twelfth centuries in Europe, textile industries began to reappear, and there was a big demand for wool. The Spaniards developed the Merino sheep, which has the finest wool and is the forerunner of all the breeds producing fine wool today.

Most wool comes from the temperate zone of the Southern Hemisphere: Australia, Argentina, New Zealand, South Africa, and Uruguay. In the Northern Hemisphere, the United States, Great Britain, Spain, France, and Italy are the leaders. Australia produces one-fourth of the world's wool. The United States produces about one-third as much as Australia. The United States, however, is the largest consumer of wool and the largest producer of wool fabrics, both in terms of yardages and dollar value.

The wool fiber is the hair of the sheep and is nature's way of protecting the animal from cold, rain, excessive heat, as well as conserving the body heat of the animal.

In the United States, most sheep are raised in Texas and the eleven Far Western states. Domestic wool is the wool from sheep grown east of the Rocky Mountains and Texas and from the Willamette Valley of Orgeon. Domestic wools compare favorably with the fine Australian wools. Territory wools are grown in the Far Western states. Sheep producing this wool seldom receive protection from the elements and are not furnished with hay. As a result the wool is often weaker and harsher than domestic wool.

Processing

SHEARING

Sheep are sheared once or twice a year, depending on their locality, by traveling crews. An expert shearer can clip as many as 100 to 200 sheep a day. The fleece is kept in one piece with the skirts and breech folded in and the flesh side outside. The fleece is tied with paper twine. One tier can keep up with two shearers. The fleeces are packed tightly into six-foot sacks. The fleeces are sometimes graded before packing but usually are graded in the warehouse before being sold. Figure 2:6, at the bottom of the preceding page, illustrates the process of shearing in the western United States.

PULLED WOOL

Pulled wool is obtained from animals which are sold for meat. The pelts are washed and brushed and then treated chemically to loosen the fibers. The yield of pulled wool is about one-fifth that of sheared wool.

Wool as it comes from the sheep and as it it is sold is called *grease wool*. It contains impurities such as sand, dirt, grease, and dried sweat called suint. The grease, in various stages of purification, is used for a wide variety of commercial purposes, such as medicines, toilet preparations, and softeners.

SORTING

Sorting is the breaking up of an individual fleece into various qualities based on fineness.

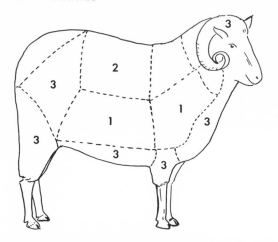

Fig. 2:7. Sorting of wool.

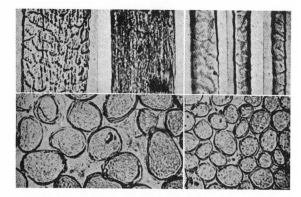

Fig. 2:8. Photomicrographs of wool fiber, showing longitudinal views above and cross-sectional views below. (From Werner Von Bergen and Walter Krauss, *Textile Fiber Atlas.* Copyright 1949 by Textile Book Publishers, Inc.)

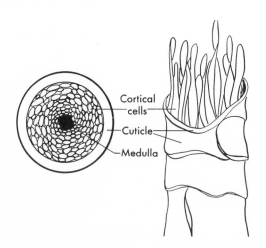

Fig. 2:9. Physical structure of wool fiber. (Courtesy of Werner Von Bergen. Reprinted by permission of *Industrial and Engineering Chemistry.*)

The diagram shows how the fleece is sorted. (*See* Fig. 2:7.) The best quality fiber comes from the sides and shoulders, the poorest quality fiber from the lower legs.

Physical Structure

Wool fibers, both sheep's wool and specialty wools, vary in length from one and one half inches to fourteen inches and in thickness from 10 to 70 microns (one micron is about 1/25,000 inch). (*See* Fig. 2:8.) Finer fiber wools (18 to 30 microns diameter) are used for clothing; coarser wools are used for rugs. The quality of wool is based on the fineness of the fiber. High quality in wool does not imply high durability.

COMPOSITION

The fiber is composed of two or three layers. (*See* Fig. 2:9.) The *cuticle*, which is the outer layer, consists of flat horny scales which overlap like shingles on a roof. The free end of the scale projects outward and points toward the tip of the hair. The scales are covered by a protective membrane. This membrane, which seems to be attached to the outer edges of the scale, may cover the entire fiber, or it may protect each individual scale. The membrane is the only non-protein portion of the fiber, and it is of a water-repellent nature, which explains why wool does not wet easily. The *cortex*, or inner structure, is made up of millions of small spindles called cortical cells. They comprise 90 per cent of the fiber. Some very coarse wools and some of the specialty fibers contain a *medulla*, which may be a completely open canal or may be filled with a loose network of open cells like honeycomb. The medulla is pigmented and gives the color to the fiber.

Wool fibers have natural crimp which is three dimensional with a combined bend and turn. (*See* Figs. 2:10 and 2:11.) The crimp is believed to be a result of uneven development of the cortical cells. The crimp in wool varies with the fineness of the fiber; fine normally in wavy lines. (These should not be confused with fiber crimp.) Even uncrimped wool fibers have molecular crimp. (*See* Fig. 2:12.) These chain molecules might be compared to springs—when the fiber is stretched, the crimp straightens out and the chains elongate; when the strain is removed, the chains go back to the original crimped state. They might also be compared to ladders in that the chains lie in a longitudinal position but are connected with cross linkages or chemical bonds. These cross linkages or rungs of the ladder help pull the fiber back to its original position after it has been stretched.

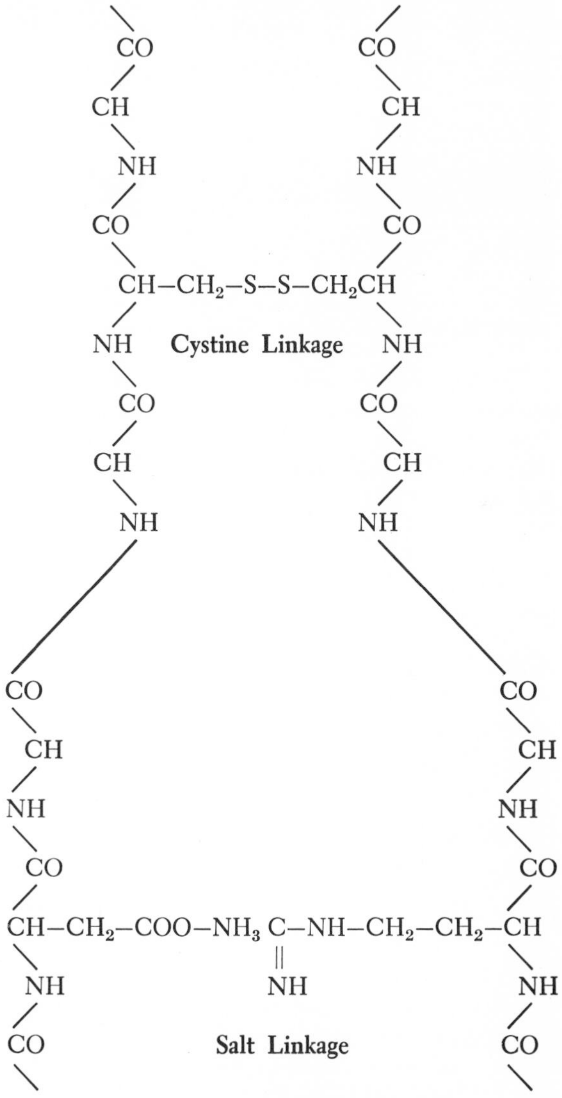

Fig. 2:10. Photo showing length of wool fiber and crimp. (Courtesy of the Wool Bureau.)

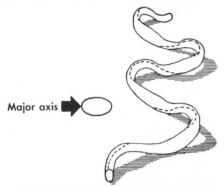

Major axis

Fig. 2:11. Three-dimensional crimp of wool fiber. (From Giles E. Hopkins, *Wool As an Apparel Fiber*. Copyright 1953 by Rinehart & Company, Inc.)

wools have as high as thirty crimps per inch, while coarse wools have few or no crimps.

Wool is a *bi-component* fiber made of two components side by side which swell differently when wet. There is a decrease in crimp on wetting and an increase on drying. The crimp helps give wool its "dry" tactile hand, its loft, and its good cohesive property.

MOLECULAR STRUCTURE

Wool is a protein called keratin. Like all proteins it is a complicated chemical compound made up of various amino acids which are linked together to form polypeptide chains cross-linked by cystine and salt linkages. This cross-linking is largely responsible for wool's resiliency. The chain molecules of keratin lie

$$CH-CH_2-S-S-CH_2CH$$

Cystine Linkage

$$CH-CH_2-COO-NH_3 C-NH-CH_2-CH_2-CH$$

Salt Linkage

Fig. 2:12. Structural formula of wool.

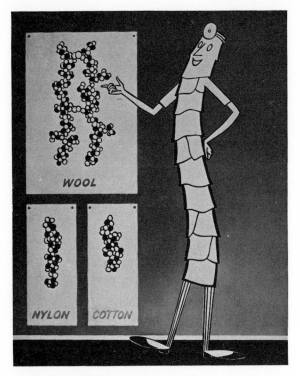

Fig. 2:13. Molecular crimp of wool fiber. (Courtesy of the Wool Bureau.)

Properties

A knowledge of the physical and chemical structure of the fiber explains its properties and indicates the kind of care required.

HEAT CONDUCTION

Wool is said to be a poor conductor of heat. However, the amount of heat conducted along the fiber is not the important factor in the *warmth* of wool. Still air is one of the best insulators and it is the air space around the fibers, in the yarns, and in the fabric which keeps the heat of the body close to the body.

Wool fibers do not pack well in yarns because of the natural crimp in the fiber and because of the scale structure. This makes wool fabrics porous, and capable of incorporating much air giving the fabrics a *lofty hand*. Wool fabrics maintain this thickness and lightness because the resiliency of the fibers enables them to recover from crushing and bending.

ABSORBENCY

The absorbency of wool is necessary to warmth. Wool does not take up water quickly. In fact, it repels it, but wool does absorb moisture of the body or the atmosphere in the form of water vapor without feeling damp. It can absorb as much as 30 per cent of its weight in moisture without feeling wet. When a wool blanket or a sweater is put into water for washing, it does not get wet quickly, as cotton does, and once wet it does not dry quickly. When water or liquid is spilled on a wool garment, the fluid tends to run off leaving droplets which can be wiped off quickly. In this respect, wool is partially water repellent. This property is thought to be due to the protective membrane covering the wool fiber.

Wool is *hygroscopic* in that it picks up moisture in vapor form. It also releases moisture slowly. As wool absorbs moisture, it actually creates heat. In winter, when people go from a dry, indoor atmosphere into a damp, outdoor one, the heat liberated by the moisture absorption of wool clothing helps to protect their bodies against the impact of the cold atmosphere.

RESILIENCY AND STRENGTH

Wool is a very resilient fiber. Its resiliency is greatest when it is dry and lowest when it is wet. If a wool fabric is crushed in the hand, it tends to spring back to its original position when the hand is opened. This crease-recovery property is important in the manufacture of fabrics because it permits energetic mechanical treatments in finishing woolens and worsteds. It is important to the consumer because it minimizes the amount of pressing needed between dry cleanings. Fabrics made of wool fibers are not all equally resilient. Some of this difference is due to fiber variation. The kind of yarn, the construction and finish of the fabric also contribute to resiliency. At present there is no scientific way to measure resiliency of fibers.

Wool also has good *press retention*. It takes and holds creases well. Creases are set by use of pressure, heat, and moisture. During pressing the fiber molecules adjust themselves to the new position by forming new cross-linkages. Creases in wool are not permanent, however, since they can be removed by moisture.

Wool fibers are *weak*, but fabrics made from them are very durable. The low strength, 1.2 to 1.7 grams per denier, is due to the large amount of amorphous areas in the fiber. Because of its high absorbency, the fiber swells when wet, and this in turn makes wool much weaker when wet. Fabrics are durable because of high extensibility, good flexing property, and resistance to abrasion. When strain is applied, the fiber first uncrimps; further strain causes the fiber to stretch up to 30 per cent of its original length without breaking. Wool fibers are very flexible—they can be bent back on themselves 20,000 times without breaking. (Sea Island cotton breaks after 3,200 flexings; silk after 1,800; and rayon after seventy-five.) The scales on the wool protect the fiber during abrasive wear.

FELTING

Felting is the term applied to the progressive shrinkage of wool. Wool and specialty wool fibers are the only natural fibers which felt. Felting occurs when wool fibers are subjected to heat, moisture, and friction. All of these conditions are present at the underarms of sweaters and shirts and in the soles of socks. To make felting possible, a fiber must possess a surface scale structure; it must be easily stretched; and it must possess the power of recovery from deformation.

While felting is not completely understood, it is believed that the following factors explain the phenomenon:

1. The scales interlock when subjected to moisture, heat, and friction. In this warm, moist condition the fibers swell and the scales open up slightly and become entangled as the fibers move. They act like fishhooks and prevent further movement of the fibers, thus forming a matted fabric.
2. Under the above-mentioned conditions, wool fibers creep or migrate toward their root end. Since the fibers are in a random arrangement in the yarn, the movement is in all directions.
3. Wool fibers tend to curl when wet, due to a difference in contraction between the cuticle and the cortex.

Felting is both an advantage and a disadvantage. This property is utilized in making fabrics directly from fiber without first spinning or weaving. It is also utilized in creating certain fabric finishes on woven or knitted fabrics. *Fulling* or milling, a finishing operation which shrinks the fabric, making it heavier and thicker, is dependent on the felting property of wool. Short wool fibers (flock) are sometimes blown or forced into a heavy woolen fabric and felted in place. In tailoring or sewing wool fabrics, extra fullness can be shrunk into shape by pressing in the presence of moisture.

Felting is a disadvantage in that it makes washing of woolens more difficult than washing of other fabrics, and it causes the formation of boardy areas in garments during wear.

Satisfactory shrink-resistant treatments (page 195) were developed during World War II for garments for the armed forces. After the war, these processes were released for commercial development.

Wool is an *amphoteric* substance. This means that it will unite with and react toward both acids and bases. Wool is fairly stable to acids; it is harmed by *alkalies*. In the manufacture of fabrics, acids are used to remove cellulosic impurities. This process is called *carbonizing*. (*See* page 199.)

Alkalies are used in cleaning fibers and in scouring and fulling fabrics. The hydrogen peroxide used in bleaching is often alkaline and must be used carefully at moderate temperatures. Very little wool is bleached to a pure white. Much of it is used as a creamy white, in natural color, or dyed without first bleaching. Vat dyes are not universally used at present since they must be applied in alkaline solution.

The consumer should take precautions during use and care of woolen goods, since wool is harmed by perspiration, bleaches, and strong soaps.

Wool is damaged by moths. Mothproofing is discussed with finishes, page 209. Moths attack the cystine linkages. Research has shown how the cross-linkages in wool can be broken and new cross-linkages built which make the fiber more resistant to the action of alkali, bleaches, and sunlight. The treated wools are also more resistant to shrinkage and to attack by moths and bacteria.

Since wool burns very slowly, it creates no fire hazard. Wool blankets will put out flames.

Identification

THE BURNING TEST

The burning test, page 18, can be used to distinguish protein from cellulose or thermoplastic fibers. Wool can be detected in a blend by the characteristic "burning chicken feathers" odor and the lack of luster of the fibers.

THE ALKALI TEST

The alkali test is a simple test which can. be used by the homemaker to identify wool and wool blends. Simple equipment, as shown in Figure 2:14, can be used.

Alkali (caustic soda) is sold on the market as lye. A hot five per cent solution will completely destroy *wool*. As it disintegrates, the fiber becomes slick, turns to a jelly-like mass, and finally goes into solution.

Recipe for 5 per cent alkali solution:
    1 tablespoon lye
    1 pint water
    Heat to boiling

The wool in a blend will disintegrate, leaving only the fibers that have been mixed with the wool.

Wool Products Labeling Act

Because there is not enough wool to meet our many needs, wool is reclaimed and used again in blends with new wool or with other fibers. The kind of wool is very difficult to judge and the consumer has only price and a sense of touch as guides, unless fabrics are labeled. Man-made fibers can be made to look so much like wool that it is difficult to tell the difference.

The Wool Products Labeling Act was passed by Congress in 1939 and became a law in 1941. The purpose of the Act is:

to protect producers, manufacturers, distributors, and consumers from the unrevealed presence of substitutes and mixtures in spun, woven, knit, felted, or otherwise manufactured wool products.

A label or tag stating the fiber content of the fabric in terms of percentages must be firmly attached to any product (except upholstery and floor coverings) containing wool.

Wool labeling terms covered by the Act are:

Wool refers to new wool. Fibers reclaimed from knit scraps and from broken threads are included.
Reprocessed wool is obtained from scraps and clips of new woven or felted fabrics made of previ-

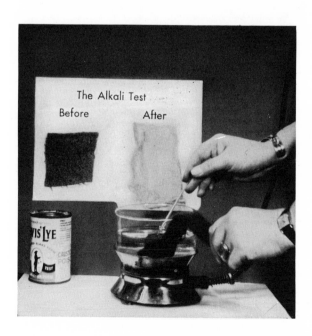

Fig. 2:14. Identifying wool fiber by the alkali test.

ously unused wool. These remnants are garnetted (shredded) back to the fibrous state and used in the manufacture of woolens.

Re-used wool, sometimes called shoddy, is obtained from rags and old clothing which have been used or worn. The rags are cleaned, sorted, and shredded into fibers. Re-used wool is usually blended with new wool before being respun. It is usually used in utility fabrics—mackinaw-type fabric which is thick and boardy, and interlinings.

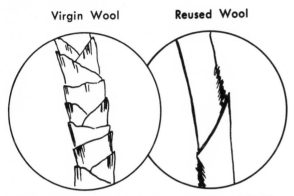

Virgin Wool   **Reused Wool**

Fig. 2:15. Virgin wool (left) and re-used wool (right).

The Wool Products Labeling Act *does not tell the consumer anything about the quality* of wool in a fabric. New wool may be fine or coarse. The consumer must rely on feel or texture to determine quality.

The term *virgin wool* is not defined in the Wool Products Labeling Act. A Federal Trade Commission rule has defined virgin wool as wool that has never been processed in any way before its complete manufacture into the finished fabric. This eliminates knitted clips and wastes from spinning and weaving included under new wool.

Virgin wool does not necessarily mean good wool.

Re-used and reprocessed fibers are important in the textile industry. These fibers, however, lose some of the desirable properties of new wool during the garnetting process because the fibers are broken and the scale structure is damaged. The re-used wool fibers are not only broken by the mechanical action of garnetting, but they are also damaged by wear. These fibers therefore are not as resilient, nor as strong and durable, as new wool.

Lamb's wool refers to fiber from lambs up to seven months. The fibers have a natural tip which is pointed. Wool is softer and possibly finer than that from older animals.

Care

Wool does not soil readily. A good brush is essential in caring for wool garments. They should be brushed after each wearing. Care should be given to the under collars and the inside of cuffs on coats and trousers. A firm, soft brush not only removes dust but it gently lifts the fibers back to their natural springiness. Fabrics which are damp should be allowed to dry before brushing.

Garments should be allowed to rest between wearings so that they hang back into shape. Wool fibers recover from deformation rather slowly. Hanging over a bath tub of hot water helps remove wrinkles. Garments should be hung so that the air can circulate freely about them as wools tend to absorb odors.

When storing woolens, be sure they are clean and free from spots. It is best to wrap them in paper and seal the edges.

Wool fabrics are not harmed by dry-cleaning solvents, and unless wet cleaning is necessary, there are usually no unsatisfactory results from dry cleaning.

Precautions must be taken when washing wool. Even shrink-resistant wools cannot receive the rough treatment given to cotton during washing. Use warm water, a mild detergent, and agitate gently. Wool should never be rubbed. Wool garments should be washed before they become very dirty. It is best to use several short sudsings and rinsings, rather than a long agitation or wash period. Because of the harmful effects of alkali on wool, be sure that all the detergent is removed. Wool garments should be placed on a flat surface to dry or hung half over the line so that the weight is evenly distributed. A blanket should be hung over two or three lines.

With the emphasis on easy-care and "wash-and-wear" fabrics, many processes are being evaluated on wool fabrics to make them competitive with the acrylic, modacrylic, and polyester wool-like fabrics.

Specialty Wools

Specialty wools are obtained from the goat family and the camel family.

Goat Family	Camel Family	Others
Angora goat— mohair	Camel's hair	Angora rabbit— angora
Cashmere goat— cashmere	Llama	Fur fibers
	Alpaca	
	Vicuña	
	Guanaco	

Specialty wools are used in less quantity than sheep's wool, and for that reason they are usually more expensive. Like all natural fibers, they vary in quality. The fibers obtained from these animals are of two kinds, the coarse, long outer hair and the fine, soft undercoat. The coarse fibers are used for interlinings, upholstery, and some coatings, while the very fine fibers are used in the luxury coatings, sweaters, shawls, suit and dress fabrics.

Mohair

Mohair, the fiber from the Angora goat, is raised in Turkey, South Africa, and the United States. Texas is the largest producer of mohair in the United States.

Mohair is our most resilient fiber and has none of the crimp found in sheep's wool, giving it a smoother surface which is more resistant to dust and is more lustrous than wool. Mohair is very strong and has a good affinity for dye. The washed fleece is a lustrous white.

Cashmere

Cashmere comes from a small goat raised in Kashmir, China, Tibet, and Mongolia. The fibers vary in color from white to gray to brownish-gray. The hair is combed by hand from the animal during the moulting season. Only a small part of the fleece is the very fine fiber, probably not more than one-half pound per goat.

Camel's Hair

Camel's hair is obtained from the two-hump Bactrian camel of Mongolia and Tibet. It is said to have the best insulation of any of the wool fibers, since it keeps the camel comfortable under extreme conditions of temperature during a day's journey through the cold of mountain passes and the heat of the valleys. The hair is collected by a "trailer" who follows the camel caravan and picks up the hair as it is shed and places it in a basket carried by the last camel. He also gathers the hair, in the morning, at the spot where the camels lay down for the night.

Because the camel's hair gives warmth without weight, the finer fibers are much prized for clothing fabrics. They are often used in blends with sheep's wool, which is dyed the tan color of the camel's hair.

There are so many qualities of cashmere and camel's hair that care should be taken by the consumer to determine the quality of fiber she is buying. The best way to judge the quality is by the feel. Consumers should be guided by the reputation of the manufacturer or retailer.

Llama and Alpaca

The llama and the alpaca are domesticated animals of the South American branch of the camel family. The fiber is eight to twelve inches in length and is noted for its softness, fineness, and luster. The natural colors are white, light fawn, light brown, dark brown, gray, black, and piebald.

Vicuña and Guanaco

Vicuña and guanaco are the wild animals of the South American camel family. They are very rare, and the animals must be killed to obtain the fiber. Vicuña is the softest, finest, rarest, and most expensive of all textile fibers. The fiber is short, very lustrous, and a light cinnamon color.

Angora

Angora is the hair of the Angora rabbit and is raised in France and in small amounts in the United States. Each rabbit produces only a few ounces of fiber, which is very fine, fluffy, soft, slippery, and fairly long. It is pure white in color.

Man-Made Protein Fibers—Azlon

The increased demand for and the scarcity of fine wools plus the high cost of wool has greatly stimulated interest in wool-like fibers. Theoretically, any protein-containing material can be regenerated into a protein fiber, and many substances have been tried and are still being investigated. Fibers from skim milk, corn, soybeans, and peanuts have been on the market briefly, but at the present time no man-made protein fibers are being produced. The generic name *azlon* has been established for a manufactured fiber in which the fiber-forming substance is composed of any regenerated naturally occurring protein.

Regenerated protein fibers were made as early as 1894 and first manufactured commercially in Italy in 1935. *Merinova*, the Italian fiber, is still being produced. *Vicara*, made in the United States, and *Ardil*, made in Scotland, were both manufactured from 1948 to 1957 but were discontinued because the fiber was economically unsuccessful.

The man-made proteins had certain properties which made them useful in blends. They were resistant to heat, acids, moth, and mildew. They took the same dyes as wool. They were absorbent, which made them comfortable and resistant to static build-up. They gave a soft, warm feel to fabrics. Their one disadvantage was low strength, which ranged from 0.7 to 1.2 grams per denier and which was more than 50 per cent less when wet. The easy care characteristics of the thermoplastic fiber and the much lower cost of the regenerated cellulose and acetate fibers account for the success of these man-made fibers.

CELLULOSE FIBERS

NATURAL CELLULOSE

Cotton
Flax
Ramie
Jute
Hemp

REGENERATED CELLULOSE

Rayon

Natural cellulose fibers are built up by nature during the growth of the plant. Man-made or regenerated cellulose fibers are made by dissolving and resolidifying natural cellulose.

Molecular Structure

The basic unit of the cellulose molecule is the *glucose unit* and is the same for both natural and regenerated fibers. The glucose unit is made up of the elements *carbon, oxygen,* and *hydrogen.*

The formula below shows how these elements are arranged in the glucose unit, and it also shows two glucose units joined together to form the cellobiose unit, which is characteristic of cellulose.

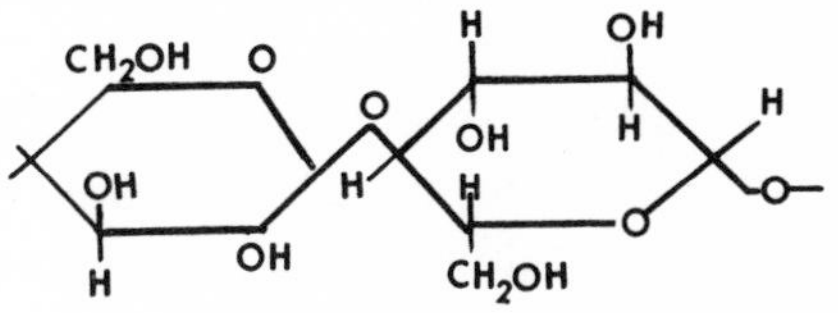

Fig. 2:16. The cellulose molecule.

The cellulose molecule is a *long, linear* chain of glucose units. The number of units in the chain depends on the origin of the cellulose. Natural and regenerated cellulose differ in the length of the molecule chain, as shown in the table on the next page.

Source	Length of Chain (DP)
Egyptian cotton	3000 to 4000
Cotton linters	1440
Pine tree cellulose	700 to 800
Regular rayon	250 to 280
High wet-modulus rayon	400 to 550

Fibers with long molecule chains are stronger than those with short molecule chains. Rayon fibers are not as strong as natural cellulose fibers for two reasons. (1) Rayon is made from cotton linters or pine tree cellulose, both of which have a shorter chain length than cotton. (2) During manufacture of rayon the chain length of this cellulose is broken down.

Polymerization is the process of joining small units together. The large unit is then called a *polymer*. Therefore, all fibers are the polymer of some fiber-forming substance. (The Federal Trade Commission definitions given in the man-made fiber section use this term.) *Degree of polymerization* refers to the number of units that have been joined to make a chain (DP).

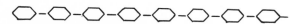

Fig. 2:17. A molecule chain.

Fibrils are *bundles* of molecule chains. These are the "building blocks" from which a cellulose fiber is made. In natural cellulose, the fibrils are closely packed, uniform bundles that are laid down side by side in spiral arrangement during the growth of the fiber. Each bundle contains forty to fifty chains. The diagram below shows one fibril bundle in its spiral path around the fiber. In regenerated

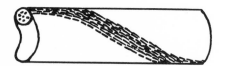

Fig. 2:18. Spiral arrangement of fibril.

cellulose the fibril bundles are irregular and randomly arranged. The molecules are held together in the bundles by forces called hydrogen bonds. A hydrogen bond is the attraction of an OH group of one glucose unit to an OH group of an adjacent unit. These operate like the attraction of a magnet for a nail. These forces are important in the wrinkle recovery of the fabric.

Hydrogen bonds are easily broken, and when a fiber is bent, the molecules on the outer edge slip past one another, breaking old bonds and forming new ones which hold the fiber in its bent position. For this reason, cellulose fibers have poor wrinkle recovery (resilience). Figure 2:19 shows hydrogen bonds before and after slippage, and Figure 2:20 shows

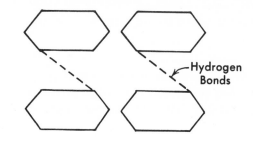

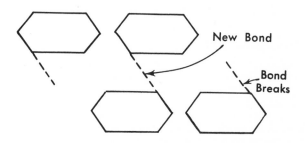

Fig. 2:19. Slippage of molecules causes breaking of bonds. Also see Figure 2:20 at the top of page 35.

the effect of bending the fiber. If stronger links can be formed between the chains, the wrinkle recovery will be improved. The cross-links will resist breaking and will pull the molecule back into place, and thus the fiber will recover from wrinkling. Wool fibers have natural cross-links. The cross-linked rayons are cross-linked before spinning. Natural cellulose fibers can be given

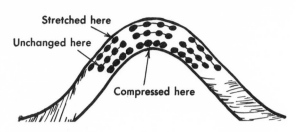

Fig. 2:20. Effect on molecules of the bending of the fiber.

cross-links by treating them with a wash-and-wear solution. (*See* Fig. 2:21.)

The random fibril arrangement of the regenerated fibers permits water to penetrate the fiber and causes it to swell when it gets wet. Water weakens the hydrogen bonds, and the regenerated cellulose fibers are therefore weaker when they are wet.

Natural cellulose fibers, on the other hand, are closely packed, and the spiral position of the bundles causes the fiber to twist and restrict the penetration of water so that these fibers actually become stronger when they are wet.

Chemical Reactivity

The chemical reactivity of cellulose is related to the three hydroxyl (OH) groups of the glucose unit. (*See* Fig. 2:21.) These groups

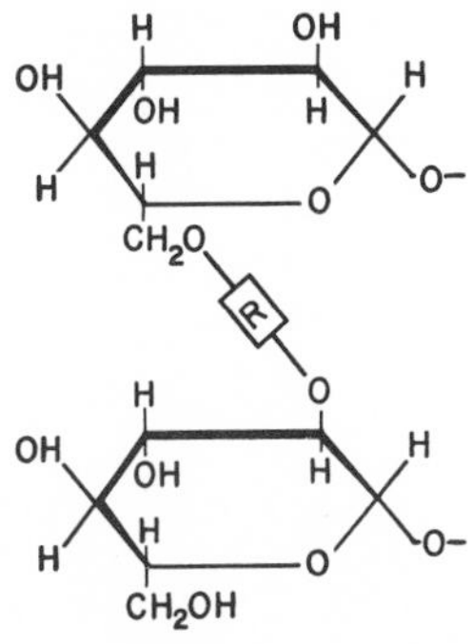

Fig. 2:21. Cross-link between molecules.

react readily with dyes and special finishes such as the wash-and-wear finishes.

Chemicals such as bleaches that cause a breakdown of the molecule chain of the cellulose usually attack at the oxygen atom and cause a rupture there. Observe in the chart on the preceding page the reduction in chain length that occurs when cellulose is dissolved to make rayon fibers.

Common Properties

All cellulose fibers have many common properties which are based on the chemical composition as well as the molecular structure. These are given in the chart below.

Property	*Importance to the Consumer*
High density (1.5±)	Fabrics feel heavier than comparable fabrics of other fiber content.
Low resiliency	Fabrics wrinkle badly unless finished for recovery.
Lacks loft. Packs well into compact yarns	Yarns can be creped. Tight, high-count fabrics can be made. Makes close wind-resistant fabrics.
Absorbency	Comfortable for summer wear. Good for towels, diapers, and handkerchiefs.
Good conductor of electricity	Does not build up static.
Good conductor of heat	Fabrics are cool for summer wear.
Can withstand high temperature	Fabrics can be boiled to sterilize. No special precautions in ironing needed.
Harmed by mineral acids. Little affected by organic acids	Fruit stains should be removed immediately from a garment to prevent setting.
Resistant to moths	Storage problem is simplified.
Attacked by mildew	Soiled garments should not be put away damp.
Inflammability	Cellulose fibers ignite quickly, burn freely, have an afterglow, and gray feathery ash. Filmy or loosely-constructed garments should not be worn near an open flame.
Moderate resistance to sunlight	Draperies should be lined.

Cotton

Low Cost
Low Resiliency
Launderability
Absorbency

Cotton is the most important cash crop in the United States, and 25,000,000 people depend on it for all or part of their income. Cotton is also the most widely used fiber. More than 10,000 items ranging from utilitarian to high fashion are made of cotton. According to the National Cotton Council, the largest single outlet is men's and boy's shirts and trousers. Other large uses are sheets, towels, baby clothes, napped fabrics, home furnishings, and military uses. In 1960 over 10,000,000,000 yards of cotton cloth were woven in the United States, and of this 4,000,000,000 were given a wash-and-wear finish.

This wide use of cotton has been the result of four revolutionary developments: early machine inventions, which made mass production possible; mercerization, which made cotton more silk-like; compressive shrinkage, which gave guaranteed size to garments; and wash-and-wear finishes, which minimized the time required for care.

The history of cotton dates back to ancient times when, from 1500 B.C. to A.D. 1500, India was the center of the cotton industry. The industry developed in Egypt at about the same time. Some of the best long staple cotton is grown in the Nile valley of Egypt. In the United States, the Pima Indians were growing cotton when the Spaniards came to this country. One of the gifts that Columbus took back to Queen Isabella was a hank of yarn.

England became the center of cotton manufacturing when the spinning jenny and spinning frame were invented by Arkwright and Hargreaves in 1769.

After the American Revolution, New England became the cotton manufacturing center in this country and remained so until after World War II, when competition from textile imports from areas of the world where labor was cheap, made it necessary to cut costs. The spinning and weaving industries began to "migrate" to the South, particularly to North and South Carolina. Wages and taxes were lower in the South, the climate was milder, and there were fewer restrictions imposed by labor unions. New modern plants and machinery made it possible to shift to continuous processing with more automation.

During the same period, cotton growing was shifting from the southeastern part of the United States to the Southwest and Far West where the weather conditions were more favorable and cotton could be grown in irrigated areas.

With increasing production costs, cotton, in 1952, for the first time became more expensive than rayon, its closest competitor. Between 1947 and 1955 cotton lost its largest single market, tire cord, to rayon, and its cotton bag industry was invaded by paper and plastics.

The wash-and-wear finishes were a boon to the industry, as they provided its chief "profit" outlet and took up the slack left by the loss of industrial markets. Today cotton's largest use is in apparel fabrics.

USES OF COTTON

	Apparel	Household	Industrial
1947	36%	28%	36%
1955	56%	28%	16%

Cotton Production

Cotton grows in any part of the world where the climate is warm. The United States, China, and Russia are the leading cotton fiber producers.

Cotton fibers are short, ranging in length from three-quarters of an inch to two inches, depending on the variety. Cotton is constantly undergoing research to develop new and better varieties. Older varieties lose out to new ones that show promise. Long staple cottons are the most valuable, the most difficult to produce, and the least abundant. The Pima strains were developed by cross-breeding the Egyptian with the American cottons. These varieties are grown in irrigated areas of the Southwest and Far West where controlled moisture gives an even rate of growth and where there is less damage from frost and rain.

Varieties of Cotton

Long staple (over 1⅛ inches)
    Sea Island—off coast of Georgia
    Pima—California, Arizona, New Mexico
    Supima—California, Arizona, New Mexico

Short staple (less than 1⅛ inches)
    Deltapine—Midsouth, Far West
    Acala—Far West
    Coker—Southeast
    Lankart—Southwest

Area of growth is a major factor affecting the quality. A variety grown in the Southwest will be more uniform than the same variety grown in the Midsouth. If a mill has particularly good machinery and operates it with skill, a lower quality of fiber can be used for a given quality of cloth.

Cotton grows on bushes, three to four feet high. The blossom appears, falls off, and the *boll* begins its growth. Inside the boll are seeds from which the fibers grow. Thus cotton is classified as a *seed hair*.

When the boll is ripe, it splits open, and the fluffy white cotton stands out like a powder puff. (*See* Fig. 2:22.)

Cotton is picked either by hand or by machine. (*See* Fig. 2:23.) One machine can eliminate twenty-three hand pickers. Complete mechanization and chemical weed control have reduced the number of man-hours required to produce one bale of cotton from 155 hours to twelve hours. More than half of the cotton crop in 1960 was picked by machine.

After picking, the cotton is taken to a gin where the fibers are removed from the seeds. Figure 2:24 shows a saw gin, in which the whirling saws pick up the cotton and carry it up to a knife-like comb which blocks the seeds as the cotton is carried through.

Fig. 2:22 (top). An opened cotton boll. (Courtesy of the National Cotton Council of America.)

Fig. 2:23 (center). Cotton-picking machine. (Courtesy of the National Cotton Council of America.)

Fig. 2:24 (below). Cotton gin. Whirling saws carry the cotton to a knife-like comb. (Courtesy of Bibb Manufacturing Co.)

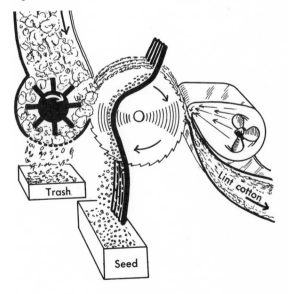

Trash

Seed

Lint cotton

The fibers, called *lint*, are pressed into bales weighing 500 pounds, ready for sale to the mills. The average yield per acre is 2½ bales. However, Arizona, the state with the largest production per acre, has averaged five bales to the acre.

The seeds after ginning look like the buds on the pussywillow. They are covered with very short fibers (⅛ inch) called *linters*. These linters are removed and used to make the spinning solution from which rayon and acetate fibers are spun. The seeds are crushed to obtain cottonseed oil.

Raw cotton is creamy white in color. The fiber is a single cell which, during growth, pushes out of the seed as a hollow cylindrical tube over 1000 times as long at it is wide.

The cotton fiber is made up of a cuticle, a primary wall, a secondary wall, and a lumen. The cross-sectional shape varies with the maturity of the fiber. Immature fibers tend to be U-shaped and the cell wall is thinner, while the mature fibers are more nearly circular with a very small lumen. (*See* Fig. 2:25.)

The *cuticle* is a waxy film on the primary or protective wall of the fiber.

The *secondary wall* contains successive layers of cellulose similar to the growth rings of a tree. One layer is laid down for each day of the twenty to thirty day growth period. Each layer is built up of fibrils (*see* page 34) which are laid down in spiral arrangement with many reversals of direction. (*See* Fig. 2:25.) These reversals are an important factor in the strength, twist, elastic recovery, and elongation of the fiber.

The *lumen* is the central canal through which nourishment travels during growth.

Identification of Cotton

Cotton can be identified as a cellulose fiber by the burning test. It burns quickly, gives off a white smoke, has an afterglow, and leaves a white feathery ash. It smells like burning paper or burning leaves. The afterglow is as important as the flame, since, if allowed to smolder, it may start a fire. The burning test does *not* distinguish cotton from the other cellulose fibers.

The longitudinal view of the cotton fiber is characterized by ribbon-like twists called *convolutions*. When the fiber matures, the lumen collapses and the reverse spirals of the fibrils cause the fiber to twist. The twist forms a natural crimp that enables the fibers to cohere to one another, so that, despite its short length, cotton is one of our most spinnable fibers. Convolutions can be a disadvantage,

Fig. 2:25. Left, reverse spirals in cotton. Right, cross section of mature cotton.

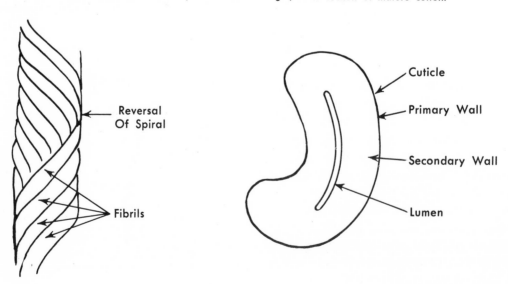

since dirt collects in the twists and must be removed by vigorous washing.

As the cotton dries upon maturing, nutrient residues remain in the lumen and give the characteristic dark central areas that can be seen in the longitudinal view of the fiber. (*See* Fig. 2:26.)

Mercerized cotton (treated with caustic soda) differs physically from regular cotton. The fiber swells and becomes shorter. Strength is increased. Some of the convolutions are removed, making the fiber almost rod-like in shape. The swelling causes a change in the molecular arrangement somewhat like the opening of a venetian blind. This makes the fiber more absorbent, and therefore dyes more easily and permanently than unmercerized cotton. Observe in the photomicrograph, Figure 2:27, the differences in fiber shape of the mercerized cotton.

The *quality* of cotton depends on the staple length, the number of convolutions, and the brightness of the fiber. (Long staple has about 300 convolutions per inch, while short staple has less than 200.)

General Properties

The general properties of cotton are similar to those of the other cellulose fibers. (*See* page 35.) It is, however, outstanding in its possession of a *combination* of low cost, easy washability, and comfort characteristics that have made it superior to the others for use in such things as summer clothes, work clothes, sheets, and towels.

The low resiliency of cotton has been improved by wash-and-wear finishes, but these still have some drawbacks, and research is continually being done to bring about improvements.

Luster has been improved by mercerization, but this is effective only on long staple cotton, so there is room for improvement in this area.

Improvements in properties related to warmth, tensile strength, and soiling resistance would give cotton many new uses.

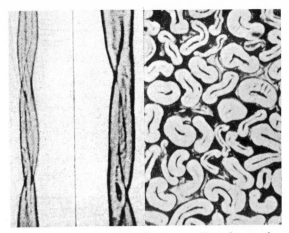

Fig. 2:26. Photomicrograph of cotton fiber showing longitudinal (left) and cross-sectional views. (From Werner Von Bergen and Walter Krauss, *Textile Fiber Atlas*. Copyright 1949 by Textile Book Publishers, Inc.)

Fig. 2:27. Photomicrograph of mercerized cotton showing longitudinal and cross-sectional views. (From Werner Von Bergen and Walter Krauss, *Textile Fiber Atlas*. Copyright 1949 by Textile Book Publishers, Inc.)

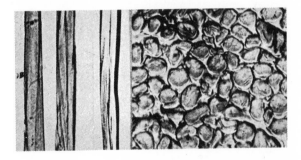

Cotton's strength is adequate for most apparel, but it cannot compete in industrial fabrics or in very sheer clothing fabrics. Check with the chart on page 12 to see how cotton compares in strength with the other fibers.

REFERENCES

1. Merrill, G. R., Macormac, A. R., and Mauersberger, H. R., *American Cotton Handbook*, New York: American Cotton Handbook Co., 1941, p. 93.
2. Mauersberger, H. R., *Matthews' Textile Fibers*, 6th ed., New York: Wiley, 1954.
3. Campbell, Kenneth S., "Preparation and Bleaching: 1. The Cotton Fiber," *Textile World*, 109:97 (Apr. 1959).

Flax

High Strength
Thick and Thin Fiber Bundles
Natural Body

The history of flax dates back over 10,000 years. Linen fabrics found in the Swiss Lake Dwellings show that Neolithic Man was skilled in the production of flax. In ancient times, Egypt was called the "Land of Linen." In the 17th century, Ireland became the center for the manufacture of linen, when a group of skilled Huguenot weavers, fleeing persecution in France, settled there. The word linen comes from the Celtic word *llin*. The flax industry in the United States dates from the early 1800's, when many Irish weavers emigrated to this country.

Production

Russia leads the world in flax production. Germany, the Baltic states, and Argentina are also large producers of flax. Flax is an important crop in Canada, both for fiber and for seed. Research programs sponsored by the Canadian industry are resulting in improved production processes there. The flax produced in Oregon is comparable in quality to that of Ireland and Belgium. Since Oregon produces only a small amount, most of the linen used in the United States is imported from Ireland and other countries.

The work involved in the processing of flax has always been extremely laborious, thus production has flourished in countries where labor is cheap. Mechanization has been slow, and although a great deal has been done, complete mechanization of this industry is still to be achieved.

The bast fibers lie in bundles in the stem of the plant just under the outer covering or bark. They are sealed together by a substance composed of pectins, waxes, and gums. To loosen the fibers so they can be removed from the stalk, the pectins must be dissolved by bac-

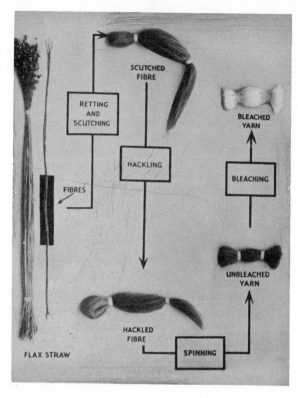

Fig. 2:28. Flax fiber at different stages of processing. (Courtesy of the Irish Linen Guild.)

terial rotting, and the woody portion of the stem broken away.

The harvesting is done by a machine that *pulls* the flax and ties it in bundles. The seeds are removed at the mill by passing the seed end of the plant through a deseeding machine.

Retting is a bacterial action which hydrolyzes the pectin and loosens the fiber bundles from the stem. This was formerly done in fields as dew-retting or in streams or pools. Now it is done in large retting tanks where the bacterial count and temperature can be carefully controlled. Controlled retting requires about a week and is one of the most important steps in flax preparation, since it determines the color and quality of the finished fiber. After the flax is removed from the retting tanks, the bundles are dried in the fields.

Breaking or *scutching* removes the woody portion of the flax stem. The fibers are passed between fluted rollers to break up the stem and the woody part is removed by agitation.

Hackling or *combing* separates the fiber bundles and removes short fibers. This is done by drawing the fibers through a series of combs. The individual fibers tend to cling together and some are broken. This gives the characteristic thick-and-thin yarn which produces the uneven "linen-like" texture of the fabric.

Physical Structure and Appearance

The long combed fibers are called *line*. Long line fibers are used in better quality linen fabrics and given the luster that is typical of good quality. The short and broken fibers are called *tow* and are used in less expensive linens. Line fibers are ready for spinning. Notice in Figure 2:28 how much the combed strands resemble combed hair. Tow fibers must be carded to prepare them for spinning.

Figure 2:28 shows the fibers before and after hackling. Further separation of the individual fibers takes place during spinning, weaving, and finishing. Fiber bundles range from 12 to 20 inches in length. The individual fibers in the bundle are from 0.5 to 2.15 inches in length.

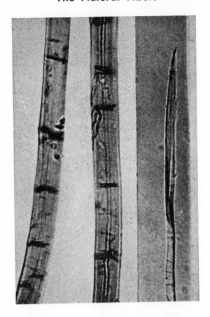

Fig. 2:30. Photomicrograph of flax showing nodes or joints. (From Werner Von Bergen and Walter Krauss, *Textile Fiber Atlas.* Copyright 1949 by Textile Book Publishers, Inc.)

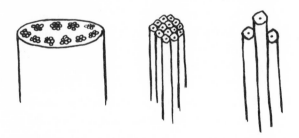

Fig. 2:29. Flax fibers before and after being removed from the stem.

Identification

Flax fibers can be identified under the microscope by crosswise markings called nodes or joints. These are shown in Figure 2:30.

The markings on flax have been attributed to either cracks or breaks during harvesting or to irregularity in growth. The fibers may appear slightly swollen at the nodes and resemble somewhat the joints in a stalk of corn. The

Fig. 2:31. Photomicrograph of flax showing cross section of fiber bundles. (From Werner Von Bergen and Walter Krauss, *Textile Fiber Atlas.* Copyright 1949 by Textile Book Publishers, Inc.)

markings are faint and difficult to see in the microscope unless staining procedures are used. Careful focusing is necessary to make the joints or nodes show clearly. Fine flax fibers are sometimes mistaken for silk, since they are about the same size and general appearance under the microscope. A small central canal is the chief lengthwise marking. The cross section is several-sided or polygonal with rounded edges.

Flax fibers are gray in color when dew-retted and yellowish in color when water-retted. Many linens are partially bleached. The finest quality linens were formerly bleached by exposure of the wet fabric to sunshine. This is seldom done now either in this country or in Ireland.

Quality in linen is determined by the length and fineness of the fiber, the character of the yarns, the degree of bleach, and the fastness of the dye.

The burning test will not distinguish the flax fiber from other cellulose fibers, since the burning characteristics are the same. It will identify flax only as a cellulose fiber. Burning characteristics are given on page 18.

Properties and Finishes

The unique and desirable characteristics of flax are its body, strength, and thick-and-thin fiber bundles.

Its chief disadvantages are low resiliency and high production cost. Although the initial cost is high, linen fabrics wear so well that they are really less expensive in the long run. Linen sheets, for example, last so long that they have become family heirlooms. Linen fabrics wear evenly and become thin all over before holes appear. Cotton fabrics often develop holes before the fabric wears thin.

Linen has had wide usage in towels because of its good wicking and quick drying properties as well as its durability.

Since flax fibers have few disadvantages, linen fabrics require few finishes. Although linen has some natural luster, most fabrics are *beetled* to increase the luster. (*See* page 178.)

Low resiliency was the chief drawback to the use of linen in clothing until the wash-and-wear finishes were developed. Table linens are not treated because they often are white and until recently resin-treated fabrics turned yellow when bleached.

Linen has natural *body;* therefore, body added by a finish is not needed on linen.

Linen has less dye affinity than does cotton. Resin finishes, mercerization, and improved dyes have improved its color fastness. Most of the Irish linens are vat-dyed.

Care of Linen

Although linen may be dry cleaned, it should be washed because proper washing increases the beauty of the fabric. Flax is a very smooth fiber and sheds dirt readily. If it is washed before too soiled, it needs no bleaching.

Starch is not needed, and any bluing that might be used (none is needed) should be completely removed from articles to be stored. Bluing contains an iron compound that sometimes oxidizes during storage and forms rust spots. These spots can be removed by a commercial rust remover or by the home remedy of salt, lemon juice, and sunshine.

Linens should be ironed while damp. Flax fibers have the same resistance to heat as the other cellulosics, but because linen is ironed very damp the temperature of the iron can be higher. Luster is increased if linen fabrics are ironed on the right side. Creases should not be pressed into the fabric and folds should not always come at the same place. It is best to roll linens on a cardboard cylinder for storing.

It is not necessary to preshrink linen fabrics when preparing them for use in home sewing. While most of the imported dress linens are not completely shrunk, if they are ironed while still damp, there will be no difficulty with shrinkage. Linen can be compressively shrunk or Sanforized.

REFERENCES

1. Mauersberger, H. R., *Matthews' Textile Fibers,* 6th ed., New York: Wiley, 1954, p. 281.
2. Schaefer, Gustav, "On the History of Flax Cultivation," *CIBA Review,* 49:1762 (Apr. 1945).
3. Irish Linen Guild, "Irish Linen," Belfast, Ire.: Irish Linen Guild, no date, p. 10.
4. Irish Linen Guild, "Care of Linen," Belfast, Ire.: Irish Linen Guild, various dates.

Ramie

High Strength
Low Resiliency
Natural Body

Ramie or grass cloth has been used for several thousand years in China. It is grown in countries that have a hot humid climate. In the United States ramie is grown in the Everglades region of Florida.

The plant is harvested by cutting. After cutting, a new growth starts immediately. Three crops a year may be harvested.

The ramie fiber bundles are removed by a decorticating machine. This machine strips the stalks as it pulls them through a series of rollers which remove all of the woody portion. After decortication, the fiber must be degummed by a mild chemical bath. The ramie fibers are longer than any of the other fibers in the bast fiber group. They range from one to twelve inches and are usually cut into desired staple length before spinning.

Much of the raw fiber is exported to Japan where it is spun into yarns and woven into fabrics. The Japanese are the largest producers of ramie yarns and fabrics in the world. Germany ranks second, and France is third.

When seen under the microscope, ramie is very similar to flax fiber. It is pure white. It is the strongest known natural fiber and its strength increases when it is wet. It has silk-like luster. Ramie also has a very high resistance to rotting, mildew, and other organisms.

Ramie also has some disadvantages. It is stiff, and low in resiliency, hence it wrinkles very easily. Ramie has the most highly crystalline molecular structure of any of the cellulose fibers. This is the reason for its high strength as well as its lack of resiliency. Ramie is low in elasticity; it is brittle, and breaks if folded repeatedly in the same place.

Ramie is used in fabrics resembling linen, such as suitings, shirtings, table cloths, napkins, and handkerchiefs.

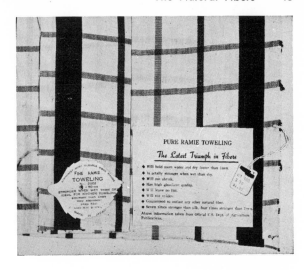

Fig. 2:32. Ramie toweling, made in Japan, with a label that lists some of the advantages of this material. Ramie is lint-free, highly absorbent, resistant to fungi, quick-drying, stronger wet than dry.

Hemp

High Strength

The history of hemp is as old as that of flax. Because hemp lacks the fineness of the better quality flax, it has never been able to compete in the clothing field. Some varieties of hemp are, however, very difficult to distinguish from flax.

Hemp production and manufacture are very similar to that of flax. In 1942 the government sponsored a hemp growing program in the United States to supply war needs. Its high strength and light weight made it particularly suitable for twine, cordage, and thread. The thread was used for stitching the soles on soldiers' shoes. After the war the demand for hemp declined, and it is now one of the less important fibers.

Jute

Weakest Cellulose Fiber
Low Cost
Natural Body

Jute was known as a fiber in Biblical times. India, the largest producer of jute, has 112 jute mills as compared to 113 for cotton. Jute is the cheapest textile fiber and is the second most widely used vegetable fiber, ranking next to cotton. The individual fibers in the jute bundle are shorter than those of the other bast fibers. It is the weakest of the cellulose fibers.

The greater part of the jute production goes into bagging for sugar, coffee, etc., or is used in twine, rope, or cordage.

REFERENCE

Mauersberger, H. R., *Matthews' Textile Fibers*, 6th ed., New York: Wiley, 1954, pp. 313–323.

III. THE MAN-MADE FIBERS

CELLULOSE	HEAT-SENSITIVE	MINERAL
Rayon	Acetate	Glass
Viscose	Diacetate	Asbestos
Cuprammonium	Triacetate	
Fortisan	Nylon	
	Nylon 66, 6, 4	
	Polyester	
	Acrylic	
	Modacrylic	
	Nytril	
	Olefin	
	Saran	
	Vinal	
	Vinyon	
	Spandex	

GENERAL DISCUSSION

Man-made fibers were first made experimentally in Europe in 1857. Commercial production in the United States began in 1910. By 1960 there were 88 man-made fiber plants producing 17 different man-made fibers and numerous types or variations.

45

Production of a new fiber is a long, expensive procedure. First, a laboratory research program is set to discover a new material. When a promising material is made, it is patented to give the producer exclusive rights to the process for a period of 16 years. Laboratory procedures must then be converted to large scale production. This is usually done in a very small plant called a *pilot plant*.

When enough fiber has been made so it can be tried out in fabric, a *development program* is set up to explore various kinds of fabric constructions and possible uses. *Consumer evaluation* is done by selling garments made from the fibers in selected areas and observing consumer reaction. All problems that arise are sent back to the laboratory, and further research is done to correct the problem.

When the fiber is ready, a full scale plant is built and an extensive advertising and *promotion* campaign is started to inform the retailers and consumers about the new fiber.

The fiber producer must be responsible for promotion that will sell his product not only to the manufacturers and the retailers, but also to his customers' customer—the consumer. Even a fiber with outstanding properties cannot be successful without a major marketing program.

In order to gain more immediate consumer acceptance, the fiber is usually promoted in an item where it has shown outstanding performance and where existing fibers have weaknesses. For example, Orlon staple fiber was first promoted in soft, lightweight sweaters because it did not shrink and required no blocking.

The producer must find many uses for his fiber if his company is to grow. No fiber has yet been designed which possesses *all* properties. The same fiber cannot be stiff for carpets and soft for clothing. Thus a continuing research program is needed to develop a *family* of fibers with properties specifically designed to fit a need. Each member of the family is often referred to by *type* number. Nylon Type 420 is a good example of a fiber modified to

fit a specific need—that of blending with cotton. On the garment label it appears as nylon 420. In the case of Dacron Type 62, however, it appears on the label as either Dacron Type 62 or Dacron T 62.

By the time the fiber is in full scale production and before any profit has been realized by the producer, he may have spent more than $50 million in development and research. A $4 or 5 million research plant must be maintained to enable the producer to meet competition from other producers who are also engaged in research programs. As one author has said, "The producer must plan his own obsolescence or his competitor will do it for him."

When consumer demand for the fiber is great enough to justify expansion, a new plant will be built. Or other companies may be licensed to produce the fiber on a royalty basis. This often happens as the time approaches for the patent to expire. In the case of nylon, there was great need for the fiber for use by the armed forces, so the government ordered that other companies be licensed to produce nylon.

Naming the Fibers

During the time the fiber is in the experimental stage it is referred to by number, as X-51 or M-27.

The *trade name* is selected by the producer and is a very definite selling tool, so the choice is an important one. It should be pleasing in both sight and sound and preferably two syllables in length. If it starts with an "A" it will have the advantage of coming first alphabetically. (All trade names are capitalized.) Some firms develop and register trade names long in advance of intended use.

Several names were considered for nylon: "No-run," then Nuron (No-run spelled backwards), Nulon, and finally nylon. The endings "on," "an," and "el" have become popular for fiber names. Some fibers are named for the company (Avisco for the American Viscose Corporation), some for the chemical composition of the fiber (Estron acetate from cellulose ester), and some, such as nylon, for fiber characteristics.

The *generic name* is the name of a *family* of fibers which all have similar chemical composition. Generic names are established by the Federal Trade Commission in cooperation with fiber producers.

Rayon (1924) was the first name adopted for a man-made fiber. It was suggested by Kenneth Lord of Burlington Industries because the bright luster of the fiber suggested the sparkling rays of the sun. The world-wide copyright for the name "rayon" is owned by the National Retail Merchants Association. Burlington Industries is the world's largest spinner and weaver of man-made fibers and often works with the man-made fiber producers in market evaluation of new fibers.

Acetate had a stormy battle getting its generic name. From 1937 to 1952 it was called rayon, but the companies producing acetate refused to use this name for their fiber because acetate was not like rayon in its properties, and they thought, and rightly so, that it deserved a distinctive name.

In 1959 and 1960 the producers of cross-linked rayons requested permission from the F.T.C. to drop the generic name "rayon" and use the generic name *lincron.* The request was denied. The producers of Zantrel Polynosic[1] rayon also requested permission to drop the name "rayon" and use the generic name *polynosic* instead. This request was denied.

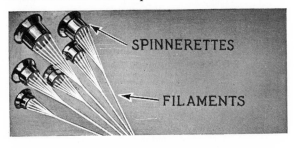

Fig. 3:1. Spinnerettes, described at right. (Courtesy of the American Viscose Corporation.)

[1] *Polynosic* was registered as a trademark in May 1961 by the American Enka Corporation and should not be used in this country as a generic name.

The *Textile Fiber Products Identification Act* was passed by Congress in 1959. It states that all clothing and household textile fibers must have the kind and per cent of fiber or fibers indicated on the label. The 16 generic names listed below were established for the man-made fibers.[2]

Acetate	Olefin
Acrylic	Polyester
Azlon	Rayon
Glass	Rubber
Metallic	Saran
Modacrylic	Spandex
Nylon	Vinal
Nytril	Vinyon

According to the TFPIA, the generic name must appear on the label. Trade names may also be used, but in addition to—not as a substitute for—the generic name.

Spinning

There are three methods of spinning man-made fibers, but the general procedure is the same.

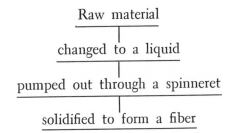

The spinneret, a small thimble-like nozzle, is one of the most important parts of the spinning equipment. The holes are smaller than the diameter of a human hair and are usually circular in shape. They are made of platinum or a similar metal which will resist acids and the effects of abrasion by the liquid. They are very expensive.

Filament fibers are spun from small spinnerets with 350 holes or less as determined by the size of the yarn to be made.

[2] Definitions according to the TFPIA are given in the individual fiber discussion section.

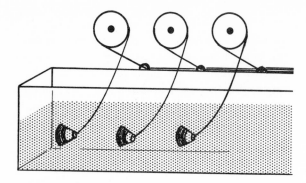

Fig. 3:2. Collecting fibers from several spinnerets to make filament tow which will be cut into staple.

Staple fibers are spun from large spinnerets with as many as 3000 holes. The product of 100 or more spinnerets is collected as a large rope called *filament tow* (Fig. 3:2), which is cut to make the staple fiber, or it is sold as filament tow. The length of the staple usually corresponds to that of cotton or wool.

Filament and staple fibers are produced in separate plants, since they are spun on different equipment.

The three spinning processes are illustrated very simply in Figures 3:3a, b, and c within the table. Additional phases common to the three processes are discussed in the section that follows.

One important advantage of man-made fibers is that the luster and color of the fibers can be controlled during the spinning process. This is done by adding pigments to the spinning solution *before* the solution is pumped out through the spinneret.

DELUSTERING

Delustering is a process in which the addition of *white* pigment (titanium dioxide) to the spinning solution reduces the amount of light reflected from the surface of the fiber.

FIBER SPINNING PROCESSES		
Wet Spinning	*Dry or Solvent Spinning*	*Melt Spinning*
Rayon Nytril Acrylic staple Vinal Modacrylic	Acetate Orlon filament Vinyon Modacrylic	Nylon Polyester Saran Olefins
1. Raw material is dissolved by chemicals. 2. Fiber is spun into acid bath. Fig. 3:3a. 3. Fiber solidifies when coagulated by acid.	1. Resin solids are dissolved by solvent. 2. Fiber is spun out into warm air. 3. Fiber solidifies by evaporation of solvent. Fig. 3:3b.	1. Resin solids are melted in autoclave. 2. Fiber is spun out into air. 3. Fiber solidifies on cooling. Fig. 3:3c.
Oldest process Most complex Weak fibers until dry Washing, bleaching, etc., required before use.	Direct process Solvent required Solvent recovery required No washing, etc., required	Least expensive Direct process High spinning speeds No solvent, washing, etc., required Fibers shaped like spinneret hole

Variation in the amount of pigment will control the degree of luster to produce *semi-dull* or *dull* fibers. Fibers which have not been delustered are referred to as bright fibers. (*See* Fig. 3:4.) The bright form of the fiber is usually the first one produced, and the delustered fibers are developed later.[3]

Fig. 3:4. Bright and dull rayon yarns. (Courtesy of the American Viscose Corporation.)

Delustered fibers can be identified under the microscope by black "peppery" dots.

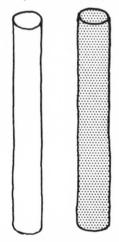

Fig. 3:5. Diagram showing a bright fiber (left) and a delustered fiber (right), as they would look under the microscope.

Fibers with high luster are limited in use to silk-like fabrics, decorative fabrics, and to fabrics which will be exposed to sunlight for periods of time. Delustered fibers are much

[3] This can be observed in the charts of fiber history included in the discussion of individual fibers.

more rapidly degraded by sunlight than high-luster fibers, because the light is absorbed rather than reflected. Also, the colors in delustered fibers fade more rapidly than in bright fibers.

The initial strength of a delustered fiber is also less than that of a bright fiber. Rayon, for example, is three to five per cent weaker when delustered.

SOLUTION DYEING

The addition of *colored* pigments to the spinning solution is called *solution dyeing*, *dope dyeing*, or *spun dyeing*.

This process was developed as a remedy for the gas-fading of blue and green colors used in acetate fibers. This is discussed in detail on page 68.

Black is usually the first color used, and other colors are then added as suitably fast pigments are made.

Solution dyed fibers are usually sold for ten to fifteen cents more per pound than uncolored fibers. This difference is offset later by the cost of dyeing yarns or fabrics.

The fastness of solution dyed fibers is excellent. They have been used in automobile upholstery, curtains, and in swim suits where chlorine and/or salt water are factors in color loss.

Trade names for solution dyed fibers indicate that the color was added to the spinning solution, as Jetspun, Chromspun, Colorspun, or Color-sealed.

Fabrics made from solution dyed fibers may be solid colors, plaids, checks, or woven designs.

A disadvantage of these fibers from the manufacturer's standpoint is that he must carry a large inventory to be able to fill orders quickly and he is less able to adjust to fashion changes in color. It is not possible to strip the color from these fabrics and redye them.

Size or Denier

Another advantage of man-made fibers is that *size* and *shape* can be controlled. As mentioned previously, the natural fibers are subject to growth irregularities and are therefore not uniform in size or in development. Manmade fibers can be made uniform in diameter, can be varied in diameter shape, and can be made thick and thin at regular intervals throughout their length. Additional information is given in the discussion of each individual fiber.

Filament yarns and fiber size or number are measured in denier. *Denier* is the weight in grams of 9000 meters of fiber or yarn. The smaller the denier number, the finer and more flexible the fiber will be.

Clothing fibers range from one to five denier. The same denier fiber is not suitable to all uses. Clothing fibers do not make good carpets and vice versa. One of the early mistakes made by the carpet industry was the use of clothing fibers for carpets. They were too soft and pliable, and the carpets did not have good crush resistance. In 1953, a rayon carpet fiber was especially designed. (*See* Fig. 3:6.)

Fig. 3:6. Carpet wool on the left; carpet rayon on the right. (Courtesy of Bigelow-Sanford.)

Even clothing wools have never been suitable for carpet use. Carpet wools used in the United States have always been imported from Asia or Africa. After World War II, when trade with China was restricted, the supply of carpet wool was reduced. Agricultural development in the underdeveloped areas of the world was also a factor in reducing the supply. As herdsmen shifted to mechanized kinds of agriculture, they ceased to raise the kind of sheep that produced the coarser fiber.

With the reduced supply of carpet fiber, there was a need for man-made carpet fibers. Especially designed carpet fibers have been produced in most of the different fiber families.

Carpet fibers range in denier from 15 to 24. Carpet fibers, other than denier size, have the same characteristics as the other fibers in the family to which they belong. For example, neither carpet wools nor clothing wools are readily inflammable, and both have good crush resistance. Study the sections discussing the various fibers and make a comparison of the properties of the various kinds of carpet fibers.

Many other properties can be built into man-made fibers. Some of these are *strength*, improved *heat resistance, high or low shrinkage*, and *high and low elongation*.

CELLULOSE FIBERS

Rayon
Most Versatile Fiber
Low Cost

Rayon is a manufactured fiber composed of *regenerated* cellulose, as well as a manufactured fiber composed of regenerated cellulose in which substituents have replaced not more than 15 per cent of the hydrogens of the hydroxyl groups.[4]

[4] F.T.C. definition.

1664 Idea suggested by Robert Hooke

1857 First cuprammonium rayon

1884 Nitrocellulose rayon; Chardonnet

1889 Rayon clothing at French Fair

1890 Cuprammonium plant in France

1892 Viscose patent; Cross and Bevan, England

1905 Courtaulds buys viscose patent
Courtaulds plant in England
Topham invented spinning box

1910 American Viscose Company in U.S.

1914 Zinc salt added to spinning bath

1916 Industrial Rayon Corporation

1918 Viscose staple—Germany

1921 Du Pont Rayon Plant at Buffalo

1923 Rayon transparent velvet; France

1924 Rayon adopted as name for cellulose-base fibers

1926 Delaware Rayon Corporation
Skenandoa Rayon Corporation
Beaunit Mills—cuprammonium
Warp sizing developed
Delustering of bright viscose
High tenacity rayon

1927 Crepe yarn techniques

1929 New Bedford Rayon Company
Celanese Corporation of America
North American Rayon Corporation
American Enka Rayon Corporation

1930 Resin finishes for crease resistance

1934 Nitrocellulose discontinued in U.S.

1935 Z-twist yarns produced

1937 Tire cord yarn
Cuprammonium staple
Thick and thin yarn
Rayon blankets
Crimped carpet fiber

1939 Latent crimp viscose; Japan

1941 Fair Haven Mills
Continuous spinning process

1943 Tire cord surpasses cotton

1946 Viscose largest user of linters

1949 Beaunit Mills Inc. viscose
Viscose continuous spinning process

1951 Bigelow-Sanford buys Hartford Co.
Mohawk buys New Bedford and Delaware companies
Latent crimp—Fiber E by Du Pont

1952 Rayon separated from acetate as fiber group

1953 Courtaulds, Inc.
Carpet fiber—especially designed for carpets by Hartford Rayon

1954 Spun-dyed viscose by Enka
High tenacity license to Firestone
Surgical dressings of rayon
Courtaulds doubles Le Moyne plant
Marcus Hook (oldest plant) closes
Buffalo plant closes

1955 American Enka Staple rayon plant (six acres floor space)

1956 Solution-dyed carpet staple
"Super L" designed specifically for carpets
Research plant; Courtaulds
Research plant doubled; Marcus Hook

1957 Delaware plant closes
Roanoke plant closes (fiber and machinery obsolete)
Tufted carpets, 4½ million pounds
Textured yarn; air-jet process; Enka

1958 High tenacity 50% stronger
Cross-linked staple rayon; Courtaulds
Microfibers by American Viscose Company

1959 Slubbed filament "Ondelette" by Du Pont
Hollow filament "Civona" by Du Pont
Flat straw fiber "Strawn"

1960 GOLDEN ANNIVERSARY of rayon in U.S.
High wet-modulus rayon
Zantrel Polynosic by Hartford Fibers *
Avlin (Fiber 40) by American Viscose Company
Moynel (SM-27) by Courtaulds
Fiber 500 by Enka
Multicellular rayon
Avlin (RD-100) by American Viscose Company
High strength rayon
Avron by American Viscose Company

1961 **

---

* Purchased by American Enka in December 1961.
** It is suggested that the student use the space above for listing new developments for this period. These developments can be found in current textile magazines, particularly the *Textile Organon*, from which many of these were taken.

The Rayon Family		
Viscose Rayon	Cuprammonium Rayon	Fortisan Rayon
Regular	Regular	
Delusterd	Delustered	
Spun-dyed	Thick and thin	
High tenacity		
Carpet staple		
Multicellular		
Hollow filament		
Latent crimp		
Cross-linked		
High wet-modulus		

History

December 19, 1960 marked the Golden Anniversary of commercial production in the United States of viscose rayon, the oldest man-made fiber. The plant was located at Marcus Hook, Pa. and owned by the American Viscose Company, a subsidiary of Courtaulds of England. Previous to 1910, all rayon fiber production had been on an experimental basis or in pilot plants. In 1954, after 44 years of operation, fiber production was discontinued at the Marcus Hook plant because it was too small and uneconomical; the machinery and fiber had both been made obsolete by many new improvements and developments. The research plant located there was retained, however, and in 1956 its capacity was doubled.

During the 1920's, a number of new rayon producing companies were established and in the early 1950's several closed due to a shift in demand away from the type of fiber they were set up to produce. A study of the accompanying historical record will show that at about the same time the older plants were closing, new plants were being built. These were larger, modern, all-on-one-floor plants rather than the older, uneconomical multistory plant.

The development of rayon was a hard struggle for its manufacturers. Rayon was a potential competitor for silk, but because it was so inferior, not many people thought it would ever be a major textile fiber. The manufacturers had so much confidence in rayon, however, that in less than fifty years they succeeded in making it second only to cotton in amount consumed. It is now *considered the most versatile fiber* on the market.

Perhaps the most important factor of rayon as a textile fiber is that it can be produced at a low cost so that people at every economic level can buy fabrics that have the beauty of appearance, hand, and color of silk, wool, and linen.

Rayon's battle for expansion in the textile field can best be illustrated by its use in the tire cord market. The tire cord market is steady, and therefore a large dependable outlet for fiber, whereas the apparel market fluctuates with fashion.

Cotton had had no competition in the tire cord market until high tenacity rayon was developed. Because the heat generated by high speed has less tendency to cause rayon to separate from the rubber, rayon had captured a large part of the market by 1943. Nylon was introduced about this time, and by 1957, one out of every three tires made was nylon. ($\frac{6}{10}$ of a pound of nylon is equivalent to one pound of rayon.) A new high tenacity rayon with 50% greater strength was introduced in 1958 for more effective competition with nylon.

Although rayon's first uses were in the clothing field, by 1957, 65% of it was used for industrial purposes or for home furnishings. Notice in the historical record that in 1951, two carpet companies bought rayon plants in order to produce their own fibers, and then in 1953, a new type of rayon was designed especially for carpets. Thus the rayon carpets on the market in the late 1950's were quite different from the rayon carpets on the market before that time.

In 1952 rayon for the first time was cheaper than cotton. Cotton weavers, who were experiencing rising costs, falling profits and competition from low-cost cotton imports, began to blend small quantities of rayon with cotton without announcing this fact. Since the use of larger amounts of rayon or the use of 100% rayon was limited by (1) poor laundering stability (unless resin treated) and (2) inability to be mercerized, an accelerated research and developmental program was initiated. This resulted in the production of (1) cross-linked and (2) high wet-modulus types to be used in the wash-and-wear market. (*See* page 58.)

Manufacture

A knowledge of the manufacturing process gives a basis for understanding *why* there is more than one *kind* of rayon and *why* each kind of rayon can be varied to make different *types* of rayon. All rayon is made from cellulose obtained by purifying cotton linters or wood pulp. The production processes differ in the chemicals used to put the cellulose into solution; in the kind of ingredients added to the solution and the length of time it is aged; in the concentration, temperature and ingredients in the acid bath; and the mechanical treatments during and after spinning. A comparison of the viscose and cuprammonium processes are given below.

THE CUPRAMMONIUM PROCESS

Purified cellulose sheets are dissolved by Schweitzer's reagent, a solution of ammoniacal copper sulfate, at a low temperature.

The solution is filtered and aged. It is then pumped through spinnerets which have fairly large holes. These spinnerets are fitted into the top of a glass cylinder containing a long tapering funnel. A slightly acidic coagulating bath is allowed to enter the cylinder and flow

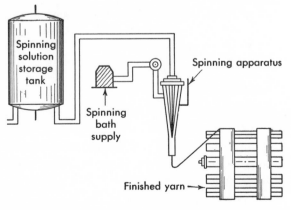

Fig. 3:7. Cuprammonium process. (Courtesy of American Bemberg.)

up to the spinneret and then flow down with the fibers as they are spun into the funnel.

The force and flow of the acid bath stretches the filaments as they are spun out. This is *stretch spinning*, a process used exclusively for cuprammonium rayon.

The yarns are passed through a sulfuric acid bath for final coagulation, wound on reels or bobbins, decoppered, washed, soaped, and dried. Washing removes any traces of blue copper color so the fibers need no bleaching.

THE VISCOSE PROCESS

Purified cellulose sheets are steeped in caustic soda for about an hour, the excess liquid is squeezed off and the sheets are shredded into crumbs which age for two or three days. They are then treated with *carbon disulfide* (Xanthation) which turns them orange in color. The crumbs are next dissolved in dilute caustic soda to make the viscose solution. The solution is aged four to five days, filtered to remove air bubbles and undissolved particles, and pumped through spinnerets into an acid bath. The acid causes the cellulose xanthate to coagulate, thus forming the fibers.

The filaments are drawn up and around a glass godet stretching wheel and collected on bobbins or in pots. The cakes and bobbins of yarn are washed, desulfured, bleached, oiled, dried, and wound onto spools for shipping.

Cuprammonium rayon is produced by American Bemberg, a subsidiary of Beaunit Mills. Although produced in small quantity as compared to viscose rayon, there has been

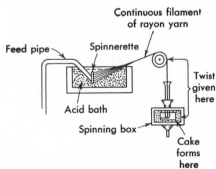

Fig. 3:8. Viscose process. (Courtesy of the American Viscose Corporation.)

Fig. 3:9. Steeping the cellulose. (Courtesy of the American Viscose Corporation.)

Fig. 3:10. Shredding the cellulose. (Courtesy of the American Viscose Corporation.)

a good market for it since it provides a quality rayon in fine denier. Recently a thick and thin yarn (denier changes within the filament), called Cupioni, has been popular in fabrics of irregular linen-like texture.

Continuous Viscose Spinning

Because the conventional pot spinning method has many handling operations and processing steps, continuous spinning processes have been developed in which the yarn travels continuously from the coagulating bath through the final operations of washing, bleaching, etc., and is then wound on bobbins.

While this is more economical of handling operations, it results in higher cost for maintenance, replacements, and changeover from one denier to another. It is also difficult to get a yarn of minimum shrinkage since the yarn is under stress from beginning to end in a continuous process.

STAPLE FIBER MANUFACTURE

The viscose solution for spinning staple is the same as that used for spinning filament. The spinnerets, however, have many holes (1000 or more) and the product of 100 or more spinnerets is collected into a large rope called *filament tow* as shown in Figure 3:2. The fibers are cut while wet, and when the tensions from the spinning are released, the fibers shrink and take on a permanent crimp. (*See* Fig. 3:2.)

Fig. 3:11. Permanent crimp in rayon staple. Figure 3:2, page 48, shows the production process.

Identification of Rayon

There is no difference in the appearance of staple and filament rayon when seen under the microscope. Cuprammonium rayon is round, rod-like, and of small diameter. (*See* Fig. 3:12.)

The longitudinal view of regular type viscose, Figure 3:13, is characterized by lengthwise lines called *striations*. These are the results of "wrinkles" that form when liquid is lost from the fiber during coagulation. The cross-section view shows a serrated, circular shape. (*See* Fig. 3:13).

Some of the types of viscose differ from regular viscose in fiber shape. These are shown and discussed later.

THE BURNING TEST

Cellulose fibers cannot be distinguished from one another by the burning test, and one kind of rayon cannot be distinguished from another by burning. However, if the fabric is made of filament fibers rather than staple fibers it can be identified as rayon because *rayon is the only cellulose fiber that is a filament.* Burning characteristics of cellulose are given in detail in the charts that you will find on pages 18 and 35.

Characteristics and Development

The first rayon had a number of drawbacks. Poor hand due to fiber stiffness and high luster were the first drawbacks to be corrected. Zinc salts added to the spinning bath improved the hand, and delustering pigments added to the spinning solution gave luster control, from very dull to semi-bright. (*See* page 49.) The high luster is due to light reflectances from the sharp serrated edges of the fiber.

Low resiliency was improved when, in 1930, resin finishes for crease resistance were developed. This also resulted in improvement in the body of rayon fabrics. Rayon (regenerated cellulose) has better resistance to acids than has cotton, so it suffered less damage from the acid catalysts used with the first resin finishes.

Solution-dyed rayon was developed in 1954. (Acetate spun-dyed fibers had been developed in 1951.) Some trade names are Jetspun, Coloray, Kolorlok (carpets), Color-sealed, and Colorspun. One of the first uses of solution-dyed rayon was in car upholstery.

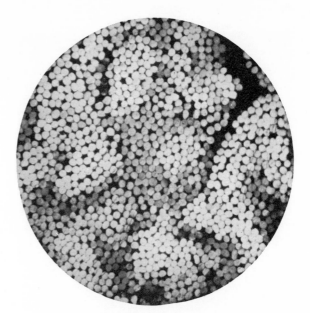

Fig. 3:12 (above). Photomicrograph of cuprammonium rayon showing cross section of the fiber. (Courtesy of American Bemberg.)

Fig. 3:13 (below). Photomicrograph of longitudinal and cross-sectional views of viscose rayon fiber. (Courtesy of E. I. du Pont de Nemours & Company.)

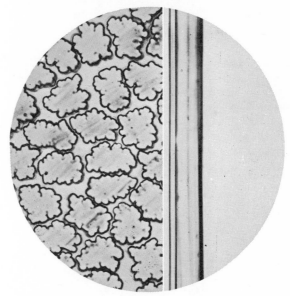

Chemical properties are, in general, similar to those of cotton. Most differences are the result of the shorter molecule chain length. Rayon is more absorbent and dyes more easily. Bright rayon fibers which reflect light are more resistant to light damage.

Rayon does not melt when the iron is too hot. *It scorches!*

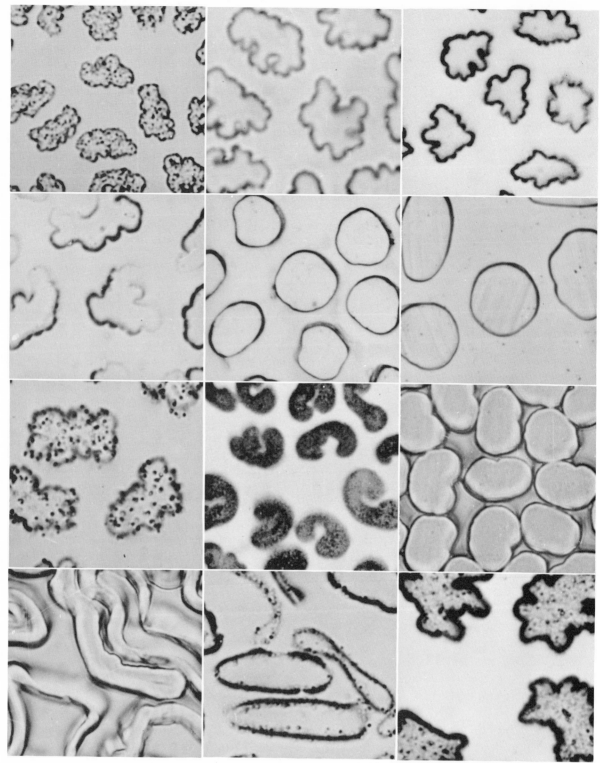

Fig. 3:14. Photomicrographs of new rayon types. Top row, left to right: 5.5 dull regular, 3.0 bright regular, 1.5 bright regular. Second row: 3.0 bright crimped, 8.0 bright smooth Super L, 15.0 bright smooth Super L. Third row: 3.0 dull V-22 intermediate strength, 1.5 XL (Avron), 1.5 bright Fiber 40 (Avril). Bottom row: 3.0 bright RD-100 (Avlin), 1.5 dull RD-100 (Avlin), Avicolor. (Courtesy of the American Viscose Corporation.)

Rayon's short molecule chain and random fibril arrangement were weaknesses that limited its use in utilitarian and washable fabrics. Study the chart below.

Weakness	*Limitation*
High wet swelling and elongation	Weaker when wet
	Seldom used for sheets, wash clothes, etc.
	Sanforization was impossible
Low dry strength	Seldom used for work clothes
Poor resistance to alkali	Mercerization was impossible; caused fiber to swell to a gel
	Could not be blended with cotton

New Rayon Types

In recent years several new types of rayon with improved properties have been developed by various manufacturers.

HIGH STRENGTH RAYON

High tenacity rayon for industrial uses was developed in 1926. Avron rayon, developed by the American Viscose Corporation in 1960, was the first high-strength rayon apparel fiber.

High tenacity rayon refers to a rayon fiber with a tensile strength of three or more grams per denier. The table below gives tensile strength figures for the cellulose fibers.

Fiber	*Strength in Grams/Denier*
Flax	6.0 g/d
Cotton	3.8 g/d
Rayon	2.0 g/d
High tenacity rayon	3.0 g/d

High strength manufacturing techniques were first developed in 1935, when it was discovered that a night foreman was keeping the doors to a factory closed, and thereby raising the temperature of the factory so the fiber was being stretched at a higher temperature.

High strength rayon is made from a normal spinning solution and spun into a coagulation bath which has a higher zinc salt concentration and a higher temperature than that used for regular type rayon. The zinc salt causes rapid coagulation of the cellulose forming a *skin* on the fiber and preventing rapid coagulation of the interior. This, plus the high temperature, makes it possible to develop good orientation when the fiber is stretched.

After the fiber leaves the coagulation bath, it is run through a 90°C hot water bath (100°C is boiling) between two godet wheels which revolve with enough difference in speed to stretch the fibers just short of the breaking point.

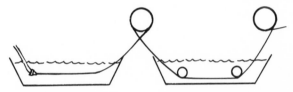

Fig. 3:15. Stretching rayon fiber in hot water baths to increase strength.

Avron is a high elongation fiber suitable for use with the other high elongation fibers such as nylon and the polyesters. It can also be used in washable sheers. It has good abrasion resistance, can be resin treated, but does not have the resistance to shrinkage or mercerization of the high wet-modulus types of rayon. Avron has a kidney bean shape, and a smooth, unserrated surface.

Fortisan is a high tenacity rayon which started out as an acetate, because acetate can be stretched to a greater degree than rayon. This greater degree of stretching gives Fortisan a highly crystalline molecular structure, and makes it one of the strongest fibers known. After the fiber is stretched it is treated with caustic soda (saponified) which changes the acetate back to regenerated cellulose. (Celcos is a rayon staple which is made by partial saponification of acetate. It is used in the manufacturing of carpets and mattresses.)

MULTICELLULAR RAYON

Multicellular rayon fibers have a unique, thin-walled, broad, flat cross-section—Figure 3:14—which imparts crispness and luster, or in dark shades, a glitter to the fabric. The fibers when wet *will bond* to one another or to other fibers as they dry. No adhesive is necessary. The flat surface of the fiber permits larger areas of contact between adjacent fibers. The bonds can be broken by mechanical action but more bonds form on rewetting and drying. The shape of the fibers permits them to intertwine and restricts the movement of other fibers in a blend. This prevents packing and thereby gives a firm hand which is permanent.

Avlin is a multicellular fiber made by the American Viscose Company. It is used in fabrics with a linen-like texture. It requires a resin finish for crease resistance.

CROSS-LINKED RAYON

Cross-linked rayons have been defined as three-dimensional polymers of cellulose units chemically combined through methylene ether linkages. (*See* page 35.) Because of this structural difference, the producers requested permission from the F.T.C. to use the generic name "lincron," but this request was denied.

Corval and *Topel*, the first cross-linked fibers, were produced by Courtaulds in 1958. By 1960, improvements in cross-linking techniques gave fibers greater stability and these new fibers were called Corval III and Topel II. The difference is in degree of cross-linking.

The outstanding advantage of these fibers is that they need *little or no resin* in blends of 50% with triacetate, acrylic, and polyester fibers, and when used alone, they need very little resin to produce satisfactory wash-and-wear garments.

They exhibit no progressive shrinkage, can be mercerized, and in blends with heat-sensitive fibers, can be satisfactorily heat-set into permanent pleats and stable fabrics. Dyeing properties are like those of regular rayon. The fibers are crimped staple with more bulk and

cover and a firmer hand than regular rayon. The appearance under a microscope is also the same.

Corval was designed for blending with wool-type fibers and Topel was designed for blends with cotton.

HIGH WET-MODULUS RAYON

Regular type viscose is the most versatile fiber. However, it has several disadvantages that have limited its use in blends with cotton and the synthetics, and also in washable fabrics such as sheets, and shirts. The limitations result from a high (25 to 45%) moisture absorption which causes excessive swelling, weakening, and elongation of the fiber. Such fabrics exhibit *progressive* shrinkage and cannot be Sanforized, mercerized, or finished by continuous processing.

A research program designed to improve the washability of rayon has resulted in the production of a type designated as high wet-modulus rayon; one of the most outstanding developments in rayon research.

The first high wet-modulus fiber, Toramomen, was made by Dr. Shozo Tachikawa of Japan in 1938. Little interest was shown in the fiber by American producers but a series of articles was published in 1951 in the *Modern Textiles Magazine*. However, in Europe, a group of fiber producers became interested in the Japanese fiber and obtained an option on the process and adapted it for commercial production. A license was granted to them in 1958 and they began production of a fiber called Zantrel Polynosic. Small amounts were imported into the United States, and because the fiber is of cellulose base, the Federal Trade Commission required that it be called Zantrel Polynosic Rayon. In 1960, the Hartford Fibers Company [5] began production of Zantrel in the United States. The company appealed to the F.T.C. for permission to use the generic name "Polynosic" rather than rayon but the appeal was denied.

[5] Purchased by American Enka in December 1961.

Meanwhile, research work in the United States resulted in the development in 1959 of three new high wet-modulus fibers, namely:

Avril (Fiber 40)

by the American Viscose Corporation

Moynel (SM 27)

by Courtaulds Ltd.

Fiber 500

by American Enka Corporation

High wet-modulus fibers have low elongation and higher wet and dry strength than regular rayon.[6] The production process is based on the concept of maintaining maximum molecule chain length and regularity in fibril structure. This is done by preventing, in so far as is possible during the dissolving and resolidifying of the fiber, the breakdown of the natural molecule and fibril structure which occurs with regular rayon.

These are some of the differences in processing as compared to that of regular rayon, page 54.

Use of very dilute spinning solution.
Elimination of aging and ripening.
Dissolving in water rather than alkali.
Use of low concentration of acid bath.

Fabrics made of high wet-modulus rayon have the following advantages:

Stability equal to cotton.
Can be Sanforized.
Can be mercerized.
Can be plisséd.
Hand more like that of cotton.
Strength is close to that of cotton.

[6] Modulus means measure. High wet-modulus is a measure of wet breaking strength divided by breaking elongation. For example:

$$\frac{\text{Wet breaking strength}}{\text{breaking elongation}} = \text{cotton } \frac{4.20}{12} \text{ or } .35$$

$$\text{Avril } \frac{2.4}{10} \text{ or } .24$$

$$\text{Zantrel } \frac{3.4}{12} \text{ or } .28$$

$$\text{Regular rayon } \frac{1.60}{30} \text{ or } .05$$

$$\text{Avron } \frac{3.0}{35} \text{ or } .085$$

TABLE OF DRY AND WET STRENGTH		
Fiber	Strength: Dry	*Wet*
Cotton	3.8	4.8
Regular rayon	2.0	1.0
High wet-modulus rayon (Zantrel)	3.4	2.7

In addition to increased use in washable fabrics, high wet-modulus rayon will be more suitable for use in draperies since it does not exhibit the "elevator effect" of regular rayon draperies which lengthen when a high moisture content in the atmosphere increases the weight of the drapery fabric, and then as the air dries, shorten again.

LATENT CRIMP RAYON

Latent crimp is not present in a fiber when it is spun, but the potential is there and the crimp is developed later. In this respect it differs from inherent or natural crimp which is present from the beginning.

The two halves of a latent crimp fiber are *not* alike. Consequently, when the fiber is wet, the surface tension is lowered more on one side than it is on the other and curling results. This can be easily demonstrated by wetting a piece of paper on one side only. This lowers the surface tension and the paper then curls toward the dry side.

Two methods may be used to make a fiber with latent crimp. In the first method a change is made in the coagulation bath. The acidity is lowered and the salt content raised. Differences in the rate of coagulation of the inside and the outside of the fiber cause the "skin" to burst on one side and a new skin forms which is thinner and has deep serrations. This gives the difference in surface tension of the two sides of the fiber which causes the fiber to curl.

Fiber E which was introduced in 1951 by the Du Pont Company, but which has since been discontinued, was a fiber of this type.

Avicron is another latent crimp fiber cur-

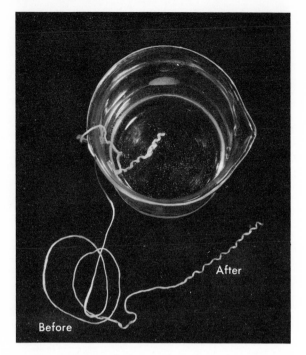

Fig. 3:16. Avicron latent crimp fiber curls when immersed in water.

rently being produced by the American Viscose Corporation. Figure 3:16 shows Avicron before and after crimping.

A second method of making a fiber with the two sides different is to spin each side from a different spinning solution. This is done by placing the two solutions (one of which is an aged solution; the other is not) side by side in different containers and spinning them out through the same spinneret hole. (*See* Fig.

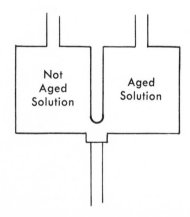

Fig. 3:17. Aged and unaged viscose solutions are spun out together to make latent crimp fiber.

3:17.) The aged solution develops a thick skin and the new solution a thin skin when in the coagulating bath. Thus, the fiber swells more on the thin skin side and crimps in a coil-like shape. Fibers of this type are called conjugate fibers. (Orlon Sayelle is a fiber of this type.) (*See* page 81.)

Characteristics

Most latent crimp rayon fibers are filament fibers. They are without crimp as they are spun and the crimp is not developed in most instances until after the garment or article has been made.

These fibers are used in rugs, upholstery, draperies, toys, and have limited use in apparel.

Advantages are the permanence of the crimp and the fact that because the fibers are filament, there is no shedding or linting.

REFERENCES

1. Welch, I. H., and Sollenberger, W. S., "New Cellulosic Fibers," *American Dyestuff Reporter*, 49:138 (Sept. 1960).
2. Moncrieff, R. W., *Man Made Fibers*, 3rd ed., New York: Wiley, 1957, p. 225.
3. Hamburger, W. J., "Dyeing and Finishing of New Cellulosic Fibers," *American Dyestuff Reporter*, 50:35 (Jan. 1961).
4. Cheatham, F. A., "An Introduction to Textile Properties of Corval and Moynel Fibres," *Canadian Textile Journal*, 77:55 (Dec. 1960).
5. Sevison, T. B., "Modified Rayons," *Textile World*, 112:49 (May 1962).

HEAT-SENSITIVE FIBERS

Acetate	Modacrylic	Vinal
Nylon	Nytril	Vinyon
Polyester	Olefin	Spandex
Acrylic	Saran	

Although the eleven fiber families listed above differ in chemical composition and structure, they are grouped together because

Property	*Importance to Consumer*

Heat-sensitive.	Glazes or melts with hot iron or hot object. Melts with hot tobacco ashes.
	Advantages:
	  1. Embossed designs and novelty fabrics.
	  2. Crush-resistant pile.
	  3. Durable pleats and shape.
	  4. Stabilized size.
	  5. Knits do not need to be blocked.
	Disadvantage:
	  1. "Set" creases are hard to remove in pressing or altering garments.

Low moisture absorption.	Advantages:
	  1. Spot resistant, easy spot removal.
	  2. Washable.
	  3. Quick drying.
	Disadvantages:
	  1. Difficult to dye.
	  2. Builds up static electricity charges.
	  3. May feel cold or clammy or hot and uncomfortable.

Resilience, elasticity, and elongation are good.	Resists wrinkles and recovers from wrinkles. Maintains air space for warmth.
High resistance to moths, mildew, insects, mold, etc.	Simplifies storage problems, little loss from these causes.
* Good strength and abrasion resistance.	Resistance to pulling and rubbing in wear.
* Wet strength is comparable to dry strength.	No danger of holes due to agitation or abrasion during washing or wearing.

* Exception: acetate.

they have a number of common properties of which heat-sensitivity is the most outstanding. These fibers are also referred to as synthetic,[7] thermoplastic, or chemical fibers.

[7] Acetate is not a synthetic, but is a thermoplastic fiber.

None of these group names has been officially adopted, however.

Heat-sensitivity is that property of a fiber that causes it to shrink, soften, or melt when heat is applied. This property is *not* possessed by the cellulose and protein fibers.

Properties common to the heat-sensitive fibers and their importance to the consumer are given in the chart at left.

The fiber families differ in degree of heat-sensitivity and even within a family the individual fibers and fiber types may vary. For example, Orlon Type 38 will shrink 20% or more when heat is applied, whereas regular Orlon has very little shrinkage. This high-shrinkage property is used to advantage in factory processes to create bulky yarns or three dimensional effects in pile and upholstery fabrics. To create these effects, the high-shrinkage and low-shrinkage fibers are blended. Heat is then applied and the high-shrinkage fibers shorten, causing the others to "buckle" and create bulk. (*See* page 114.)

In home use, ironing is the highest temperature to which a fiber or fabric is normally subjected. Therefore, precautions must be taken *to adjust the iron setting* so it is within safety limits for that particular fiber.

If the iron is too hot, the fiber will soften enough to be flattened by the pressure of the iron, or it will melt. Flattening of the surface is called *glazing*. (*See* Fig. 3:18.) The use of a soft pressing pad will permit edges and seams to sink down into the pad when pressure is applied and will prevent glazing.

Before

After

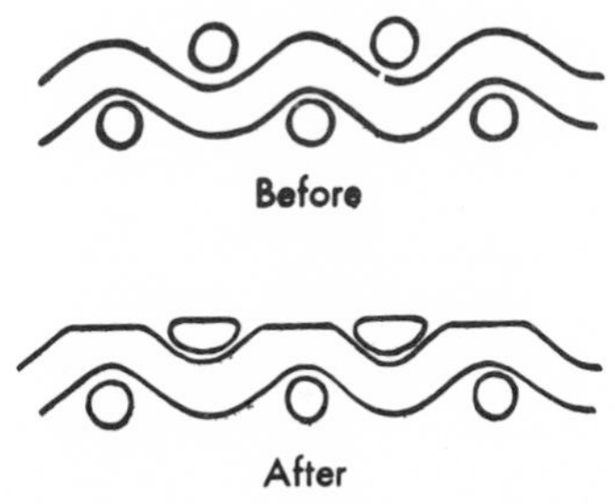

Fig. 3:18. Heat and pressure cause permanent flattening of the yarns or glazing.

The chart below gives the ironing temperature for the heat-sensitive fibers.

Safe Ironing Temperature for Heat-Sensitive Fibers

Arnel triacetate	485°F	Compare with the natural fibers listed below.	
Polyesters			
Kodel	425	Flax	450°F
Dacron	365	Cotton	425
Nylon		Rayon	375
66	365	Silk	300
6	300	Wool	300
Acetate	350		
Acrylics			
Zefran	350		
Acrilan	325		
Creslan	300		
Orlon	300		
Olefins	300		
Modacrylics			
Verel	275		
Dynel	225		

Fabrics made of heat-sensitive fibers were at first considered very difficult to sew and tailor. However, when tailoring wool, a great deal of work is also involved, such as steaming, pressing, and pounding. Nevertheless, tailoring of the fabrics made from the new fibers did *not* require any more work than wool; it simply *required different techniques.* Because ironing and pressing temperatures vary for the fibers in this group, it is advisable *to try out* the temperature of the iron and the reaction of the fabric. Nylon, for example, resists creasing, so if sharp creases are desired, it is necessary to top stitch or edge stitch the crease. Creases in Orlon, on the other hand, are easily pressed in and out.

The following suggestions are helpful when sewing: use lower temperatures; check the temperature of the iron carefully, or use moisture from a press cloth or steam iron to eliminate the human element in temperature control; use light pressing on seams that may need to be changed or altered to prevent permanent creasing; use soft pressing pads to prevent glazing.

Fullness cannot be shrunk out, so changes must be made in the pattern in areas where fullness is usually controlled by shrinking. For example, the fullness in the top of the sleeve can be reduced by changing the sleeve cap or by increasing the size of the armhole of the blouse.

Seam puckering, which is caused by the higher elasticity of the fabric or by nylon thread, must be controlled by changing the tension on the machine, or by using a smaller needle and a smaller hole in the bed of the machine. Medium pressure on the presser foot and maintenance of a slight tension on the fabric, by using both hands as the seam is stitched, will aid in controlling puckering. If puckering is a serious problem with a fabric, it may be best to select a simple pattern with few seams.

Do not mark with waxy chalk, because when pressed, it will leave an oily mark on the fabric that is difficult to remove.

Heat-Setting (Manufacturing Process)

Heat-setting is defined as a heat treatment that gives a shape and size that will not change (stabilizes) under conditions of intended use. The heat used for setting must be higher than any temperature that will be used later, since later use of a higher temperature will cause the fabric to lose its "set."

Heat-setting may be done on the yarn, fabric, or completed article. (*See* Fig. 3:19.) Heat-setting before scouring prevents setting of wrinkles during scouring. All heat-setting is done before or during dyeing. Fabrics may be partially heat-set at one stage of manufacture and completely heat-set later.

During the heat treatment, the yarn, fabric, or garment must be held in the shape in which it is to be set. It must be allowed to shrink some during setting or there will be possible future shrinkage as the molecules readjust themselves to their original unstretched condition.

Heat-setting is done in boiling water, in a steam oven, or hot air. The time of treatment

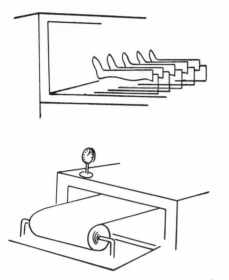

Fig. 3:19. Heat setting nylon hosiery and yard goods. (Courtesy of E. I. du Pont de Nemours & Company.)

and the degree of heat determine the success of the process. Interesting fabric effects are achieved by combining or alternating heat-set and nonheat-set yarns in fabric. (*See* Fig. 3:19.)

Problems and Care

Static electricity is generated by the friction of a fabric rubbing against itself or against other objects. If the electrical charge is not conducted away, it tends to "build up" on the surface. Then when the fabric comes in contact with a good conductor, the shock or rapid transfer occurs. This transfer may produce sparks that in a gaseous atmosphere can cause explosions. This is always a hazard in dry cleaning plants and hospital operating rooms. Nurses are forbidden to wear nylon or acetate uniforms in operating rooms because of danger from ether fumes.

People who live in areas of extreme coldness and dryness find it a particularly annoying problem since it is increased under these conditions. Static electricity causes soil and lint to cling to the surface of dry fabrics and dark colors become very unsightly. Brushing simply increases the difficulty.

The resins used for crease-resistant finishes and shrinkage control on cotton, linen, and rayon also cause the building up of static electricity. These fabrics pick up and hold lint from the wash water.

Static can spoil the draping qualities of a fabric by causing it to cling to the body. Static causes fabrics to cling to machinery, tables, and even to other fabrics making cutting and handling very difficult. It is responsible for increased defects and makes a higher percentage of seconds.

There are some solutions to the problem of static. The choice of the fabric from which the garment is made is a big factor in overcoming this problem—cotton, rayon, or linen fabrics do not build up static. High moisture content in the air of the home will cut down on static build-up.

Antistatic finishes [8] have been developed for use in the rinse after washing. There are also spray-bomb antistatics on the market. Many ready-to-wear garments are sold with an antistatic finish. No static finish made so far is permanent or durable, although much research is being done in this field. Some of it is concerned with changing the fiber itself so its static properties are altered.

Wash-and-wear garments can be made from all of these fibers, except the diacetates. When made in knit construction, they give outstanding performance. Satisfaction may, however, depend on the care used in washing.

The following recommendation has been made for wash-and-wear garments made of thermoplastic fibers. Wash the garment three minutes; rinse three minutes. Remove it before the spin cycle, do not wring but allow the garment to drip dry. The weight of the water will press it as it dries. After laundering a suit, hang the jacket on a well-shaped hanger and pad the shoulders with wash cloths. Smooth the shoulders. Trousers should be hung by the cuffs.

Surface pilling that might occur on the right side can be reduced by turning all garments wrong-side-out during laundering.

[8] Glim, Slipease, Sta-puf, Downy, etc.

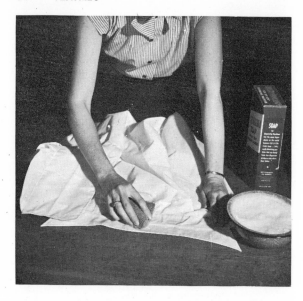

Fig. 3:20. "Cold spotting" heavily soiled areas in a Dacron shirt, helpful to remove body oils.

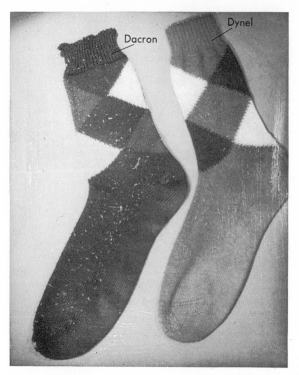

Fig. 3:21. Pilling. Sock made of Dacron on the left, sock made of Dynel on the right. Both were worn one day a week for 14 months and washed after each wearing.

Laundry research has shown that many oils, including body oil, are not removed at low temperatures and at high temperatures greasy soil penetrates into the thermoplastic fibers. When areas such as collars and cuffs are heavily soiled with body oil, the following cold treatment is suggested by the Du Pont Company. Figure 3:20 illustrates the procedure. Work a *strong* solution of detergent into the spot with a sponge. Rinse in *cold* water. Be sure to manipulate the spotted areas thoroughly or until the water is clear. Then wash in the regular manner.

Any method of laundering that avoids wrinkles in the final extraction or removes them during drying is best.

PILLING

Pilling is the balling up of fiber ends on the surface of a fabric. When nylon and the polyesters came on the market, pilling became a serious problem. Formerly pilling had occurred on napped fabrics of cotton or wool but the pills often broke off before the garment became unsightly. However, the nylon and Dacron fibers were so strong that the pills accumulated.

Pills are of two kinds: fabric pills and lint pills. Fabric pills are less unsightly since they contain only fibers from the garment. Lint pills become very unsightly because they contain fibers picked up in the wash water or through contact with other garments and even through attraction by static charges.

Figure 3:21 shows two socks, of which one has lint pills and one has fabric pills. Observe the difference in appearance.

Because pilling was such a serious problem (even filament fabrics of nylon and Dacron pilled), a great deal of research was done on the problem. It was found that *singeing* when properly done is the best single treatment. (*See* pages 78, 175.)

The following statements give further information about causes and cures of pilling.

1. All fabrics of a lofty type staple will pill.
2. The construction of the fabric has more to do with pilling than does the fiber content. Long nap pills more than short nap.

3. Loose fitting fabrics pill faster than fabrics held under tension.
4. Low twist yarns pill more. Higher twist and plied yarns are recommended. Increasing the twist for yarns with 1½ inch staple gives good resistance to pilling without appreciably changing the covering power of the yarn. Increasing the twist with longer staple gives some change in covering power.
5. Some of the hydrophobic fibers pill less than others. Strong fiber pills hold to the surface, while weak fiber pills usually break off.
6. Round, smooth fibers like nylon and Dacron are more easily "teased" out of a fabric than irregular shaped fibers. This may explain why the sock of Dacron pilled more than the Dynel sock.
7. Water-repellent finishes lubricate the fibers and make pilling easier.
8. Resin finishes seem to anchor the fibers in the yarn and reduce pilling.
9. Fulling of wool or wool blend fabrics tightens the construction and reduces pilling.
10. Wool resists pilling because of its scale structure.

Acetate

Low Cost
Natural Body
Hand and Drape

Acetate is a manufactured fiber in which the fiber-forming substance is cellulose acetate. Where not less than 92% of the hydroxyl groups are acetylated, the term triacetate may be used as a generic description.[9]

The history of acetate as a separate fiber group began in 1952 when the Federal Trade Commission passed a regulation that separated acetate from the rayon family to which it had belonged since the 1924 ruling that designated all cellulose-base fibers as rayon. Acetate fiber producers had been unhappy about the 1924 ruling because they felt that acetate was different in chemical composition and properties,

[9] F.T.C. definition.

CHRONOLOGICAL HISTORY OF ACETATE FIBERS

1869 Cellulose triacetate made
1899 Filaments made in Germany
1903 Diacetate made
1914 Solvent recovery process
    Acetate film by Lustron
1919 Filament commercial production
    Lustron Corporation
1925 Celanese Corporation
1927 Celanese-Lustron merger
1929 Tubize Rayon Corporation
    American Chatillon Corporation
    Du Pont Company
1930 Tubize-American Chatillon merger
    American Viscose
1931 Tennessee Eastman Company
    Delustered filament
1935 Staple produced
    Crimped staple
1946 Celanese-Tubize merger
1951 Solution-dyed fiber
1952 Generic name ACETATE established by
        F.T.C.
    Triacetate fiber X-100 (Arnel) announced
1954 Crystal acetate fiber—Celanese
    Latent crimp Type C by Du Pont
1955 Arnel commercial production
    Texturized yarn process used
1957 Y-cross section fibers
    Celacloud Type F by Celanese
    Celafil Type K by Celanese
    Type 20 by Du Pont
    Hollow filament
    Eastman 50
1959 Filament designed for texturizing
    Eastman 75
    Celaloft by Celanese
1962 *

* Student can add new developments in this space.

---

so it should be considered as a separate fiber. Their protests resulted in the 1952 ruling that made the two fiber groups separate. Thus, in 1952, a big promotion campaign announced acetate to the consumer. There was, and still is, a great deal of confusion about this "new" fiber.

The process of making acetate was known as early as 1869. However, the acetone which was used as a solvent was expensive so that acetate could not compete costwise with the other fibers made from cellulose. Then, during World War I, a method of recovering acetone was discovered and acetate manufacture became economically possible.

Diacetate was the first *kind* of acetate fiber to be manufactured successfully. Triacetate was used experimentally in 1914, but because there was no suitable solvent at that time, it was not produced commercially until 1953 when the Celanese Corporation introduced *Arnel.* The chart on the previous page gives a history of acetate and lists improvements and developments.

Acetate is an *ester* of cellulose which differs both physically and chemically from pure or regenerated cellulose.

The ester is formed by treating cellulose (an alcohol) with glacial acetic acid and acetic anhydride, a process called *acetylation.* Diacetate has fewer hydroxyl groups which have reacted with the acid than has triacetate. (*See* Fig. 3:22.)

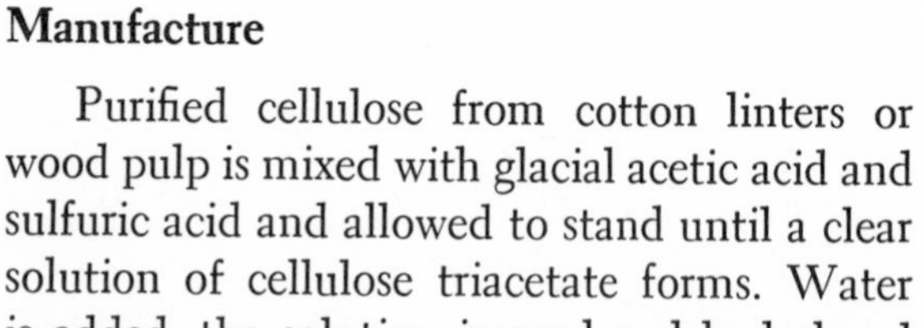

Fig. 3:22. Acetate molecules.

Manufacture

Purified cellulose from cotton linters or wood pulp is mixed with glacial acetic acid and sulfuric acid and allowed to stand until a clear solution of cellulose triacetate forms. Water is added, the solution is aged and hydrolyzed to a cellulose diacetate. This is then precipitated as acetate resin flakes. The flakes are dissolved in *acetone* to make spinning solution.

Delustering pigments or pigment colors can be added to the solution to make dull or semi-dull fibers, or solution-dyed fibers.

The solution is forced out through a spinneret into a column of warm air. The fibers harden as the solvent evaporates and are stretched to orient the molecules and increase fiber strength, and finally, they are given a slight twist and wound on bobbins.

Unlike rayon, the yarn is now ready for spinning or weaving without further processing.

The acetone is recovered to be used again.

Staple fibers are cut, crimped, lubricated, dried, and baled for shipment.

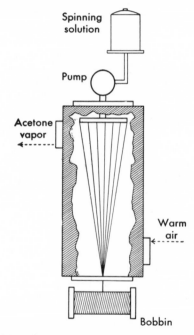

Fig. 3:23. The acetate spinning chamber. (Courtesy of the Tennessee Eastman Company.)

Identification

Acetate fiber, as well as the acetate resin flake, will dissolve in acetone. As no other fiber will immediately dissolve in this solvent, *acetone solubility is a specific test* for acetate fibers.

Figure 3:24 shows a dropping bottle, watch glass, rod, and cleansing tissue for use in making the acetone test. (Nail polish and fountain

Fig. 3:24. The acetone test for identification of acetate fiber. See the text below for full instructions. (Courtesy of Opal Roberson.)

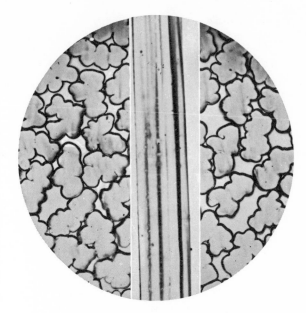

Fig. 3:25. Photomicrograph of longitudinal and cross-sectional views of acetate fiber. (Courtesy of E. I. du Pont de Nemours & Company.)

pens are acetate plastics which will dissolve in acetone.) How to test:

Ravel off both warp and filling yarns. Place on a watch glass, keeping the two sets separate. Drop a small amount of acetone on the yarns. Rub a stirring rod across the dampened part. If it dissolves readily, the fibers are acetate.

Use a small sample and test at one corner. If there is a small amount of acetate in the fabric no change may be noticed until the fabric dries. Then a definite stiffening can be felt. Note: The acetone will evaporate and the dissolved material will harden on the watch glass, so clean it off with a paper tissue before the solution hardens.

MICROSCOPE IDENTIFICATION

The cross-section of acetate, Figure 3:25, is lobular or flower-petal shaped. This shape results from the evaporation of the solvent as the fiber hardens. One of the lobes or "petals" shows up in the lengthwise view, Figure 3:25, as a false lumen.

IDENTIFICATION BY BURNING

Acetate fibers burn as easily as cotton or rayon. In brushed, napped, or pile fabrics, how-ever, acetate does not burn with quite the speed or flash flame of the others since it melts and forms small beads on the loose fibers. When acetate is burned, it has a characteristic vinegar-like odor and leaves a black plastic residue. See page 18 for directions for the burning test.

Diacetate Fibers

Since 1952, when acetate was renamed, it has been promoted as the "Beauty Fiber." It has many silk-like qualities and is often used in blends with silk. The properties of high luster, silkiness, crisp hand, and body and drape have made fashion fabrics such as taffeta, bengaline, satin and tricot one of the major outlets of diacetate fibers. For this reason, more filament than staple has been produced.

In 1959, 74 million pounds of acetate staple and 229 million pounds of filament were manufactured.

All staple is crimped and most of it is used in draperies, upholsteries, or in blends with rayon for suitings and dresses. Acetate has *natural body* and when mixed with rayon, gives better texture to suitings, crepes, and satins than can be obtained with 100% rayon.

The market for fashion fabrics is a fluctuating one and the development of new fiber types has influenced fashion trends and stimulated demand for acetate. Some of these developments were the result of research to eliminate fiber disadvantages, while others were produced in an effort to widen the market for acetate. Some of these developments are discussed below.

Solution-dyed fibers [10] brought an important plus value on colorfastness and stimulated the use of acetate in curtains and swimsuits, as well as apparel and household items. Acetate has little affinity for cotton and viscose dyes, so a new class of dyes, called acetate dyes, was developed for dyeing acetate. Those acetate dyes which contained blues and greens were unstable to atmospheric gases and would fume or gas-fade. Blue and gray took on a pinkish hue and green colors turned brown. Gas-fading is the result of a chemical reaction between the dye and the nitrous acid formed by nitrogen dioxide and moisture in the air. Inhibitors, such as resins, were tried but were only temporary measures. Dyes resistant to fume fading are more expensive. The addition of colored pigments to the spinning solution gave colors which were fast to gas fading and to washing but were not suitable for all uses and had some disadvantages from the production standpoint. Trade names are: *Chromspun* by Tennessee Eastman (the first solution-dyed fiber of any kind), *Celaperm* by Celanese, *Color-sealed* by Du Pont, and *Colorspun* by American Viscose Corporation.

Crystal acetate gained wide acceptance in bridesmaids' dresses, formals, and draperies. It is a flat fiber spun out through a narrow slit rather than a round hole in the spinneret. It gives an optical effect of scintillation which cannot be obtained by regular acetate. Flat fibers tend to be more brittle than other shapes and this was the basis for some of the early dissatisfaction in the dry cleaning performance of crystal acetate.

[10] See pages 49 and 203.

Bulked acetate fiber was a development that increased the use of acetate in blends with cotton, in decorator fabrics, and in stuffings for pillows and comforters. Each new type of fiber product gives designers a new medium to work with and widens the possibilities for end-uses.

Type C acetate, by Du Pont, is a latent crimp fiber and was one of the first of this type produced. It had no crimp when spun but the crimp developed when the yarn or fabric was immersed in the hot water of the dye bath.

Type 20, also by Du Pont, and *Celacloud Type F*, by Celanese, are Y-shaped fibers that bulk in hot water. *Celafil Type K*, a similar fiber, was made specifically for use in pillows. *Eastman 50*, a hollow doughnut-shaped fiber, gives increased bulk, luster, and tear strength.

DISADVANTAGES

Low heat-sensitivity and poor washability have been the chief disadvantages of the diacetates. The triacetates which excel in these areas, have won wide acceptance in end-uses where these factors are important. Figure 3:26 shows the effect of high temperature on the two kinds of acetate.

COMMON PROPERTIES

The diacetates and triacetates both have similar physical appearance, weight, and low strength properties. They are resistant to damage from light, mildew, moths and mold. Both can be heat-set in durable pleats or embossed designs. Triacetate, however, has good washability.

Triacetate

Arnel, the first triacetate fiber, was promoted by the Celanese Corporation as the Ease-of-Care fiber. Its advantages were listed as washability, dimensional stability through many launderings, rapid drying, freedom from damage by high ironing temperatures (*see* Fig-

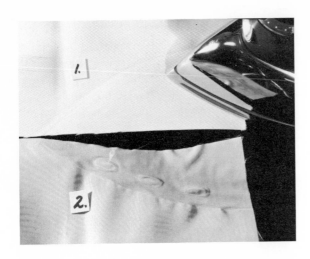

Fig. 3:26. Effect of heat on (1) Arnel and (2) acetate.

ure 3:26), high resistance to glazing and the ability to take durable pleats.

Washability of Arnel is related to its low absorbency (Arnel 3.0% and diacetate 6.5% regain of moisture). The higher number of reacted hydroxyl groups in the triacetate molecule block the water molecules and prevent swelling.

Arnel is outstanding in its resistance to damage by heat. It melts at 512°F as compared to 482°F for nylon and Dacron, and 474°F for the diacetates. Because it has high heat resistance, it can be heat-set at higher temperatures and will satisfactorily hold heat-set shapes such as pleats. The heat-set treatment of Arnel fabrics also causes better molecule arrangement, thus increasing crystallinity, a factor which reduces water absorption. (*See* page 14.)

Further developments in triacetate fibers will probably be in the production of a fiber with improved wet and dry strength.

Saponification (Iron-Proofing)

Acetate fibers can be treated with a caustic soda to reverse the acetylation reaction and restore the cellulose to a regenerated state. Since regenerated cellulose is rayon, these fibers (Fortisan and Celcos) are discussed in the section on rayon.

Nylon

Abrasion Resistance
Elasticity
High Strength
Light Weight

(The Polyamide Fiber)

Nylon is a manufactured fiber in which the fiber forming substance is any long chain, synthetic polyamide having recurring amide groups ($-\underset{\underset{O}{\|}}{C}-NH-$) as an integral part of the polymer chain.[11]

In 1928, Wallace Carothers, a young scientist from Iowa, was employed by the Du Pont Company to head up a fundamental research program on long chain polymers. His discovery of nylon in the mid 1930's has been listed along with antibiotics, as one of the outstanding developments of the 20th century. Nylon is a family of fibers, designated by the number of carbon atoms in the amide unit. *Nylon 66* was the one developed by the Carothers research.

Nylon 6, produced in 1954 by Allied Chemical Corporation, was made from caprolactum and was sufficiently unlike Nylon 66 so that no license arrangement was needed with the Du Pont Company. Nylon 6 has a lower melting point (428°F) than Nylon 66 (482°F), a softer feel, and a better affinity for dye. The two nylons can be blended together and dyed in a single dyebath to give a two color fabric (cross-dye).

Nylon 8 has not been used as a fiber but is used as a finishing solution to give greater absorbency to fabrics.

Nylon 4, recently developed by the Minnesota Mining and Manufacturing Company, is more absorbent than Nylon 66 or 6.

Nylon 66 has been on the market much longer than the others and during this time a

[11] F.T.C. definition.

continuing fiber research and development program has resulted in the production of many variations, called types, which have improved existing fibers and adapted them to new end-uses. See the chart below.

Manufacture

Nylon is made by the melt-spinning process. Nylon 66 is made by combining an acid (adipic) with an amine (hexamethylene diamine) to form an amide salt.

Other nylons are also made by reacting acids with amines.

Nylon salt is heated in an autoclave, a piece of equipment like a giant pressure cooker. (*See* Fig. 3:27.) Heat causes the molecules to join together to form linear polymers. The molten nylon is pumped out through

---

CHRONOLOGICAL HISTORY OF NYLON

1928 Carothers research into long chain polymers, sponsored by Du Pont

1938 Nylon 66 by Du Pont
Used in tooth brush bristles

1939 Nylon fiber commercial production
Du Pont plant at Seaford, Delaware

1940 First nylon stockings

1941 Du Pont plant at Martinsville, Va.

1942 Nylon converted to war uses
Seaford plant expanded

1945 Nylon returns to civilian market
Martinsville plant expanded
Nylon 66% of hosiery

1946 Nylon lingerie
Du Pont plant at Chattanooga, Tenn.
Nylon 6 research by Allied Chemical
Staple fibers produced

1947 Sewing thread and nylon satin

1948 High tenacity by hot-stretching
Tire cord introduced
15 denier hosiery filament
First use in carpets and upholstery

1949 Permanent pleats and nylon velvet

1950 Absorbent finish Nylon 8 solution
Absorbency by crepe weave
Nylon sweaters

1951 Chemstrand license for Nylon 66
Nylon mesh shoes

1953 Chemstrand plant at Pensacola, Fla.
12 denier monofilament for hosiery
Dull or opaque Nylon Type 680
First nylon sheets and Nymo thread

1954 Textured yarn
—Helanca "stretch" socks
—Taslan in blouses, etc.
Nylon 6 commercially produced
—Allied Chemical Corp.
—Enka Rayon Corp.
—Industrial Rayon Corp.

1955 Chemstrand expands Pensacola plant
Du Pont's patent ends
Carpet fiber of Nylon 66

1956 Solution-dyed nylon
Carpet fiber of Nylon 6
Tire cord plant by Du Pont, Richmond, Va.

1957 Low-elongation Type 420 Nylon for blends with cotton
Textured yarns in carpets and sweaters
10 denier, 2 filament hosiery yarn
Nylon chiffon and georgette

1958 Tire cord expansion by four producers

1959 Non-round cross-section nylon fibers
—Antron Type 560 by Du Pont; trilobal
—"Sparkling" Type 90 by Du Pont; multilobal
—Cadon by Chemstrand; multilobal
Whiter nylon (fluorescent compounds)
Type 91 by Du Pont
Blanc de Blanc by Enka
Carpet nylon
Type 501 (trilobal) by Du Pont
Nylon 22 by Industrial Rayon
Cumuloft by Chemstrand
Textured Caprolan by Allied Chemical
Heat-resistant Nylon Type 109 industrial
Nylon 4 by Minnesota Mining and Mfg. Co.

1960 Industrial Rayon sold nylon plant to Hercules Powder Co. for conversion to production of olefin fibers
Type 228 for textured yarns
Seaford plant expansion for 501 carpet fiber

1961 *

---

* Student can add new developments here. Information source: *Textile Organon*.

Fig. 3:27. Nylon spinning process.

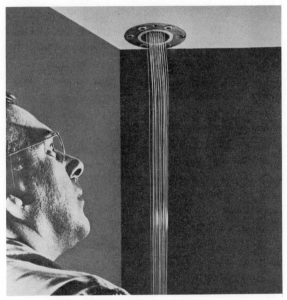

Fig. 3:28. Spinning nylon fiber. (Courtesy of E. I. du Pont de Nemours & Company.)

tiny holes in a spinneret, which is a metal disc about the size of a silver dollar. (*See* Fig. 3:28.)

As the nylon fibers emerge from the spinneret and hit the air they solidify and are gathered into a yarn. Next, the yarn is stretched or *cold-drawn* between a system of rollers.

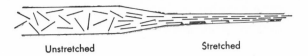

Unstretched   Stretched

Fig. 3:29. Orientation of molecules during stretching or cold drawing.

An interesting change takes place during stretching. In the undrawn fiber, the long chain-like molecules are arranged helter-skelter, like straws in a haystack. But drawing aligns the molecules into an orderly array, places them parallel to one another, and brings them closer together. Fiber diameter is also reduced in size. Figure 3:29 illustrates this: the molecules are represented by short lines. When nylon is cold-drawn, it becomes very strong, tough, and elastic, and the yarn develops translucency and luster. After drawing, the filament yarns are carefully inspected and packed for shipping to the weaving mill.

Nylon staple is made by crimping continuous nylon filament tow and then cutting it into short uniform lengths. It is shipped in large 500-pound packs much like bales of cotton. Some nylon staple is obtained by reprocessing nylon by a system similar to that used for reused wool. (*See* page 111.)

The process of melt-spinning can be demonstrated by a simple laboratory experiment

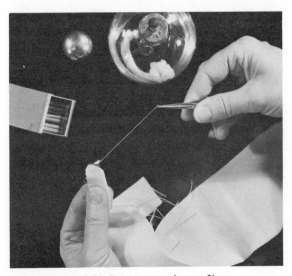

Fig. 3:30. Spinning a melt-spun fiber.

which is fun to do. Use any material which is made by melt-spinning, such as nylon or Dacron (polyethylene bags are good too), a flame and a pair of tweezers. A fabric with heavily delustered fibers may not spin satisfactorily. Allow the material to burn until quite a little melt has formed and quickly draw out a fiber with the tweezers.

Identification

Nylon and the other melt-spun fibers are unique in that they will keep the shape of the spinneret hole through which they are spun. The first nylon fibers could be identified under the microscope by the round, rodlike shape and absence of structural markings. However, nylon types of non-round shapes have been developed since and these are listed on the chart and discussed later in this section.

Fig. 3:31. Photomicrograph of nylon fiber. Inset is cross-sectional view. (Courtesy of E. I. du Pont de Nemours & Company.)

The burning test is a good method of identifying nylon. The fibers melt and drip and some of the flame is occasionally carried down with the drip. The odor is celery-like and a white smoke is given off. When the melt hardens it is tan in color unless the cloth has been dyed certain colors. A large enough amount should be burned to be sure the results observed are characteristic since there are some similarities to the burning characteristics of the polyesters. Pure nylon without any finish is resistant to flaming.

Characteristics of Nylon

It is rather interesting to note that nylon achieved its first success in women's hosiery and lingerie, whereas Dacron, which was developed later, was first promoted in men's washable suits. Both of these fibers, unlike the acrylics, are used in large quantities in filament form.

Transparency, *high strength*, and *elasticity* are properties responsible for nylon's success in hosiery. The transparency of the nylon fiber is evident in Figure 3:31. The one fiber in the crosswise direction can be clearly seen through the others.

Observe on the historical chart the progress in the development of finer denier fibers which could be used in stockings with the "bare-leg" look. (See Fig. 5:59, page 167.)

Transparency was a drawback, however, in lingerie. Opaque fibers were made by the addition of delustering agents and also by the use of a Schreinered finish (see page 176) which flattened the knit stitches to reduce the open spaces between the yarns (give better cover). Tricot fabrics finished in this way were called nylon "satinette." The *tenacity* of nylon varies from four to seven grams per denier. This, combined with its elasticity and abrasion resistance, has made nylon fabrics very durable. Sheer fabrics are strong and garments of nylon are seldom discarded because of worn places but rather because of failure in the "appearance life" of the garment. Nylon fibers are so strong and durable that they sometimes "shear-off" or cut through other kinds of fibers with which they are blended. Snagging of filament yarn fabrics is a problem resulting from nylon's high strength. The fibers do not break as weaker fibers do but pull and cause the fabric to pucker. The puckering of the slip in the photo-

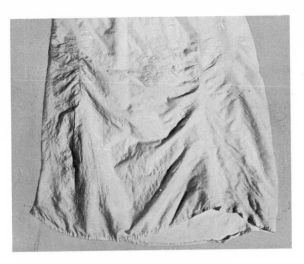

Fig. 3:32. Snagging of nylon slip.

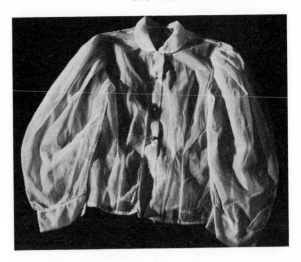

Fig. 3:33. Heat-set wrinkles in nylon blouse.

graph was caused by garters. Pilling, an accumulation of fiber balls on the surface, is also caused by strong fibers which do not break off when abraded.

High tenacity nylon is used in tire cords and is competing well with rayon.

The *high elongation* of nylon fibers made nylon incompatible with cotton when used in blends. When the fabric was pulled or stretched, the cotton fibers broke while the nylon was still elongating. *Nylon Type 420* was developed especially for use in cotton blends. It has been called the most striking example of making the fiber fit the need. It is a high-strength, low-elongation fiber with an initial modulus similar to that of cotton. The Nylon 420 fiber is usually blended with the warp yarn of the cloth rather than with the filling, since the chief end-use is work clothing and in these fabrics the warp yarn is exposed on the surface to a greater extent than the filling yarn. Nylon 420 was first sold for $1.28 per pound so it was used in a way that would help keep the fabric cost competitive with that of 100% cotton. The addition of 25% Nylon 420 is sufficient to increase the wear-life 70%.

Nylon's *abrasion resistance* is outstanding. Scissors and fabric cutting knives have to be sharpened frequently when used on nylon. This has been one of the reasons that nylon corduroys are not on the market. The pile surface is made by cutting yarn floats on the surface of the gray goods and no way has yet been devised for keeping these small, circular cutting knives sharp enough to do an efficient job with nylon.

The *heat-sensitivity* of nylon is high enough to make it possible to permanently heat-stabilize fabrics against shrinkage and to heat-set pleats, embossed designs, etc. It is a drawback in that it is difficult to press sharp creases in home sewing and difficult to press out heat-set wrinkles acquired in washing. (See Fig. 3:33.)

Although nylon is one of the most *elastic* fibers, its ability to be heat-set has made it possible to produce fabrics or garments with 300 to 400% greater elasticity. Permanently accordion pleated hosiery was the first attempt. "Stretch" yarns made by a heat-setting process (Helanca) were more successful. They were first used in "one-size" hosiery. Although one size did not fit everyone, stretch yarns did make it possible to reduce the number of sizes. These yarns found wide use in knit goods such as leotards, and underwear. By the early 1960's they were being used in woven fabrics in anything from sheer blouses to heavy sportswear. Stretch can be controlled to almost any amount and fewer sizes are needed, a factor which simplifies the retailers inventory. Because of the success of nylon fiber in textured

Fig. 3:34. Removing a nylon "damasque" housecoat from an automatic dryer after washing.

yarns, a fiber *Type 228* was specifically designed for this purpose.

Nylon's *low absorbency* which caused discomfort in summer wear, was one of the first consumer disappointments. The first nylon shirts were uncomfortable because the fabric was not properly designed. One manufacturer, interested in profits rather than repeat sales, made these shirts against the advice of the Fabric Research Department of the Du Pont Co. Since then, fabrics with good comfort rating have been developed by use of open-work "window pane" effects, crepe weaves, and others. *Nylon 8*, a finishing solution made of a nylon with a higher absorbency than regular nylon has been used, not only on nylon, but on the other low absorbency fibers. *Nylon 4* is also a lower absorbency fiber. Texturized yarns contribute to comfort by lessening the amount of skin contact.

The *chemical resistance* of nylon is generally good but nylon is damaged by strong acids. Soot from smoke in industrial cities contains sulfur which, on damp days, combines with atmospheric moisture to form sulfuric acid which has been responsible for epidemics of runs in stockings. Pencil erasers, which are rather effective in removing picks and pulls in stockings, set up a chemical reaction which weakens the stocking. Commercial laundries have had to change the marking ink formula because regular ink dissolved the nylon.

Raised design fabrics, such as nylon damasque (sculptured nylon) are made by shrinkage with chemicals. The raised areas are created by printing phenol on that part of the fabric which is to be the background. The phenol causes the nylon to shrink, thus the untreated areas pucker. The background may be printed with a metallic pigment of either copper or aluminum color. These fabrics are washable. The house coat, which is shown in Figure 3:34 as it is being taken from the dryer, was washed in an automatic washer. After drying, there was no evidence of damage to the metallic print and there were no wrinkles.

The *light resistance* of the first nylon fibers was rather low. They could not be used satisfactorily at windows on the south side of the house. In 1960 the Chemstrand Corp. announced that a new light resistant factor had been added to all Chemstrand nylon fibers. This means that nylon's use in upholstery, drapery fabrics, and rugs can be greatly increased, also.

WHITER NYLON

White nylons have a tendency to develop a discoloration not satisfactorily removed by bleaches. This was a drawback to its use in underwear, particularly in girdles, because bleaches have a very damaging effect on rubber and also cause some weakening of the nylon.

The new whiter type nylons are made by adding a fluorescent compound to the spinning solution. *Type 91 Nylon* by Du Pont and *Blanc de Blanc* by Enka were the first extra white nylons produced.

NON-ROUND NYLONS

One of the most interesting of the new nylon fiber developments is that of non-round cross-section fibers. It was previously mentioned that melt-spun fibers maintain the shape of the spinneret holes. Therefore change in fiber cross-section shape is accomplished by changing the shape of the spinneret holes. The cross-section shape is important to properties which relate to hand, cover, bulking properties, opaqueness, and luster. In all of these properties the fibers with circular cross-section are deficient.

"Sparkling" Type 90 Nylon was the first one produced. It is a multilobal fiber which gives high light reflectance and sparkle. It is made in 15 denier for use in hosiery for evening wear. It also has limited use in other evening clothes.

Cadon by Chemstrand is another multilobal nylon which is used in apparel fabrics. It has a silk-like luster and greater clarity of color in prints due to the manner of light reflectance. Furthermore, it has superior covering power which gives opacity to light weight fabrics.

Antron (Type 560) is the Du Pont trilobal fiber produced by a fiber development program designed specifically to create a fiber with true silk-like properties. (This research is discussed on page 77.) Antron is also the first nylon trade name adopted by the Du Pont Company since 1939 when nylon was patented.

Type 501 is a trilobal fiber designed for use in nylon carpets. (*See* page 50.) Cumuloft by Chemstrand is another carpet fiber.

Polyesters

Crease Resistance
Press Retention, Wet or Dry

A polyester fiber is a manufactured fiber in which the fiber forming substance is any long chain polymer composed of at least 85%

by weight of an ester of dihydric alcohol and terephthalic acid (p-HOOC—C_6H_4—COOH).[12]

Dacron (pronounced day-cron), the first polyester fiber, was introduced in 1953. In 1946, exclusive patent rights to production in the United States had been obtained by the Du Pont Co. from the Calico Printers Assn., Ltd., of England, whose process was based on the giant polymer research of Dr. Carothers. Imperial Chemical Industries, Ltd. of England obtained the patent rights for the rest of the world and now produce Terylene in England and Canada. They also license companies in other countries to produce polyester fibers under other trade names.

From 1946 to 1953 Dacron went through a period of market evaluation and fiber development. During this time it was called *Fiber* V and later named Amilar, but this name was soon changed to Dacron to avoid confusion with the trade name Amilan.

Dacron found immediate acceptance in easy-care, wash-and-wear garments such as tricot blouses and men's suits. Comfort properties were improved when cotton was blended with Dacron and a 65% Dacron, 35% cotton fabric became a staple item. Demand for this fabric became so great that a second plant was built especially for production of one-and-one-half inch staple for use in Dacron/cotton blend fabrics.

In 1959 three new polyester fibers entered the market. Two were produced under license arrangements with the Du Pont Company until the expiration of patent rights in 1961.

Fortrel, formerly known as Teron, is produced by Fiber Industries, Inc., a subsidiary of Celanese and I.C.I., and is marketed by Celanese through their promotion department.

Vycron is produced by the Beaunit Mills, Inc.

Kodel, the third fiber, was developed by the Tennessee Eastman Co. and is fundamentally different from the other polyesters so no

[12] F.T.C. definition.

license arrangement was needed for its production.

1930 Carothers basic research in U. S.

1940 Research in England
   Patent by Calico Printers Assn.

1946 Du Pont bought patent rights for production in U. S.

1947 Imperial Chemical Industries bought rights for rest of world

1950 Fiber V pilot plant

1951 Fiber V named Amilar
   Name Amilar changed to Dacron
   Market evaluation of Dacron

1953 Dacron commercial production
   Plant at Kinston, N. C.
   Research plant at Kinston

1954 Dacron film "Mylar" developed *
   Terylene in Canada
   Dacron Type 54 for blends with cotton

1955 Dacron/rayon blends
   Dacron for bedding

1956 Kinston plant increased 25%
   Fiberfil for pillows

1957 Metalized Mylar *

1958 Dacron Type 64 for blends with wool
   Dacron/cotton voile
   Kodel fiber by Tennessee Eastman
   Teron fiber by Fiber Industries

1959 Dacron evaluated for tire cord
   Teron renamed Fortrel
   Dacron Type 61—high shrinkage; industrial
   Vycron fiber by Beaunit Mills
   Dacron Type 62 fiber

1961 Fortrel commercial production
   Du Pont plant at Old Hickory to produce one-and-one-half inch staple for cotton blends

1962 **

---

* See yarn section, page 96.
** Add new developments in the space provided here.

The following chart gives some of the differences between the properties of Kodel and Dacron.

Property	Dacron	Kodel
Ironing temperature	365°F	425°F
Specific gravity	1.32	1.22
Tensile strength	3 to 8	2.5 to 3.0

Kodel is more resistant to pilling than regular type Dacron. However, Type 64 Dacron, which was developed for use in blends with wool, also has improved resistance to pilling.

Manufacture

The manufacturing process for the polyesters is similar to that for the nylons. Both fibers are *melt-spun*. Ethylene glycol and terephthalic acid are polymerized at high temperature in a vacuum. The polymer is solidified and cut into cubes which are melted and spun into fibers. The fibers solidify in air and are then hot-stretched to orient the molecules and reduce the denier of the fiber. The fiber is heat-set before use.

Polyester fibers are produced in filament and staple form, in bright and dull lusters, in regular and high tenacity strength, and can be solution dyed.

The molecule units in Dacron are heavy, stiff, and resilient. They resist bending but recover rapidly from bending. The molecule chains are held together by numerous bonds of such a nature that they cannot be relaxed by moisture. This is the reason for Dacron's *outstanding resistance to wrinkling when wet*.

Appearance and Identification

The polyester fibers, when seen under the microscope are so much like nylon that identification is difficult. Both longitudinal and cross-sectional views of Dacron are shown in Figure 3:35.

The fibers have the smooth rod-like shape and round cross-section which is typical of melt-spun fibers.

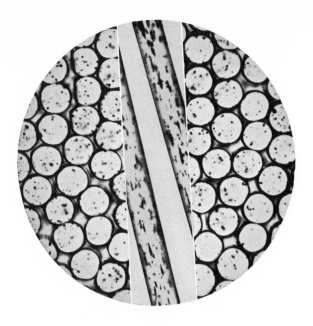

Fig. 3:35. Photomicrograph of longitudinal and cross-sectional views of Dacron polyester fiber. (Courtesy of E. I. du Pont de Nemours & Company.)

Dacron Type 54 (not shown) is of ribbon-like shape which blends better with cotton. Dacron Type 62 (*see* next page) has a trilobal shape which is similar to that of silk.

Although nylon and the polyesters burn alike in some ways, they can be distinguished from one another by the odor and the smoke.

Both melt and drip and some of the flame is occasionally carried down with the drip. Both are relatively non-flammable in the unfinished state. Both form a tan bead when the melt hardens. Some dyes may, however, cause a darker bead to form.

Polyesters have an aromatic odor and a heavy black smoke containing particles of soot. Nylon's odor is celery-like and the smoke is white. (Be sure to burn a large enough quantity to get adequate results.)

Dacron Type 62 is a trilobal, semidull fiber of normal tenacity with a silk-like appearance and hand. It is more susceptible to acids and alkalies and dyes more easily than regular Dacron. Dacron Type 62 and Antron nylon were the result of a study by the Du Pont Co. in cooperation with a silk finishing company to investigate the effect of the different stages of the silk finishing processes on the aesthetic properties of silk fabrics, since silk fibers seemed to acquire added richness in the fabric form.[13]

The man-made filament fibers have in the past lacked the unique combination of aesthetic properties possessed by silk. The development of a fiber with these properties has been a long time goal of the man-made fiber industry. Dacron Type 62 and Antron nylon marked the achievement of this goal.

Sericin makes up about 30% of the silk fabric weight. The boil-off finishing process removes the gum or sericin and creates a looser, more mobile fabric structure. If the fabric is in a relaxed state while the sericin is being removed, the warp yarns take on a high degree of weave-crimp. This crimp plus the looser structure of the fabric combines to create the liveliness and suppleness of the silk fabric. This suppleness has been compared to the action of the coil spring "slinky" toy.

The properties are quite different when the boil-off is done under tension. The weave-crimp is much less and the response of the fabric is more like that of a flat spring, thus the supple nature is lost.

Man-made fibers are normally processed under tension by a continuous processing rather than a batch processing method. Because of the results of the research study of silk, Dacron Type 62 and Antron nylon are processed in a completely relaxed condition. Finishing starts with a heat-setting process which stabilizes the fabric to controlled width, removes any wrinkles and imparts resistance to creasing.

The next step is a very important caustic soda (alkali) treatment. As mentioned before, Dacron Type 62 is susceptible to the action of caustic and in this treatment a controlled amount of the fiber is dissolved away. This step is comparable to the degumming of the silk fiber. As a result, the fabric structure is

13 See "Silk-like Fabrics from Man-made Fibers," *Textile Industries*, **124**:93 (Aug. 1960).

more mobile. To get maximum weave-crimp, the remaining finishes of bleaching, coloring, washing and a final heat-setting to fix the color and assure stability are all done with the fabric under completely relaxed conditions. An antistatic is applied to the fabric.

The finishing of Antron nylon is similar except that there is no modification of the fiber structure such as occurs in the caustic treatment of Dacron Type 62.

The trilobal shape of the fiber results from the shape of the spinneret holes. Melt-spun fabrics possess the ability to retain the shape of the spinneret holes. Figure 3:36 shows the cross-section shape of Dacron Type 62.

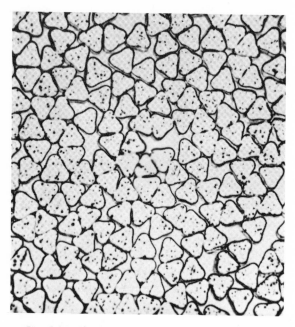

Fig. 3:36. Photomicrograph of cross-sectional view of Dacron Type 62 polyester fiber, a modified cross-sectional filament. (Courtesy of *Textile Industries*.)

The outstanding advantage of the polyesters is their wrinkle resistance, either wet or dry. Their wrinkle resistance when wet has given them an advantage over wool in tropical suitings, since wool has poor wrinkle resistance when wet. Under conditions of high atmospheric humidity and body perspiration, Da-

cron suits do not shrink and are very resistant to wrinkling. However, when they do acquire wear wrinkles, as often happens at the waist band of a shirt where body heat and moisture "set" the wrinkles, it is necessary to remove them by pressing. (Washing and pressing directions are given on page 63.) The polyesters are naturally white and are unaffected by cotton bleaches. Although they are usually washed, they can be dry cleaned very satisfactorily.

Dacron has found wide use in bedding and furniture batting because of its resiliency and washability. It can be sterilized without damage, and dries quickly so is useful in hospital pillows, etc. The first batting was made from waste apparel fiber and was not very satisfactory. *Fiberfill* was designed especially for this purpose and has recently been offered as "sewn-in" batting.

Mylar polyester film is another development that has increased the washability of metallic yarns. (*See* page 121.)

The polyester fibers have wear resistance comparable to that of nylon. They have been evaluated for use in tire cords. They are also comparable in heat resistance, and heat-set pleats in wash-and-wear are highly satisfactory.

Pilling is a common problem with Dacron fabrics. (Type 64 Dacron, which was developed for blending with wool, as mentioned previously, is pill resistant.) Type 54 Dacron, which was developed for use in blends with cotton, requires a finishing treatment to prevent pilling.

Singeing is the most important means of controlling pilling. This should be done thoroughly, preferably after brushing and shearing, with a two flame exposure at the slowest possible speed. The flame melts the fuzz and gives the fabric a smooth surface. Heat-setting (at 385° to 420°F) combined with singeing gives added pill resistance. The fabric becomes plastic, shrinks and the strains of yarn and fabric processing are released. When cooled, the fibers are set and locked in the yarn and fabric structure. Both treatments improve the hand, and heat-setting improves drape, and wash-and-wear performance.

The polyesters are more *electrostatic* than the other fibers in the heat-sensitive group. This is a distinct disadvantage because the static charges attract lint to the surface and it is difficult to keep dark colored fabrics looking neat. Dirt and dust are attracted to curtains so they become dingy looking in much less time than cotton curtains. Dacron has been popular in curtains because it has good light resistance.

Fig. 3:37. Crocking of color on the collar of a Dacron blouse. Many printed Dacrons may become unuseable before being worn out, because of crocking.

Color crocking has been the source of trouble with many of the printed Dacrons. The color is usually a pigment print which is bound to the surface with a resin binder. Garments may become unuseable, before the fabric is worn out. Dacron has an affinity for oil and the collar is an area which soils quickly and must be spot cleaned to remove the oil. The extra rubbing used to remove the soil also removes the color. This has happened to the blouse shown in the picture above. Other areas subject to such abrasion are the underarm, pockets, button and buttonhole openings, and the abdomen.

Acrylics

Light Weight

Bulk

Cover

Loft

Easy Care

Acrylic fibers are manufactured fibers in which the fiber forming substance is a synthetic polymer composed of at least 85% by weight of acrylonitrile units.[14]

$$CH_2-\overset{\displaystyle H}{\underset{\displaystyle CN}{C}}$$

Acrylic fibers are produced by four companies and marketed under the trade names Acrilan, Creslan, Orlon, and Zefran. The success of these fibers is due, perhaps, to the combination of wool-like qualities and easy care.

These fibers account for about 20% of the non-cellulose man-made fiber market. They were first used in knitted outer wear where good cover, texture, and fabric stability are important. They are widely used in men's, women's, and children's sweaters. In this field, their high bulk, resiliency, and ease-of-care make them superior to all other man-made fibers. Their non-scratchiness and non-felting is superior to that of wool. In spite of the fact that most acrylic sweaters pill, many people prefer them. They are used in fur-like fabrics, both for outer shells and for liners in coats, jackets, etc. Acrilan has been very successful in carpeting because of its resiliency, bulking power, and good resistance to abrasion. The fact that acrylic fibers can be made in any diameter gives them a plus value over wool which must be selected for carpeting on the basis of fiber coarseness. None of the wool grown in the United States is suitable for carpeting, thus

[14] F.T.C. definition.

the cost of the acrylics compared with imported wool may very well mean that they will take over, or at least be very competitive in, this large market.

The future for the acrylics seems bright. They have better durability characteristics than rayon or acetate, they give better wool-like textures than nylon or polyesters, and they have easy-care characteristics that are desired by consumers.

The chart below shows the historical development.

HISTORICAL DEVELOPMENT OF ACRYLICS

1948 Orlon. Du Pont, after experimentation and market research with Fiber A, announced plans to produce this fiber under the trade name "Orlon."

1950 Orlon commercial production of type 81 filament and type 41 staple.
Acrilan. Production plans announced by Chemstrand.

1952 Acrilan commercial production.

1953 Orlon 42 staple with better dyeability.

1954 Acrilan R (round cross-section) replaces first Acrilan (dog-bone cross-section).
Creslan. Pilot plant production of X51 and X54 by American Cyanamid.

1956 Creslan announced as trade name for X51 and X54.
Zefran. Dow Chemical Company announced plans to produce nitrile alloy fiber. Pilot plant designation was Q1240.
Orlon 81 discontinued because of difficulty in dyeing.

1958 Zefran commercial production.
Acrilan fiberfill for pillows.

1959 Creslan commercial production.
Orlon filament "Cantrece" introduced.
Orlon Sayelle reversible crimp staple introduced.

1960 Acrilan solution dyed.

Manufacture

Acrylonitrile is produced in the United States by four companies: American Cyanamid Co., Union Carbide and Chemicals Co., B. F. Goodrich Co., and Monsanto Chemical Co.

The largest amount is used in the production of fibers.

Acrylonitrile can be used alone as a homopolymer or it can be combined with other substances such as basic, acidic or polar non-ionizing monomers which are introduced into the polymer to increase dye affinity. The first acrylic fibers were very difficult to dye, a factor which led to their use as the white or light colored fiber in heather effect fabrics. This also led to the development of new dyeing techniques.

In fiber manufacture the polymer is dissolved in a suitable solvent, usually dimethyl formamide, and either wet spun or dry spun. Fibers cannot be melt spun because acrylonitrile decomposes when melted. After spinning the fibers are stretched 300 to 1000% of their own length, dried, crimped, heat-set and marketed as cut staple or tow. (Orlon Cantrece is the only filament fiber in this group.)

PROPERTIES COMMON TO ALL ACRYLICS

Property	*Importance to the Consumer*
Low density	Fabrics feel light and airy
Low to medium strength	Satisfactory
Slight loss in wet strength	Durability only slightly impaired
Differential shrinkage and good resiliency	Warmth, good cover, maintains loft, makes high bulk possible
Excellent resistance to weathering	Good for outdoor furniture and awnings
Low moisture absorption and wicking	Quick drying, easy spot removal, may build up static charges
Thermoplastic	Can be heat-set. Durable pleats, dimensional stability
Resistant to insect and microbiological attack	No storage problem

All of the acrylonitrile fibers are similar in their properties because of the high percentage of acrylonitrile present. They differ somewhat in their affinity for dyes, and slightly in absorbency and strength. See the chart below.

PROPERTIES OF ACRYLIC FIBERS

	Acrilan	*Creslan*	*Orlon*	*Zefran*
Cross-section	Round or bean	Round	Dogbone	Round
Tenacity	2.27	2.5	2.4	3.5
Density	1.17	1.18	1.16	1.19
Moisture regain	1.5	2.2	1.5	2.5
Sticking temp.	470–480°F	410°F	455°F	490°F
Resistance to acids	—Good to excellent—			
Resistance to alkalies	—Fair to good for weak alkali—			
Dyes used	Basic Disperse Acid Chrome Naphthol	Acid Chrome	Acid	Vat Sulfur Naphthol

Orlon

Orlon, the first acrylic fiber made by Du Pont, was the first acrylic fiber on the market. Research started in 1938. Since its initial production as Orlon, many changes and modifications have been made to make it a better fiber for specific end-uses. In 1960 the following types were on the market:

Type 21. Orlon Sayelle is the trade name for Du Pont's "bicomponent" acrylic fiber, which has a three dimensional crimp similar to that of wool. The spinning solution is modified chemically so the fiber has different swelling properties on each side and when the fiber is heated one side shrinks more than the other, giving a high degree of crimp. Unlike the other man-made fibers it has reversible crimp, which means that it elongates when wet and crimps again as it dries. The effect in fabrics is in aesthetics, loft, fabric elasticity, and resistance to permanent heat deformation. Fabrics of Orlon Sayelle have characteristics of wool plus the easy-care properties of the synthetics. Uses are: sweaters, knit and woven fabrics, pile fabrics, and socks.

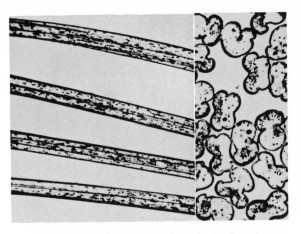

Fig. 3:38. Photomicrograph of longitudinal and cross-sectional views of 3.0 denier, semidull Orlon Sayelle. (Courtesy of E. I. du Pont de Nemours & Company.)

Type 24. Orlon Sayelle is three denier (very fine) staple designed especially for full fashioned, fine gauge knits, and light weight woven fabrics. In wool, comparable yarns are 64s and 80s, which are too costly for mass production.

Type 25. Staple for blending with cotton and rayon for outerwear.

Type 28. High shrinkage staple with a crisp, but not scratchy, hand for brushed knits and outerwear. Animal-effect fiber with a low crimp and rich luster.

Type 36. Carpet staple for use in 100% Orlon carpets. Fibers are soil and static resistant, and are comparable to wool in cleanability.

Type 38. High shrinkage tow for deep-pile coats. Fibers have 40 to 50% shrinkage. Can be used effectively in fur-like fabrics with two pile heights when combined with fibers which have low shrinkage. When exposed to heat, type 38 shrinks, forming the down hair component in the fabric.

Type 39. Staple for use on the woolen spinning system for blankets and coatings. Anti-static protection is built in. This is especially important in blankets and electric blankets.

Type 42. Regular Orlon has a reasonably good combination of properties for many uses.

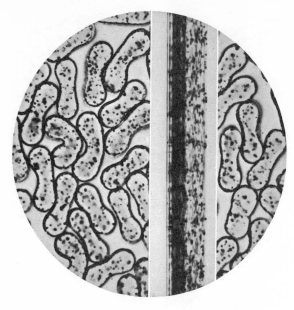

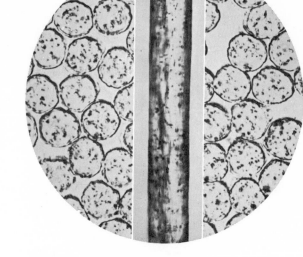

Fig. 3:39. Photomicrograph of Orlon acrylic fiber; longitudinal and cross-sectional views. (Courtesy of E. I. du Pont de Nemours & Company.)

Fig. 3:40. Longitudinal and cross-sectional photomicrograph of Acrilan acrylic fiber. (Courtesy of the Chemstrand Corporation.)

Type 44. Tow designed to give cross-dyed effects when combined with type 42.

Type 72. A 1.5 denier for use in skin contact fabrics. It wets readily and moisture evaporates rapidly.

Type 75. Staple to be used in blends with cellulose fibers. Whiteness is equal to bleached cotton. Retains softness and is dimensionally stable in washing.

Orlon Cantrece was the only filament acrylic fiber. It was used especially in silk-like knits intended for high fashion clothing. Production was discontinued in 1962.

Orlon Cantrece, Orlon Sayelle and the animal-effect fibers have been designed for prestige items. Orlon Sayelle is expected to find wide use in clothing.

All Orlon fibers are produced in a wide range of deniers, in lengths from 1½ to 4½ inches, or in mixed deniers and varied staple lengths. They may be bright or semi-dull.

Acrilan

Acrilan (pronounced ak-ri-lan) is the acrylic fiber of the Chemstrand Corporation which is jointly owned by the American Viscose Company and the Monsanto Chemical Company.

The first Acrilan fiber was introduced on the market in 1952, twelve years after research started. It was made principally of acrylonitrile with other chemicals added to make it more acceptable to dyes.

Acrilan was the first acrylic fiber to be used in carpeting and the first real competitor with wool for this end-use. Acrilan is made in two types, 16 and 1656, each of which takes dye differently. It is available in deniers ranging from 1.0 to 15.0 and in lengths from 1⁹⁄₁₆ to 5 inches, as high bulk or regular fiber, and in bright or semi-dull lusters. All fiber is crimped mechanically. Acrilan fiberfill is produced for use in pillows and comforters. The Chemstrand Corporation has established standards for blankets, carpeting, fiberfill, and upholstery. The Seal of Quality on a blanket, the Acrilan label on fiberfill or upholstery, or Acrilan ® on carpets means that the manufacturer has met the performance standards set by the fiber producer.

Fig. 3:41. Photomicrograph of longitudinal and cross-sectional views of Creslan acrylic fiber. (Courtesy of the American Cyanamid Company.)

Creslan

Creslan is the acrylic fiber of the American Cyanamid Company. Like the other acrylic fibers it contains substances other than acrylonitrile to give it a better affinity for dyes. It is produced in deniers from 2 to 15 and in length from 1¼ to 6 inches. It is available in bright or semi-dull lusters and is crimped mechanically.

Creslan fibers are sold by the fiber producer to the manufacturer under a protected identification program which requires that products can carry the Creslan trade name if they meet certain performance standards. Otherwise, they can be labeled only as acrylic fiber.

Zefran

Zefran, the newest acrylic fiber, is produced by the Dow Chemical Company. It is described as a nitrile alloy with a graft copolymer of dye receptive groups on a backbone of acrylonitrile. Graft polymerization is being used with many of the synthetic fibers. In this process side chains of a different molecular composition are attached to a finished polymer chain. These grafted molecules give different properties to the fiber, usually better dye affinity or better absorbency.

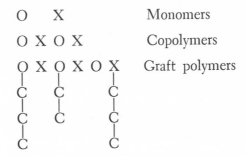

This may mean that the acrylonitrile was polymerized alone or with a small amount of another substance and then copolymerized with the dye receptive polymer. Zefran differs from the other acrylic fibers in that it can be dyed with vat dyes. Zefran is produced in deniers from 2 to 6 and in staple lengths from 1½ to 4½ inches, as bright or dull fiber, and is mechanically crimped.

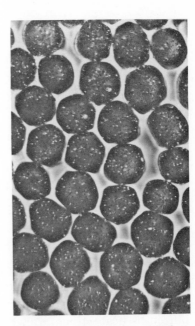

Fig. 3:42. Photomicrographic cross section of Zefran, the newest of the acrylic fibers. (Courtesy of The Dow Chemical Company.)

Modacrylics

Very Heat-Sensitive
Chemically Inert
Easy Care

Modacrylic fibers are manufactured fibers in which the fiber forming substance is any long chain synthetic polymer composed of less than 85% but more than 35% acrylonitrile units.[15]

$$CH_2-CH$$
$$|$$
$$CN$$

These fibers are modified acrylics. *Dynel*, produced by the Carbon and Carbide Company, is a copolymer of 60% vinyl chloride, $CH_2=CHCl$ and 40% acrylonitrile. While the composition of *Verel* has not been announced, it probably contains vinylidene chloride, $CH_2=CCl_2$, and other substances in addition to acrylonitrile. Verel is produced by the Eastman Chemical Products, Inc. The chart below shows the historical development of the modacrylic fibers.

HISTORICAL DEVELOPMENT OF MODACRYLIC FIBERS

1948 Vinyon N filament produced by Carbide and Carbon Chemical Co. Later discontinued.

1951 Dynel staple produced by Carbide and Carbon Chemical Co.

1954 Dynel whiter fiber for blending with cotton for underwear.

1956 Verel announced by Eastman Chemical Products, Inc.

1957 Verel commercial production.

1960 Verel H. B. high bulk staple for carpets.

1961 Filament fiber.

Manufacture

The raw material, in the form of a copolymer resin, is dissolved in acetone, wet spun as filament tow, stretched, cut, crimped, and stabilized by heat-setting. Stretching is done during the manufacturing process to orient the

[15] F.T.C. definition.

molecules in the fiber and thus increase fiber strength.

The modacrylics are heat-sensitive. (*See* Fig. 3:43.) They must be ironed or pressed with the lowest iron setting and a press cloth placed over the fabric. In blends with natural fibers, the press cloth may not be needed. This

Fig. 3:43. Dynel test fabric pressed with steam iron. Note shrinkage.

heat-sensitivity has several advantages. Fabrics can be set in pleats which are durable to washing. High count, lightweight constructions suitable for rainwear when fibers used in the unstabilized form are shrunk during finishing. In deep-pile fabrics, the shrinkage holds the pile yarns or fibers firmly in place and makes a more dense, fur-like pile. When used in combination with stabilized fibers or yarns, textured or three-dimensional fabrics can be made or the "guard hair" effect of true fur can be simulated.

The modacrylic fibers are *self-extinguishing* when burned, a property which makes them superior to the acrylics in this characteristic when used in highly napped or deep-pile fabrics or carpets.

The modacrylics are used in chemically resistant clothing and in industrial cloths because they are resistant to the action of most chemicals. These fibers are heavier than the acrylics so do not make as light clothing.

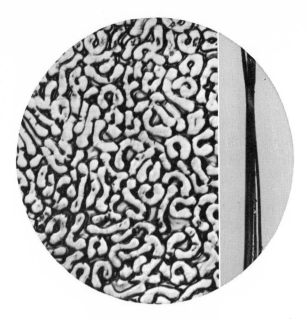

Fig. 3:44. Photomicrographs of Dynel modacrylic staple fiber; cross-sectional and longitudinal views. (Courtesy of the Carbide and Carbon Chemical Company.)

The properties of Dynel and Verel are contrasted below.

Property	Dynel	Verel
Cross-section	Irregular	Dog-bone
Density	1.35	1.37
Tenacity	2.5–3.3	2.5–2.8
Moisture regain	0.04	3.5–4.0
Effect of heat	Softens at 300°F.	Stiffens above 300°F.
Effect of acid	Resistant	Resistant
Effect of alkali	Resistant	Resistant
Effect of moths, mildew, and microorganisms	Resistant	Resistant
Flammability	Self-extinguishing	Self-extinguishing

Both fibers are produced in denier sizes suitable for clothing and carpets. They are produced in either heat-set or unheat-set fiber and as staple (1½ to 5 inches) or filament tow. Both fibers are widely used in deep-pile fabrics (face and backing) and in carpeting.

By proper heat finishing, Dynel fibers can be given a high polish (page 165) which makes them look like fur. Dynel has been blended with wool to make felt fabrics which can be heat molded into men's hats. Bondyne is a suit fabric made of a blend of Dynel and wool. Dynel has been used for doll wigs which look very much like real hair and can be washed, set, brushed, and combed.

Verel fiber is produced with different amounts of shrinkage:

Regular Verel — 1 to 13% shrinkage

Type I Verel — 9 to 11% shrinkage

Type II Verel — 19 to 23% shrinkage

Photomicrographs of Dynel and Verel are shown at left and below.

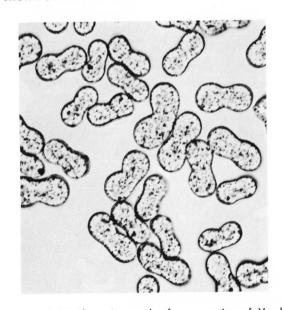

Fig. 3:45. Photomicrograph of cross section of Verel modacrylic fiber. (Courtesy of Eastman Chemical Products, Inc.)

Olefins

Lightest Fiber Made
Insulates Better Than Wool
Low Cost

Olefin fibers are manufactured fibers in which the fiber forming substance is any long chain synthetic polymer composed of at least 85% by weight of ethylene, propylene or other olefin units. (Propylene-CH_2—CH_2—CH_2—.)[16]

The olefins are the newest man-made fiber family and show signs of becoming one of the most important. Polyethylene, an olefin product, has been widely used for plastic bags and squeeze bottles but has such low heat resistance that it has found little place in the apparel field.

Polypropylene fibers were developed in Italy after six years of basic research and are produced there under the trade name *Meraklon*; the name was taken from Merak, one of the stars of the Big Bear. The Novamont Corporation at Neal, West Virginia is a subsidiary of the Italian firm and produces Meraklon in this country. *Herculon* by Hercules Powder Company, *Reevon* by Reeves Bros., *Eastman* by the Tennessee Eastman Company, and *Olane* by Avisun Corporation are other polypropylene trade names. The Hercules Powder Company, in 1960, purchased the nylon plant of the Industrial Rayon Corporation and converted it to the production of polypropylene fiber. Conversion was economical since both nylon and the olefins are melt spun.

Manufacture

The olefins are melt spun by the same techniques used for nylon and the polyesters. Polypropylene is spun from a molten solution, cooled in the air to solidify it and then drawn and heat-set. These fibers, like all melt-spun fibers which will retain the shape of the spinneret holes, are circular in cross section and rod-like. They contain nothing but carbon and hydrogen and have excellent chemical resistance.

The fibers are produced as staple, tow, or conventional filament.

The low cost of the fibers relate to three factors:

> Melt-spun fibers are simple to produce.
> Petroleum, the raw material, is readily available.

[16] F.T.C. definition.

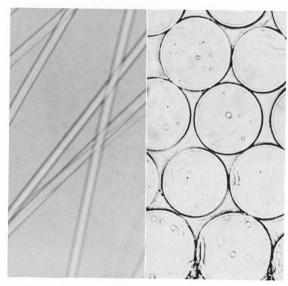

Fig. 3:46. Photomicrograph of Herculon. (Courtesy of Hercules Powder Company.)

Because it is the lightest of the fibers, a pound of it will make more fabric than a pound of the other fibers.

Characteristics

Polypropylene is the lightest fiber made.

Fiber	Specific Gravity
Polypropylene	0.91
Cotton	1.5
Rayon	1.5
Dacron	1.38
Wool	1.34
Acrylics	1.17
Nylon	1.14

The figures below give the weight of a square yard of cotton poplin as compared to the same fabric made with polypropylene.

Cotton poplin	3.8 oz. per sq. yd.
Polypropylene poplin	2.7 oz. per sq. yd.

Because of its light weight it is used in coatings, blankets, etc. Its insulation power is higher than that of Australian wool and it has good transmission of humidity.

Cohesiveness is another outstanding property. The fiber-to-fiber contact resembles that of wool more than that of other man-made fibers. This means that the staple is easily spun into yarns on conventional spinning machinery. Other properties are:

Very low static.
Low pilling.
High wrinkle resistance.
Good elasticity.
Tenacity—4.8 to 7.5 g/d.
Excellent washability.
Suitable to wide range of end-uses.

Polypropylene softens and melts at 320 to 330°F. It must be ironed with an iron of controlled temperature or with a steam iron or a press cloth. Because it has good washability with wrinkle resistance, little ironing should be needed.

Future research will probably develop more heat-resistant types.

REFERENCES

1. *Textile Organon*, **31**:110 (June 1960).
2. Fior, A., "The Propylene Story," *Textile Industries*, **124**:105 (Aug. 1960).

Nytril

Softness
Easy Care

Nytril fibers are manufactured fibers in which the fiber forming substance is any long chain synthetic polymer composed of at least 85% vinylidene dinitrile.[17]

$$CH_2 = C(CN)_2$$

Research on nytril fibers was started during World War II by the B. F. Goodrich Company. In 1950 laboratory tests indicated that the fiber had excellent crease recovery and was similar to wool in many of its properties. The

[17] F.T.C. definition.

first fiber was produced in 1955 at Avon Lake, Ohio under the trade name Darlan and later renamed *Darvan*. In 1960 the Celanese Corporation acquired exclusive world rights to the patent and process and started an extensive research and development program to overcome certain dyeing and finishing problems. Goodrich continued to produce the fiber for Celanese until 1961 when production in the United States was discontinued. The Celanese Corporation then entered into an agreement with Farwerke Hoechst AG of Germany to form a new company, Bobina Faserwerke to produce a fiber trademarked *Travis*. Production of this fiber was begun in 1962. The fiber may ultimately be made in the United States again.

Nytril fibers are unique in that they are almost completely amorphous and strength is relatively unimpaired at temperatures below 320°F.

Properties of Darvan

Darvan had a tenacity of 1.7 to 2.2 g/d and a moisture regain of 2.6%. The fiber was not stretched after spinning, which accounted for its low strength and also its absorbency. A comparison of Darvan and wool is interesting since Darvan was used in wool type fabrics. Wool is somewhat weaker and loses much strength when wet, while Darvan retained most of its strength. The densities and elongations are similar and the wool is much more absorbent.

Darvan was thermoplastic and could be heat-set to hold its shape. In deep-pile fabrics "sit-marks" would shake out, tufting resistance was high and the pile was *softer* than with other synthetics. Cleaning of deep-pile Darvan fabrics could be done with less care since steaming did not change the hand of the fabric.

Darvan was similar to the acrylics in chemical resistance and similar to the polyesters in dyeability. X-7 was a modified Darvan developed for improved dyeability. Darvan was

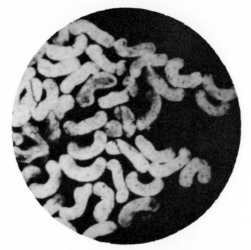

Fig. 3:47. Photomicrograph of cross section of Darvan nytril fiber. (Courtesy of the Celanese Corporation of America.)

available in deniers from 1.5 to 8.0, in staple lengths from 1½ to 4½ inches, in bright or semidull and in heat-set or unheat-set forms. The cross-sectional shape shown above is irregular and thus the fiber gives good cover and bulk characteristics to the fabric.

REFERENCES

1. Reuter, L. F., and Johnson, R. D., "The Technological Story of Darvan," *Canadian Textile Journal*, 76:25 (Dec. 1959).
2. Moncrieff, R. W., *Man Made Fibers*, 3rd ed., New York: Wiley, 1957, p. 443.

Saran

Self-extinguishing
Water Resistant
Low Cost

Saran is a manufactured fiber in which the fiber forming substance is any long chain synthetic polymer composed of at least 80% by weight of vinylidene chloride units ($CH_2 CCl_2-$).[18]

[18] F.T.C. definition.

Saran is a vinylidene chloride and vinyl chloride copolymer developed in 1940 by the Dow Chemical Company. *Velon* is a saran fiber made by Firestone Industrial Products Company.

The raw material is melted, spun, and stretched to orient the molecules. Both filament and staple forms are produced. Much of the filament fiber is produced as monofilament and used as yarns for seat covers, furniture webbing, screenings, luggage, shoes, and handbags. Monofilaments are also used in doll's hair and wigs.

The staple form is made either straight, curled, or crimped. The curled form is unique in that the curl is inherent and closely resembles the curl of natural wool. The staple is used in rugs, draperies, and upholstery.

In addition to its use as a fiber, saran has wide use in the plastic field.

Properties

Saran has good weathering properties, chemical resistance, and resistance to stretch. Its clothing uses are limited because of its low resistance to heat. It is an unusually tough, durable fiber. The fiber as seen under the microscope is perfectly round and smooth. It does not catch and hold gritty dirt particles that, when embedded in a rug, set up an abrasive shearing action.

Saran absorbs little or no moisture so that it dries rapidly. It is difficult to dye and for this reason, solution dyeing is used.

Saran does not support combustion. When exposed to flame, it will soften, char, and decompose.

A new development by Dow Chemical Co. is *Rovana*, a micro-tope yarn, which can be woven directly into fabrics. Rovana is a thin, slit film which is folded into a continuous ribbon-like strand. The advantage of this form over the conventional yarn is that it has better cover in a fabric. In addition to the other properties of saran, it is said to make a very tear resistant fabric. Compared with cotton fabrics of the same weight, Rovana fabrics have three to four times the tear strength. Rovana fabrics can be molded into three dimensional fabrics. They can be pressed together by thermal or electronic methods instead of being sewed together.

Rovana is being tried in various end-uses; draperies, luggage, place mats, wall coverings, tobacco shade cloth, and automobile seat covers.

REFERENCES

1. Saran Yarns Co., "Saran Fibers," Odenton, Md.: Saran Yarns, no date.
2. Mauersberger, H. R., *Matthews' Textile Fibers*, 6th ed., New York: Wiley, 1954, p. 1004.
3. Abernethy, Nelson W., "Rovana, Dow's New Saran Micro-tape," *Modern Textiles Magazine*, **41**:99 (May 1960).

Vinyon

Very Heat Sensitive
Chemical Resistant

Vinyon is a manufactured fiber in which the fiber forming substance is any long chain synthetic polymer composed of at least 85% by weight of vinyl chloride units (CH_2CHCl).[19]

Vinyon was introduced to the textile trade in 1939 by the American Viscose Corp. It is a copolymer of vinyl chloride, 88%, and vinyl acetate, 12%. Polymerization is obtained by heating the monomers in the presence of a catalyst. The co-polymer is dissolved in acetone, extruded in air.

The first fiber was in filament form. The filaments were twisted in the wet state, stretched about 800%, which gave them a tenacity of 3.4 g/d.

Vinyon HH, produced by American Viscose, is a staple fiber with a round cross-section. These fibers have a tenacity of 0.7 to 1.0 g/d which indicates that they are not stretched

[19] F.T.C. definition.

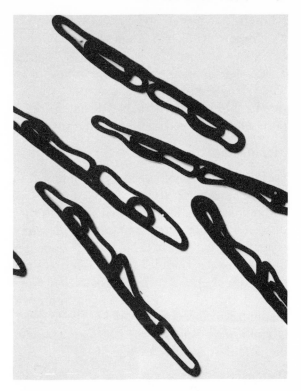

Fig. 3:48. Photomicrograph of cross section of Rovana microtape. (Courtesy of The Dow Chemical Company.)

after spinning. These fibers, which are amorphous, have a warm, pleasant hand.

Vinyon is very heat sensitive. The fibers soften at 150–170°F, shrink at 175°F and do not withstand boiling water or normal pressing or ironing temperature. They are unaffected by moisture, chemically stable, resistant to moth and biological attack, poor conductors of electricity, and do not burn.

Their properties make them especially good for bonding agents in rugs, papers and non-woven fabrics.

Vinal

Chemical Resistant
More Absorbent Than
Other Vinyl Fibers

Vinal fiber is a manufactured fiber in which the fiber forming substance is any long chain synthetic polymer composed of at least 50% by weight of vinyl alcohol units (CH_2CHOH).[20]

No vinal fiber is produced in the United States but Kuralon is imported from Japan. The Japanese use the generic name "vinylon" for this fiber and trade names Kuralon for exports and Cremona for their home market.

Manufacture

Polyvinyl alcohol polymers are obtained by treating polyvinyl acetate with caustic soda (saponification). The polyvinal alcohol is then dissolved in hot water and wet spun into a coagulating bath. If nothing more is done, the fibers are water soluble and suitable for surgical purposes. For textile purposes they must be heat treated with formaldehyde in an acid medium which acetylizes some of the hydroxyl groups and thus makes the fibers water insoluble. Kuralon is 40% acetylated.

Properties

Vinal fibers are inexpensive (85¢ per pound), resistant to most chemicals, and resistant to microbiological attack. They are thermoplastic; soften at 200° and melt at 220°C. They are similar to wool in density (1.3) and in water retention. They have a dry tenacity of 3.2 g/d and lose about 25% of their strength when wet. Vinal fibers are similar to cotton because of their hydroxyl groups. They have poor crease resistance. Fibers have a ribbon shaped cross section similar to Dynel.

Vinal fibers are used in chemical work clothing, tarpaulins, hatch covers, swim suits.

REFERENCES

1. Wells, Richard D., "Vinal, What It Is, What It Can Do," *Modern Textiles Magazine*, **40**:51 (Nov. 1959).
2. Moncrieff, R. W., *Man Made Fibers*, 3rd ed., New York: Wiley, 1957.
3. Hopff, H., and Gerber, G., "Fibers from Addition Polymers," *CIBA Review*, **12**:137 (Apr. 1960).

[20] F.T.C. definition.

Spandex

Lightweight
Very Elastic
Good Holding Power

Spandex is a manufactured elastomeric fiber in which the fiber forming substance is a long chain polymer consisting of at least 85% segmented polyurethane.[21]

An elastomer is a fiber or yarn that has a high break elongation (more than 200%) and both a high degree and rapid rate of recovery. An elastomeric fiber is made up of hard and soft segments in the polymer chain. The soft segments provide the give and the hard segments tie the chains together. Varying proportions of hard and soft segments are used depending on the amount of stretch desired. The word "polyurethane" is used to describe esters, particularly the ethyl ester which has the formula $-NH_2COOC_2H_5-$.

Spandex is used in garments where light weight and stretchiness are desired: foundation garments, bathing suits, surgical hose, ski pants, football pants, garters, belts. Trade names for fibers on the market are Lycra, Vyrene and Stretchever. Other fibers are being planned; see the chart at the top of the next page.

Spandex Vs. Rubber

Spandex can be used wherever rubber is used in apparel.

Before 1930, rubber thread was quite coarse and fabrics made from it were relatively heavy. Yarns were obtained by cutting sheets of rubber into the desired yarn size. Rubber yarns are sold by core size, the size determined by the number of slices made from one inch of the sheet. Size 70, for example, means that 70 yarns were cut from each inch of the sheet. In the 1930's, a technique for making rubber yarn from liquid latex was developed. The liquid latex was extruded through spinnerets into

[21] F.T.C. definition.

HISTORICAL DEVELOPMENT OF SPANDEX FIBERS

1947   Du Pont made small amount of fiber designated as Fiber K
1950–57 Manufacturers of foundation garments experimented with Fiber K
        Du Pont pilot plant production. Fiber named Lycra
        U.S. Rubber pilot plant production of Vyrene
1960–62 Du Pont—full scale production of Lycra at Waynesboro, Va.
        U.S. Rubber—expanded capacity for Vyrene at Gastonia, N. C.
        International Latex—production of Stretchever at Bristol, R. I.
1963   Celanese Fibers Co. Fiber 32
        Firestone Tire and Rubber Company introduced Spandelle
        Globe Manufacturing Company introduced Glospan
        United States Eastampton Rubber Thread Company research program
        Goodrich Chemical research program
        Chemstrand Corporation research program
        Rhee Rubber Company research program
        American Cyanamid * is working on a stretch version of Creslan
        Eastman Chemical Co.* is working on a polyester elastic fiber, T-1700, at Kingsport, Tenn.

* These elastometric fibers are not spandex.

a coagulating bath, washed, treated, and vulcanized. These threads were much finer than the cut yarns and they were round.

Rubber yarns are covered with two layers of yarn (cotton, nylon, silk), each layer wrapped spirally around the core in a different direction. The rubber core is stretched slightly during wrapping. The yarn cover limits elongation because the cover yarns jam when the elastic is stretched. This prevents rupture of the rubber core. When the elastic is relaxed the cover yarns also jam to fix the length of the yarn at rest.

During the 1950's, synthetic elastomers (spandex) were developed. These fibers are claimed to be superior to rubber in dyeability. Rubber does not take dye readily and in col-

ored fabrics the color is in the wrapping and when the fabrics are stretched the undyed core shows. With spandex both the core and the wrapping yarns are colored thus the "grin through" is not obvious. Spandex is ⅓ lighter in weight and almost twice as strong as rubber. The specific gravity of rubber is 1.4 and of spandex is 1.0. One pound of spandex has the same holding power as 1.8 pounds of rubber. In the foundation garment industry this means that lighter weight garments of spandex have the same control as heavier ones of rubber. When spandex was first used in girdles there was some resistance both by store buyers and customers because they did not think that a light weight garment could do the same job as the traditional heavier garment. Manufacturers convinced store buyers by giving them garments to wear and suggested that they give a tape measure with each girdle so the customer could measure herself in the new garment.

Spandex has better resistance to cosmetic lotions, body powders and body oils than rubber. Spandex is more expensive than rubber. In 1961, a spandex girdle at $7.95 and a Lastex rubber girdle at $5.00 were comparable in style and both made of power net. An article in *Women's Wear Daily* compared the price of nylon tricot @ 50¢ per yard with that of spandex tricot @ $5.00 per yard.

Manufacture

Spandex is made by either dry or solvent spinning. Like all man-made fibers, the spinning solution may contain delustering agents, dye receptors, whiteners and lubricants. Fibers are produced as monofilaments or multifilaments and in sizes from fine to coarse. The multifilament yarns differ from other multifilament yarns in that they are held together by positive bridging. A pin inserted in the yarn cannot be pulled through the entire length but will be stopped by these joinings. Companies making multifilaments say the advantage of these yarns is that in sewing fabrics the machine needle will go between the fine filaments and thus there is no danger of breaking them. Companies making monofilaments say that blunt needles are used to sew elastic fabrics and they push the monofilament to one side so there is no danger of rupturing it.

Properties

Spandex has good flexlife, has good resistance to abrasion and is machine washable. The fibers are inherently white but they yellow and degrade at temperatures above 300°F. Most fibers are harmed by chlorine bleach. Garments of spandex can be dry cleaned with conventional solvents. As was mentioned in the comparison with rubber, they are light weight, resistant to body oils and can be dyed.

Lycra and Vyrene are trade names for the most commonly used spandex fibers and are compared in the chart below.

COMPARISON OF LYCRA AND VYRENE

	Lycra	Vyrene
Manufacturer	Du Pont	U.S. Rubber
Form in which sold	Bare or covered multifilament Denier size 70–560	Covered—double or single monofilament Ends or core size 75–200
Cost, 1961	$13 to $5.85 per pound	$4.50 to $10.50 per pound depending on core size and covering material

Spandelle (Firestone) and Glospan (Globe Manufacturing) are other trade names.

REFERENCES

1. "New Snap-Back Filaments," *Modern Textiles Magazine*, **40**:38 (Dec. 1959).
2. Boulware, H. M., "Vyrene, New Synthetic Elastic Yarn," *Modern Textiles Magazine*, **41**:46 (Aug. 1960).
3. Marchell, T. B., "Man-Made Elastic Yarns," *Textile Industries*, **125**:75 (Aug. 1961).
4. "Fast Growth Looms for Spandex Fibers," *Chemical and Engineering News*, **40**:34 (Jan. 1962).

MINERAL FIBERS

The mineral fibers are inorganic materials which are used mainly for fireproof fabrics and for insulation. The mineral fibers have more industrial uses than clothing and household textile uses. Fiberglas and asbestos are the most commonly used fibers.

Asbestos

Fireproof
Acid Resistant
Low Pliability

Asbestos is a natural fiber which occurs as veins or strips in rocks. While there are three minerals classified as asbestos, the most important commercial variety is the Canadian serpentine. Other deposits are found in Russia, Arizona, and Africa. The fiber is obtained by mining or quarrying. The fiber is carefully separated from the crushed rock and sorted according to fiber length.

Properties

Asbestos fibers are ⅜ inches to ¾ inches in length and are quite small in diameter. The diameter has never been definitely determined because the fibers can be split to infinite fineness and the finest ever measured was made of several fine fibers. Under the microscope the fibers look like tiny polished rods, very straight, with no rough surfaces. The physical structure of the fiber makes it very difficult to spin into yarns because it is lacking in length and cohesiveness. For textile uses, five to twenty per cent cotton is blended with asbestos.

Asbestos is white or grayish-white in color. Asbestos fibers do not take dye readily but since most textile uses are utilitarian, color is not important. Some fire screens and draperies have been printed.

Asbestos is used for padding, for laundry presses and mangles, belting for conveying hot materials, brake linings, gloves, aprons, etc.

Glass

Fireproof
Rotproof
Dimensionally Stable

The process of drawing out glass into hair-like strands dates back into ancient history. It is thought that Phoenician fishermen noticed small pools of a molten material among the coals of the fires they built for cooking on the sands of the Aegean beaches. While poking at the strange substance with a stick, they drew out a long strand—the first glass fiber. Venetian artisans of the Middle Ages had developed the art of making glass and of attenuating glass rods.

In 1893, at the Columbian Exposition in Chicago, the Libbey Glass Company exhibited lampshades woven from glass fibers and silk. A celebrated actress saw them and ordered a dress made from the fabric. Her dress was valued at $30,000. These fabrics were not practical because they could not be folded without splitting.

In 1938, commercially useful glass fiber was first produced by the Owens-Corning Fiberglas Corporation. Their fiber is called Fiberglas. Johns-Manville produces glass fiber under the trade name J-M Fiber Glass.

The major end-uses for glass fiber are curtains and draperies, insect screens for the home, wall paper, and reinforced plastics.

The raw material for glass fiber is sand, silica, and limestone, combined with additives of feldspar and boric acid. Two methods of manufacture are used: a direct method reduces the raw material batch to molten glass in small furnaces from which it is drawn out into thin streams through a group of perforated bushings; small marbles ⅝ inches in diameter are made. These glass marbles are inspected for impurities and then remelted in large electric furnaces (2400°F). For filament yarns, each furnace has 200 holes in the base of the melting chamber. Fine streams of glass flow through these holes and are carried

Fig. 3:49. Marbles from which glass fiber is spun. (Courtesy of the Owens-Corning Fiberglas Corporation.)

through a hole in the floor to a winder in the room below. The winder revolves faster than the glass comes from the furnace, thus stretching the fibers and reducing them in size before they harden.

When staple yarn is spun, the glass flows out in thin streams from holes in the base of the furnace, and jets of high pressure air or steam yank the glass into fibers eight to ten inches long. These fibers are collected on a revolving drum and made into a thin web which is then formed into a sliver, or soft, untwisted yarn.

Glass fiber has wide industrial use where weight saving, noise abatement, fire protection, temperature control, and air purification are needed. The excellent insulating properties of glass fiber are also used to advantage in the clothing and household textile field. Some of the recent household items to appear on the market are interlined hot-pads, mittens, and glass fiber batting for use in upholstery. In clothing, glass fiber has been used in interlinings for coats, jackets, and mittens. The fiber used for interlining garments differs from that used in industrial insulation.

Fig. 3:50. High-speed winder drawing Fiberglas strand. (Courtesy of the Owens-Corning Fiberglas Corporation.)

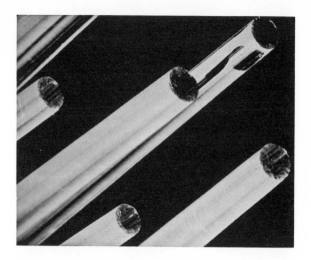

Fig. 3:51. Photomicrograph of Fiberglas. (Courtesy of the Owens-Corning Fiberglas Corporation.)

Filament glass fiber is used extensively in the decorator field for curtains and draperies. Here the fiber performs most satisfactorily if bending and abrasion can be kept at a minimum. Curtains or draperies of glass fiber should be used at windows that will not be kept open, allowing the wind to whip the curtains. The bottom of the draperies or curtains should not touch the floor or window sills. Glass-fiber fabrics are washable either in a tumble type machine or by hand. Rubbing and twisting should be avoided. They should be washed alone and preferably not more than two pieces at a time. Frequent washing should not be necessary since glass fibers resist soil, and spots or stains can be wiped off with a damp cloth. No ironing is necessary. Curtains can be smoothed and put on the rod to dry.

Glass fiber is soil-resistant and soil is easily removed. However, the oil used in finishing has been the cause of graying in white curtains. Oil holds the dirt persistently and it also oxidizes with age. Washing has not proved to be a satisfactory way of whitening the material and dry cleaning is not recommended unless Stoddard solvent is used.

Properties

Glass fiber appears as a very fine, smooth, transparent rod under the microscope (Figure 3:51). It is perfectly round in cross-section. Glass fiber is one of few fibers that is *proof* against the following:

Fire	Moisture absorption
Acid	Stretching and shrinkage
Light and age	Absorption of odors
Rot, insects, etc.	

Its disadvantages are:

Low flexibility and resistance to abrasion
Too little elongation when stretched

Until these disadvantages can be overcome, filament glass fiber will not be used for clothing.

Finishing Glass Fibers

Coronizing is a process for heat-setting, dyeing, and finishing glass fiber in one continuous operation. Heat-setting is done on the fabric to set the crimp in the woven yarn. Since glass is low in flexibility, the yarns resist bending around one another in the woven fabric. Heat-setting softens the yarn so it assumes a permanent bend suitable to the fabric construction. Heat-setting is done at a temperature of 1100°F, which is high enough to soften the yarns but not melt them. Coronized fabrics have greater wrinkle resistance and softer draping qualities.

After the heat-setting treatment, the glass fabric is treated with a lubricating oil. Then color and a water-repellent finish are added. For this treatment, the Hycar-Quilon process is used. Hycar is an acrylic latex resin which, with the color pigment, is padded on the fabric and then cured at a temperature of 320°F. This is followed by a treatment with Quilon, a water-repellent substance, and the fabric is again cured. Glass fiber is non-absorbent, but glass will get wet, as anyone who has washed and dried windows knows. The water-repellent treatment is to make the fabric resistant to wetting and to increase color fastness. The resin used in the color treatment increases the flexibility of the fiber. However, the resin is damaged by chlorinated dry cleaning solutions, so dry cleaning should be done with Stoddard solvent.

Producers of Glass Fibers

Fiberglas—Owens-Corning Fiberglas Corporation

L. O. F.—Libbey-Owens-Ford Glass Company

Vitron—Glass Fibers, Inc.

Screen printing (*see* Figure 6:41 for picture) as well as roller printing can be done by the Hycar-Quilon process since the color paste dries fast enough to allow one screen to follow another rapidly. The Hycar-Quilon process gives good resistance to rubbing off—crocking—which was one of the disadvantages of other coloring methods.

REFERENCES

1. Owens-Corning Fiberglas Corp., "Fiberglas—A New Basic Material," Toledo, O.: Owens-Corning Fiberglas, no date, p. 2.
2. Owens-Corning Fiberglas Corp., "It Can Be . . . 15 Times Finer Than Human Hair—Strong As Steel—Yet Bend Like Rubber—WHAT IS IT?" Toledo, O.: Owens-Corning Fiberglas, no date, p. 2.
3. Labarthe, Dr. Jules, Jr., "Decorative Fabrics and New Finishes and What Can Be Expected of Them," paper presented at National Home Furnishings Conference, Chicago, Ill., Apr. 28, 1953.
4. Caroselli, R. F., "The Finishing, Dyeing, and Printing of Glass Decorative Fabrics," *American Dyestuff Reporter*, **43**:327 (May 1954).
5. Thomas, J. H., "Fiberglas Screen Prints," *Rayon and Synthetic Textiles*, **31**:30 (July 1950).
6. Rogers, H. M., "Glass Fibers—How They Are Made; Where They Are Used." *Modern Textiles Magazine*, **41**:42 (Oct. 1960).

IV. YARNS

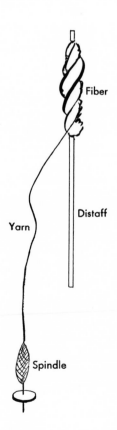

Yarn is a generic name for an assemblage of fibers, laid or twisted together. The process of making yarns from fibers, tow or liquid materials is called *spinning*. (*See* Fig. 4:1.)

The basic operations of spinning the natural fibers are the same now as they were when man first made yarns. Fibers, loosely bound to a distaff, were drawn out by the fingers and twisted by rotating a spindle at the end of the yarn. The spinning wheel, developed later, was the first device for *mechanical spinning* of fibers. It rotated the spindle while the fibers were drawn out by hand. Differences in systems were evident even in hand spinning. Wool was spun by a large wheel which permitted an intermittent motion similar to the present *mule spinning*. The large wheel was rotated one revolution, at which time the fibers were drawn out and twisted;

Fig. 4:1 (Left). Distaff and spindle used in primitive spinning of yarn.

96

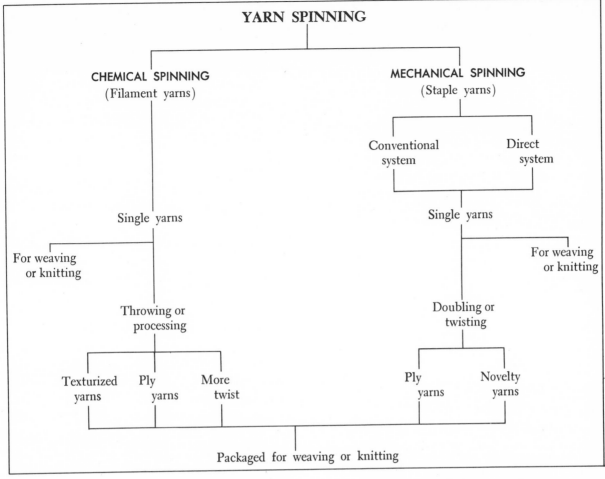

YARN SPINNING

CHEMICAL SPINNING
(Filament yarns)

MECHANICAL SPINNING
(Staple yarns)

Conventional system — Direct system

Single yarns

For weaving or knitting

Single yarns

For weaving or knitting

Throwing or processing

Doubling or twisting

Texturized yarns — Ply yarns — More twist

Ply yarns — Novelty yarns

Packaged for weaving or knitting

Fig. 4:4. Yarn spinning process diagram.

the wheel was then reversed one revolution permitting the spun yarn to be wound on a spool. (*See* Fig. 4:2.)

Flax fibers which were longer and stronger than wool were spun by a smaller wheel that twisted and wound the yarn in one continuous operation similar to *ring spinning*.

Figs. 4:2 (Left) and 4:3 (Right). Mechanical and chemical spinning. (Courtesy of the American Viscose Corporation.)

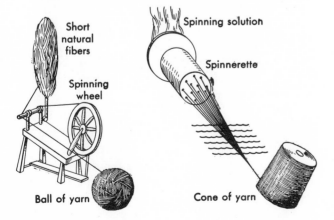

Short natural fibers

Spinning wheel

Ball of yarn

Spinning solution

Spinnerette

Cone of yarn

In making silk yarns, the filaments from six to eight cocoons were reeled (drawn off) and laid together into a yarn. The skeins of yarn were further processed in a *throwing mill*.

The first man-made fibers were silk-like and were made by forcing a solution through a spinneret and twisting the filaments into a yarn. This process was *chemical spinning* since the product was a yarn. (*See* Fig. 4:3.)

The term "spinning," therefore, includes yarn production by the following processes:

1. Chemical spinning of
    solution to filament yarn
    solution to filament tow
    solution to cut staple
2. Mechanical spinning by
    conventional spinning of staple
    direct spinning of
        tow to top
        tow to yarn

CHEMICAL SPINNING

All filament yarn except silk [1] is produced by chemical spinning at a fiber producing mill. Chemical spinning includes all of the processes from extrusion of the fibers to winding the yarns on the cone or spool for further processing or for knitting or weaving. The number of holes in the spinneret determines the number of filaments in the yarn. The number usually varies from one to 350 filaments. (*See* Fig. 4:5.)

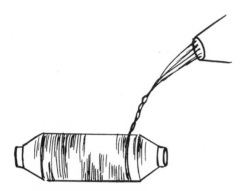

Fig. 4:5. Principle of chemical spinning.

Filament yarns are made either with or without twist as they come from the fiber spinning machine. If further twisting or processing is required to prepare the yarns for use in certain fabrics, the yarn is sent to a throwster.

Throwing is a general term which originally meant twisting, but today covers all of the processes used to put the yarns in proper condition for weaving or knitting. Throwing is often done at a separate mill. It is done to create functional end-uses rather than for purely decorative purposes as is done with novelty yarns. Throwing requires a relatively large investment in specialized equipment and skilled personnel. Throwsters work in two ways: they buy raw yarn, process it and sell the processed yarn, or they work on a commission basis in which the customer buys the raw yarn, sends it to the throwster who processes it to order and returns it to the customer, charging for his services. This latter plan bene-

[1] Silk is a natural filament produced by the silkworm.

fits the customer in that he can meet seasonal demand and fashion changes for fabrics without investing in specialized equipment.

Filament yarns in which the fibers have inherent, latent, or chemical crimp are not included in the discussion that follows because their modification is not the result of a spinning process. They are discussed in the fiber section on page 57.

REGULAR FILAMENT YARNS

Filament fibers are more expensive in price per pound than filament tow because of the smaller quantity spun at one time. However, the cost of making filament tow into staple fiber and then spinning it into yarn usually makes the cost about the same.

Regular filament yarns are smooth, silk-like, and feel cool to the touch. The filaments pack well into compact yarns which give little bulk, loft, or cover to a fabric. Because there are no protruding fiber ends, the yarns will not lint, they resist pilling and fabrics made from them shed soil readily.

Filament yarns are more lustrous than staple fiber yarns but the luster varies with the amount of delustering agent used in the spinning solution and the amount of twist in the yarn. Maximum luster is obtained by using bright filaments which are laid together with little or no twist.

Filament yarns reach their maximum strength at three turns per inch; then it remains constant or decreases. Filament yarns are stronger than staple fiber yarns of the same size and fiber content because the strength of each filament is completely utilized. In order to break the yarn, the filaments must be broken. Because of this difference in strength, filament yarns can be finer and fabrics made from them more sheer.

The more filaments in a yarn of a given denier, the softer and more supple it is. Fine filaments, however, are not as resistant to abrasion as coarse filaments, so for durability, it may be desirable to have fewer but coarser filaments in the yarn.

CHEMICAL SPINNING ─────────────────► FILAMENT YARNS

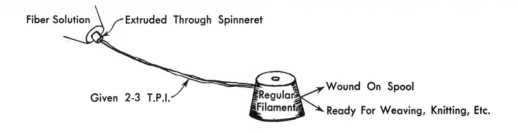

Fiber Solution — Extruded Through Spinneret

Given 2-3 T.P.I.

Regular Filament

Wound On Spool

Ready For Weaving, Knitting, Etc.

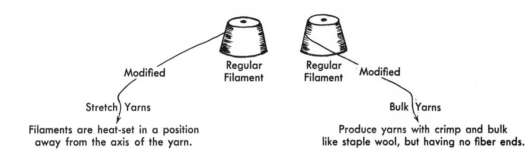

Modified   Regular Filament   Regular Filament   Modified

Stretch Yarns

Filaments are heat-set in a position
away from the axis of the yarn.

Bulk Yarns

Produce yarns with crimp and bulk
like staple wool, but having no fiber ends.

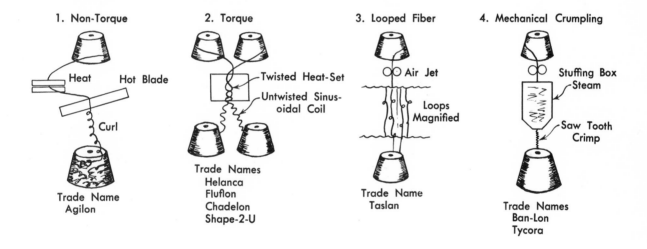

1. Non-Torque

Heat   Hot Blade

Curl

Trade Name
Agilon

2. Torque

Twisted Heat-Set

Untwisted Sinus-
oidal Coil

Trade Names
Helanca
Fluflon
Chadelon
Shape-2-U

3. Looped Fiber

Air Jet

Loops
Magnified

Trade Name
Taslan

4. Mechanical Crumpling

Stuffing Box
Steam

Saw Tooth
Crimp

Trade Names
Ban-Lon
Tycora

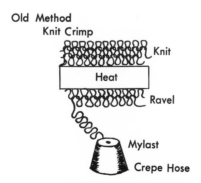

Old Method
Knit Crimp

Knit

Heat

Ravel

Mylast

Crepe Hose

Fig. 4:6. Chemical spinning process diagram.

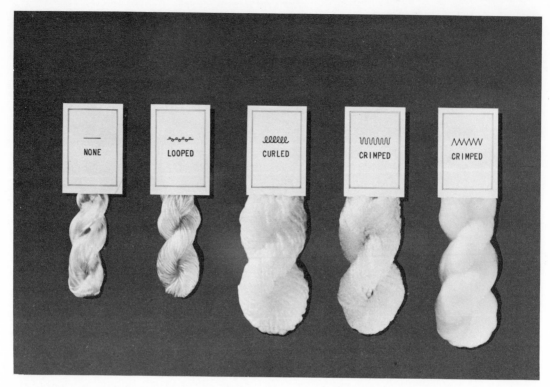

Fig. 4:7. Appearance and bulk of continuous filament textured yarns. (Courtesy of the Allied Chemical Corporation.)

TEXTURIZED FILAMENT YARNS

Texturized yarns are those in which the individual filaments are displaced from their natural and relatively closely packed position into various configurations.

Texturizing processes were developed to give regular filament yarns some of the advantages of spun yarns—namely, good cover, softness, opaqueness, warmth, and absorbency due to lower degree of skin contact, and at the same time retain the advantages of full utilization of fiber strength, resistance to pilling, and resistance to linting of the filament yarns.

Texturizing also gives a more silk-like hand to nylon and the polyester fibers, a property in which the round cross-sectional types are deficient.

The texturized yarns vary in softness, bulkiness, and stretchiness depending on the size of the filaments and on the techniques used to modify the regular yarns from which they

were originally made by the manufacturer.

Thermoplastic fibers are used in yarns which have the configurations maintained by

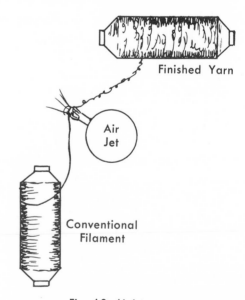

Fig. 4:8. Air jet process.

heat-setting, while any fiber may be used if some of the filaments are kept in their regular position to help maintain the configuration of the filaments which have been texturized.

Texturized yarns are classed as *bulk* and *stretch* yarns.

Bulk Type Yarns

Bulk yarns are those in which the filaments have been modified to give greater mass per unit length and are of two types; loop and crimp.

Loop type bulk yarns are made by feeding regular filament yarn over an air jet at a faster rate than it is drawn off by the take-up rolls. The blast of air forces some of the filaments into tiny loops. The rate at which the yarn is fed into the nozzle determines the amount of yarn thrown into loops; the velocity of the air affects the size of the loops. (*See* Fig. 4:8.)

Volume increase is between 50% and 150%. The yarn maintains its size and bulkiness under tension, since the straight sections of the fiber bear the strain and allow the loops to remain relatively unaffected. The yarns have little or no stretch. This process can be used on any kind of filament since heat-setting is not necessary. The looped yarn does not look like a novelty yarn when viewed without magnification. Taslan, Skyloft, and Lofted Acetate are some trade names for loop type yarns.

Crimp type yarns are bulk yarns which are made by compressing regular yarns in a stuffing box causing the individual filaments to fold or bend at a sharp angle. The yarn is then heat-set. The bulked single yarns are usually plied to hold the filaments together and minimize snagging. (*See* Fig. 4:10.)

The filaments have a wavy, irregular, zigzag, saw-tooth crimp. The apparent volume increase is approximately 200% to 300%. The yarns have some elasticity, but not enough to be classified as stretch yarns. Registered trade marks are Textralized, Ban-Lon, Spunized, and Tycora.

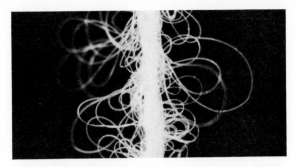

Fig. 4:9. Taslan textured yarn. "Taslan" is Du Pont's registered trademark used to designate textured yarns made in accordance with quality standards set by Du Pont. (Courtesy of the Chemstrand Corporation.)

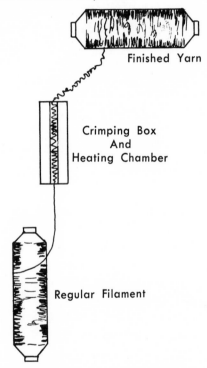

Finished Yarn

Crimping Box
And
Heating Chamber

Regular Filament

Fig. 4:10. "Stuffing box" process.

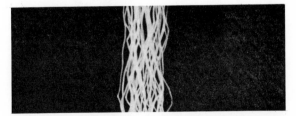

Fig. 4:11. Textralized yarn used in Ban-lon garments. "Textralized" and "Ban-lon" are registered trademarks for end-products and continuous filament yarns modified by a process licensed by Joseph Bancroft & Sons. (Courtesy of the Chemstrand Corporation.)

Stretch Type Yarns

Stretch yarns have both bulk and stretch. They are used in hosiery, underwear, sweaters, gloves, and swim suits, and they make possible the manufacture of a one-size item that fits several wearers. For the retailer this means fewer separate items, but more depth in them may be stocked. Stretch yarns are of two types; coil and curl.

Coil type stretch yarns are made in two ways. The conventional process developed by the Heberlein Co. of Switzerland is based on the twisting of two plies together, heat-setting and untwisting. In the false twist process, a single yarn is twisted, heat-set, and untwisted very quickly.

The conventional process twists the yarns from two cones with 45 to 125 t.p.i.; the plied yarn is then heat-set in a pressure steam box. The yarn is then untwisted and wound on bobbins. Figure 4:12 shows this as a continuous process, but it is not.

When the yarn is in the relaxed state, the effect is that of soft staple or spun yarn. The yarns have a bulk increase of 300%. They stretch 300% in heavy denier and 400 to 500% in finer yarn. Helanca is the trade name of the process. Helanca Hi-Test is the yarn with maximum stretch.

The false twist coil type yarns are made by a continuous process which is much faster because it reduces the number of operations and because the false twist spindle runs faster than conventional spindles. The twisting and untwisting is done in a four to ten inch space and takes less than a second. The yarn is led from the supply package to a heating chamber to the false twist spindle which consists of a rapidly revolving tube with an electrically located guide or hook. The yarn is twisted, heat-set, and untwisted as it travels through the tube. (*See* Fig. 4:13.) The false twist process can be demonstrated by tying the ends of a string together into a loop, holding the

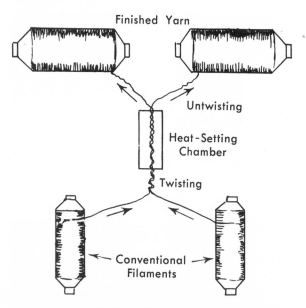

Fig. 4:12. Conventional stretch process.

The yarn is twisted by one machine and the twist removed by another. The yarn may be used as singles with alternating S-twist and Z-twist yarns in the fabric or they may be plied by twisting singles of opposite twist together.

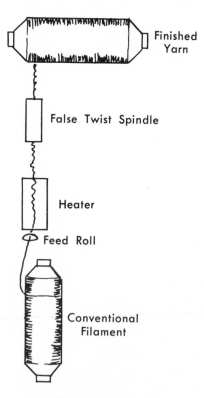

Fig. 4:13. "False twist" process.

Fig. 4:14. Technique for demonstrating false-twist principle.

loop over the thumb and forefinger, inserting a pencil between the two strands and twisting. As the pencil turns, there will be an S-twist on one side of the pencil, and a Z-twist on the other. (*See* Fig. 4:14.) As the pencil is moved up between the fingers, the twist is removed; as the pencil turns around, twist is put in.

Variations in the yarn can be obtained by differences in the amount of false twist, differences in the heat-setting temperatures, and differences in the degree of tension on the feed roll. The yarns can be given a right or left twist, or they can be given alternate right and left twist by reversing the false twist spindle at controlled time intervals. The yarn can be

used as a single or yarns can be plied by combining singles of right and left twist.

Superloft, Fluflon, Saaba, Helanca SS, and Helanca SW are trade marks for false coil type yarns. Helanca can be used for both conventional and false coil yarns if the producer maintains the quality set by the Heberlein Co. One requirement for Helanca yarns is that the yarn must be capable of being extended at least 200%. (*See* Figs. 4:15 and 4:16.)

Curl type stretch yarns are made by drawing regular filaments around a heated roll to soften and plasticize them and then over a dull knife edge which deforms the filaments into a series of spirals and imparts elastic and bulk properties to the yarn. The yarn is then cooled. The effect is similar to that obtained by pulling Christmas ribbon over scissors to curl it. This process can be used on monofilaments as well as multifilament yarns. The yarn is used in hosiery, underwear, carpets, and knit constructions and is being tried out in woven fabrics as well. Agilon is the trade name for

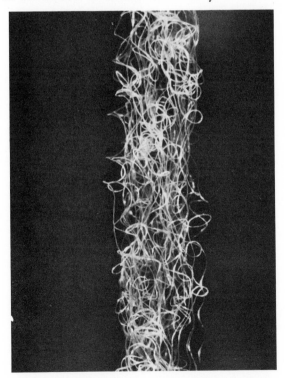

Fig. 4:15. Helanca (conventional). "Helanca" is the registered trademark of Heberlein Patent Corporation. (Courtesy of the Chemstrand Corporation.)

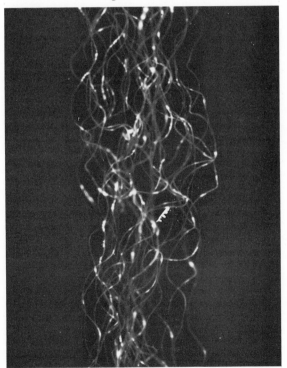

Fig. 4:16. Fluflon. "Fluflon" is a registered trademark of Marionette Mills, Inc. (Courtesy of the Chemstrand Corporation.)

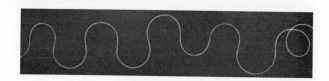

Fig. 4:17. Agilon (Top Left). (Courtesy of Deering Milliken Research Corporation.)

Fig. 4:18 (Below Left). Non-torque stretch process.

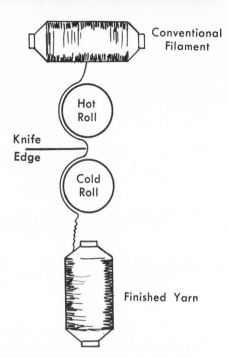

Conventional Filament

Hot Roll

Knife Edge

Cold Roll

Finished Yarn

the curl type yarn developed by the Deering-Milliken Research Corporation. (*See* Figs. 4:17 and 4:18.)

At the present time, these textured yarns are identified by trade names which are confusing to the consumer since the yarn names are similar to fiber and finish names. It may be that in the future, there will be generic names for yarns as there are now for fibers, with certain limits defined for bulk and stretch.

REFERENCES

1. Chemstrand Corp., "Textured Nylon Yarn," *Modern Textiles Magazine*, 40:37 (Aug. 1959).
2. "A Mill Man's Guide to Textured Nylon Yarns," *Modern Textiles Magazine*, 40:35 (Sept. 1959).
3. Press, J. J., ed., *Man-Made Textiles Encyclopedia*, New York: Textile Book Publishers, 1959, pp. 234–243.

MANUFACTURERS, TRADE NAMES, AND CHARACTERISTICS OF TEXTURIZED YARNS

Yarn Type or Configuration	Trade Mark	Company Producing	Fibers Used	Bulk	Stretch	Other Characteristics
Loop	Taslan	Du Pont	All fibers	50–150%	— —	
	Skyloft	American Enka	Rayon	+	— —	
	Lofted Estron	Tennessee Eastman	Acetate	+	— —	
	Lofted Chromspun	Tennessee Eastman	Acetate	+	— —	Interesting color effects
	Bulked Celaperm	Celanese	Acetate	+	— —	
	Aerocor	Owens-Corning	Fiberglas	+	— —	
Crimp	Textralized	Joseph Bancroft	Nylon, polyester	200–300%	200%	
	Ban-Lon	Joseph Bancroft	Nylon, polyester	200–300%		
	Spunized	Spunized Co.	Nylon, polyester		Limited	Fabrics made of texturized yarns
	Tycora *	Textured Yarn Co.	Nylon, polyester			
	Mylast	Clarence Meyers	Nylon, polyester		Limited	
	Duclé	Clarence Meyers	Nylon, polyester	+	+	
Coil—conventional torque (twist)	Helanca **	Heberlein Patent Corp.	Nylon, polyester	300%	300–500%	
	Helanca Hi-test	Heberlein Patent Corp.	Nylon, polyester			Maximum twist
Coil—false-twist torque (twist)	Helanca SS	Heberlein Patent Corp.	Thermoplastics	Maximum	Minimum	Smooth sweater yarn
	Helanca SW	Heberlein Patent Corp.	Thermoplastics	Some	Minimum	Sweater yarn, bouclé type
	Superloft	Leesona Corp.; Universal Winding Co.	Thermoplastics			Greatest yield with least stretch
	Fluflon	Marionette Mills	Thermoplastics		400%	
	Saaba	Universal Winding Co.	Thermoplastics	High	Minimum	Crepe-like yarn
	Glacé-lon	Textile Equipment Sales	Thermoplastics			
	Gro-Lon	Grove Nylon Co-Pilot Mfg. Co.				
	Cumuloft	Chemstrand	Nylon			
	Livilon	Chadborun Gotham				Monofilament
	Chadalon	Chadborun Gotham				
	Burmilized	Burlington Mills	Nylon	+	+	Monofilament
	Shape 2U	Burlington Mills				
Curl	Agilon	Deering-Milliken	Thermoplastics	+	400%	Mono- or multifilament

* Trademark refers to texturized yarn produced by various methods.
** Helanca can be used for conventional or false twist process providing the yarns meet standards set and maintained by the Heberlein Patent Corporation.

MECHANICAL SPINNING

Spun yarns (made of staple fibers) are produced at yarn spinning mills by either the conventional spinning system (page 107) or the direct spinning system (page 111). (*See* Fig. 4:19.)

The conventional system is long and expensive since each operation is performed by a different machine, and much hand labor is needed to move materials from one machine to another. It is used for spinning both natural and man-made staple fibers.

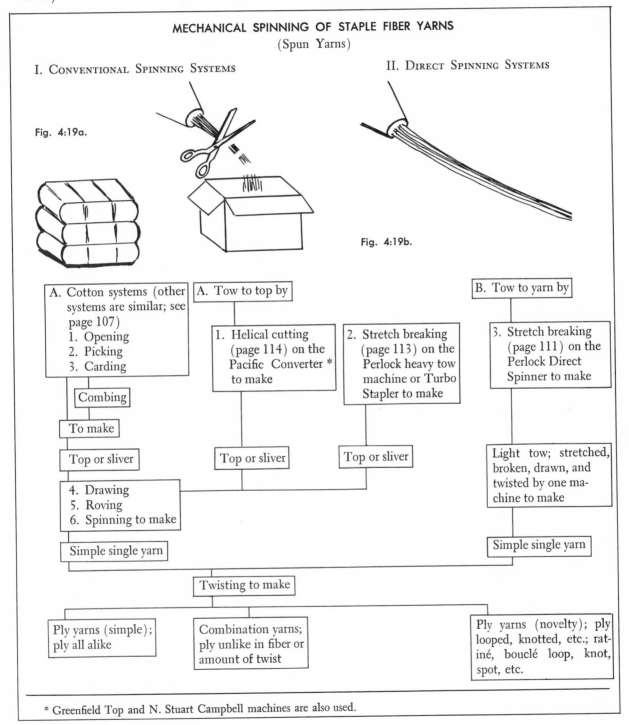

MECHANICAL SPINNING OF STAPLE FIBER YARNS
(Spun Yarns)

I. CONVENTIONAL SPINNING SYSTEMS

Fig. 4:19a.

II. DIRECT SPINNING SYSTEMS

Fig. 4:19b.

A. Cotton systems (other systems are similar; see page 107)
1. Opening
2. Picking
3. Carding

Combing

To make

Top or sliver

4. Drawing
5. Roving
6. Spinning to make

Simple single yarn

A. Tow to top by

1. Helical cutting (page 114) on the Pacific Converter * to make

Top or sliver

2. Stretch breaking (page 113) on the Perlock heavy tow machine or Turbo Stapler to make

Top or sliver

B. Tow to yarn by

3. Stretch breaking (page 111) on the Perlock Direct Spinner to make

Light tow; stretched, broken, drawn, and twisted by one machine to make

Simple single yarn

Twisting to make

Ply yarns (simple); ply all alike

Combination yarns; ply unlike in fiber or amount of twist

Ply yarns (novelty); ply looped, knotted, etc.; ratiné, bouclé loop, knot, spot, etc.

* Greenfield Top and N. Stuart Campbell machines are also used.

It has always seemed wasteful to cut man-made filament tow into staple lengths and then spin it into yarn by the expensive conventional system. The direct spinning system was developed as a way of by-passing some or all of the steps of the conventional system without disrupting the continuity of the strand of filament tow.

Classification of spun yarns is based on length of staple and parallelism of arrangement. *Combed* and/or *worsted* (wool) yarns are made of long staple fibers with parallel arrangement. *Carded* yarns are made of short fibers with relatively parallel arrangement. *Woolen* yarns differ from the others in that the fibers are distributed at right angles to the length of the yarn. Short staple fibers are used in woolen yarns. (Remember that woolen has a specific meaning and is not a synonym for the word "wool." (*See* Figs. 4:20 and 4:21.)

Worsted Yarns

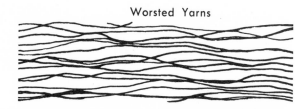

Fig. 4:20. Combed yarn made of long staple wool fiber.

Woolen Yarns

Fig. 4:21. Carded yarn made of short staple fiber.

See page 11 for discussion of fiber strength, yarn strength, and fabric strength.

CHARACTERISTICS OF SPUN YARNS

Spun yarns are characterized by protruding fiber ends. Longer fibers with orderly arrangement have few protruding ends. Protruding ends contribute to a dull, fuzzy appearance, the shedding of lint, and the formation of pills. They can be removed from the yarn or fabric by the singeing operation described on page 175.

The strength of a staple fiber yarn is dependent on the cohesive properties (clinging power) of the fibers, and upon the points of contact resulting from the pressure of twist. Individual fiber strength is relatively unimportant. The friction of one fiber against another gives resistance to lengthwise slippage of fibers within the yarn. A smooth surface creates less friction than a rough surface (wool scales, for example). The greater the number of points of contact, the greater the resistance to slippage. Fibers with crimp or convolutions, make a greater number of points of contact.

Staple fiber yarns are suited to fabrics for clothing where absorbency, bulk, and warmth are desired. The fiber ends or crimp hold the yarns away from close contact with the skin, and are more comfortable on a hot humid day than the smooth filament yarns.

The length and parallelism of the fibers and the amount of twist have a definite influence on fabric properties and end-uses as illustrated by the comparison of woolen and worsted fabrics given below.

Worsted Fabrics *	*Woolen Fabrics*
Yarns have medium to high twist.	Yarns have medium to low twist.
Lighter weight.	Less strength. Bulkier, softer, rougher texture.
Smoother surface.	
More firmly woven.	Fuzzier surface.
Do not sag.	Do not hold shape as well as worsteds.
Take and hold a press better.	
Longer wearing, stronger.	Become baggy at areas of stress.
Widely used for men's suits and women's suitings.	Tensile strength relatively low.
Tailor well.	Widely used for blankets, soft fabrics, casual type apparel.

* Worsted takes its name from the English village of Worstead, where this type of fabric was first manufactured.

CONVENTIONAL SPINNING SYSTEMS

Conventional spinning systems differ in the number of operations and the length of the fibers processed. The combing operation is seldom used with man-made fibers since they are usually uniform in length and parallelism can be achieved in the drawing operation. A comparison of the systems is given in the chart below.

System	Length of Staple	Comment	Cost
Cotton	1½ inch	Smooth, even yarn. Less elastic and soft.	Low
American *	Various lengths	Modified cotton system for longer staple. Spins worsteds.	Low
Woolen	Short, coarse	Coarse count yarns, fuzzy. Can use waste and noils.	Low
Bradford	Long staple	Lofty, soft yarn. Strength without excessive twist.	High
French	Variety of lengths	Soft, smooth, lofty, elastic. Warm hand.	Expensive

* Has largely replaced the French and Bradford Systems.

Fig. 4:22. Opening cotton fibers. (Courtesy of Coats & Clark, Inc., New York, N.Y.)

The cotton system is representative of the others so is discussed in detail.

COTTON SYSTEM

Operations	Purpose
Opening	Loosens, blends, fluffs fiber.
Picking	Cleans, forms fiber lap.
Carding	Cleans, straightens, forms sliver.
Combing	Straightens, removes short fibers.
Drawing	Parallels, blends, and reduces size.
Roving	Reduces size, forms roving.
Spinning	Twists and winds the final yarn.

Opening and picking are the first operations.

The cotton arrives at the spinning mill tightly packed in a bale. It varies considerably from bale to bale in uniformity and quality. It is, therefore, necessary to blend together a number of bales to insure a uniform product. Layers from six to nine bales are fed into the opening machine which loosens and fluffs the fibers to an immense fluffy mass ten to fifteen times as bulky as it was in the bale. The fibers are cleaned of leaves, dust, and so forth, and are then blown through tubes to a storage room where they are conditioned to a certain moisture content so they will not be brittle during the rest of the spinning process. (See Fig. 4:22.)

The picking machine continues the loosening and cleaning of the fibers and forms them into a continuous sheet called a *lap*. (See Fig. 4:23.)

Fig. 4:23. The lap formed by the picking machine. (Courtesy of Coats & Clark, Inc., New York, N.Y.)

A new machine developed [2] in 1960 makes cotton processing continuous and automatic from opening through carding by eliminating the picking machine. In the "Carousel," cotton is plucked by four beaters from twelve bales which move in a circular path above the beaters like a merry-go-round. The cotton is carried pneumatically to an Automixer for further blending and then to the carding machine. No lap is formed.

The *carding* machine consists of two cylinders covered with card clothing—a heavy fabric embedded with many especially bent wires. The fiber lap is fed between the two cylinders which straightens the fibers and forms them into a thin filmy sheet. This sheet is then brought together as a soft rope called a *card sliver*. (*See* Fig. 4:24.)

Fig. 4:24. Carding. (Courtesy of Coats & Clark, Inc., New York, N.Y.)

A *sliver* is a loose, soft strand of fibers without any twist, produced in the carding, combing, or drawing operations.

Average or short staple fiber is processed on the carding machine.

Combing is a straightening operation for long staple, good quality fibers. The fiber lap is fed into the combing machine, short fibers are combed out and the long parallel fibers

[2] *Textile Industries,* **124:**91, Nov. 1960.

emerge as a *combed sliver*. (*See* Fig. 4:25.) Combed wool sliver is also referred to as wool *top*.

Fig. 4:25. Combing. (Courtesy of Coats & Clark, Inc., New York, N.Y.)

Combing is expensive since long staple fiber costs more per pound and as much as one-fourth of the fiber is waste. A combed yarn fabric may cost more than twice as much as a carded yarn fabric. See page 106 for a comparison of combed and carded yarn properties.

Fig. 4:26. Drawing operation. (Courtesy of Coats and Clark, Inc., New York, N.Y.)

Drawing blends several slivers together and parallels the fibers. Blending produces a more uniform yarn. Notice in Figure 4:26 the number of slivers being fed into the drawing machine.

Drawing is done by four sets of rolls, each set running successively faster than the preceding set. The speed is adjusted so the sliver that comes out is comparable in size to the individual slivers that go in, and it comes out much faster than the slivers feed in.

Figure 4:27 is a diagram of the drawing rolls.

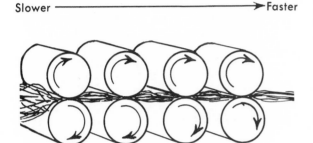

Slower ⟶ Faster

Fig. 4:27. Diagram of drawing rolls.

Roving is a term applied to both a process and its product. The purpose of the process is to draw out (draft) the sliver to a size suitable for spinning. This drawing is done by a set of rollers similar to those of the drawing machine. (*See* Fig. 4:28.) It increases the parallelism of the fibers, and when two or more slivers are drawn out together (doubling), the uniformity of the yarn will be improved.

Roving, the product, is not coiled in a can as was the case with the sliver which had very little strength, but is given a slight amount of twist and wound on a bobbin. The twist is inserted by the flyer shown in Figures 4:29 and 4:30.

Fig. 4:29. The roving machine. (Courtesy of Coats & Clark, Inc., New York, N.Y.)

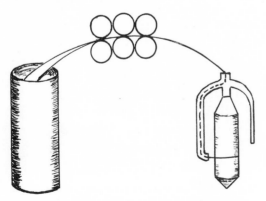

Fig. 4:28. Diagram of roving machine.

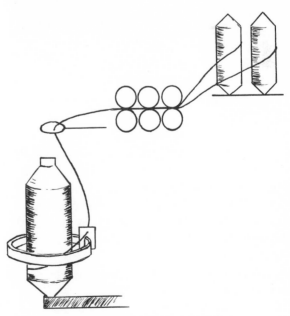

Fig. 4:30. Diagram of spinning machine.

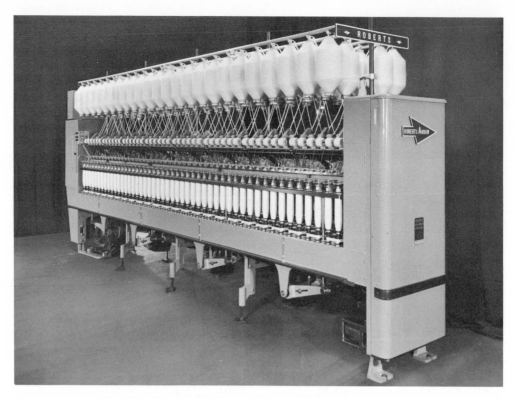

Fig. 4:31. The spinning frame. (Courtesy of the Roberts Company.)

A *roving* is a continuous, soft, slightly twisted strand of fibers produced from sliver. A roving is comparable in size to a thin pencil.

Spinning is the final operation in the making of single yarns.

The *ring spinning* frame,[3] a down-twisting machine, is a continuous, simultaneous drawing, twisting, and winding operation. Drafting rolls draw out the roving to its final size. A traveler, which glides freely around a ring, inserts the twist as the spindle rotates the bobbin on which the yarn is wound. (*See* Fig. 4:30, page 109.)

Mule spinning is done on a spinning frame with an intermittent action, used in the woolen spinning system. The yarn is drawn out and twisted, then the twisting stops while the twisted part is wound up on the bobbin.

Winding is the operation in which the yarn is wound from the bobbins to spools or cones.

Creeling is the winding of yarns from the

spool on to a warp beam. This may be done at the yarn spinning mill, or the spools and cones may be shipped to the weaving mill and the creeling done there. Figure 4:32 shows a creel which holds a large number of spools of yarn, and the warp beam on which they are being wound.

---

[3] A frame is a multiple machine with a number of individual units.

Fig. 4:32. Winding yarns on a warp beam. (Courtesy of the Barber-Colman Company.)

Slashing

Before the warp creel-beam is placed on the loom, the yarns are unwound from it and run through a starch bath to seal the fiber ends and strengthen the yarns. (*See* Fig. 4:33.) This treatment helps them withstand the tension and friction to which they will be subjected during weaving.

Garnetting

Garments that have been discarded and cutter's scraps may be shredded and reduced to fiber so that the fibers can be made into yarns and woven into fabrics.

Many consumers are familiar with reused and reprocessed wool garments. Few, however, are aware that fabrics of cotton, rayon, silk, and nylon are also reclaimed for use. The source of supply is the same as that for wool—cutter's scraps, waste from spinning and knitting, and worn out, discarded clothing. Two machines usually do the work of reducing the old cloth to fibers—a rag picker and a garnetting machine. The cutter's scraps and rags, after being sorted, are sprayed with a lubricant to make them more pliable.

In the rag-picking machine, the garments, scraps, and waste pass around a cylinder covered with metal teeth or spikes that pull the fabric apart and reduce it to small pieces. These pieces go to the garnetting machine which thoroughly breaks them up and reduces them to the fibrous condition necessary for use on the conventional yarn spinning system.

The same garnetting machine cannot process all kinds of fiber fabrics. Nylon, for example, must be processed on a special garnet.

Some of the rag materials are reduced to flock (very short fibers) for use in electro-coated designs and imitation suedes. Some of the rayons are put back into solution and are respun into new fibers.

DIRECT SPINNING SYSTEMS I
(Tow-to-Yarn)

Direct spinning systems were developed as an economical, efficient way of reducing continuous filament tow to staple sliver (tow-to-top process on page 112), or to spun yarns (tow-to-yarn process discussed below) without disrupting the continuity of the strand. Direct spinning by-passes some or all of the conventional spinning operations.

In the tow-to-yarn process, all stapling (making filament tow into staple) and spinning operations are performed by a single machine—the Direct Spinner. This is a Perlock light tow machine which processes 4400 denier high tenacity viscose rayon.

The tow is fed into the machine through leveling rolls, passes between two nip rolls, across a conveyor belt to a second pair of nip rolls which travel at a faster rate of speed and create tension that causes the fibers to break at their weakest points. The strand is then

Fig. 4:33. Slashing of warp yarn. Yarn enters from the right.

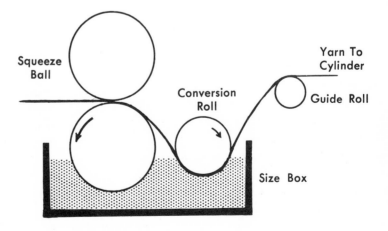

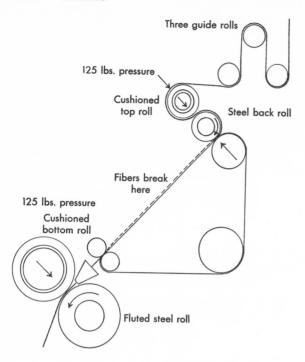

Fig. 4:34. Diagram of direct spinning. Perlock light tow-to-yarn system.

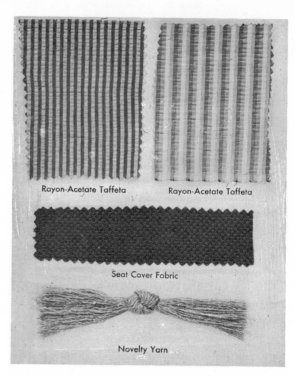

Fig. 4:35. Direct spun yarns and fabrics.

drawn out to yarn size, twisted and wound on a bobbin. (See Fig. 4:34.)

Direct spun yarns have a higher degree of strength and uniformity than conventionally spun yarns. They can be distinguished from conventionally spun yarns by "backing" the twist out of a single yarn. The fibers will have a staple length in excess of six inches whereas conventionally spun yarns have fibers which are usually less than two inches in length.

There is no control over the average staple length and there is not sufficient time after stretching and before winding for the fibers to relax, so that the yarns have high potential shrinkage, 14% in wet finishing operations. This shrinkage makes it possible to produce fabrics such as those in Figure 4:35. High shrinkage yarns in the filling are alternated with low shrinkage yarns. In wet finishing, the low shrinkage yarns are puckered by the contraction of the high shrinkage, direct spun yarns.

Dense, compact rainwear fabrics can be made by using the direct spun yarns in the filling direction. When these shrink, they bring the warp yarns closer together.

Novelty yarns are produced by combining a high shrinkage ply with a low shrinkage ply to produce a bouclé effect. (See Fig. 4:35.)

The strength of direct spun yarns is best utilized in upholstery fabrics.

Disadvantages are expense, lack of crimp, and no way of producing blends.

DIRECT SPINNING SYSTEMS II
(Tow-to-Top)

The tow-to-top direct spinning process may be performed by either of two machines which reduce the filament tow to staple, and form it into sliver: the Perlock machine discussed below, and the Pacific converter which is discussed on page 113.

The Perlock heavy tow machine operates on the principle that, when tow is stretched, the fibers will break at their weakest points (random breakage) without disrupting the continuity of the strand. A sheet of filament

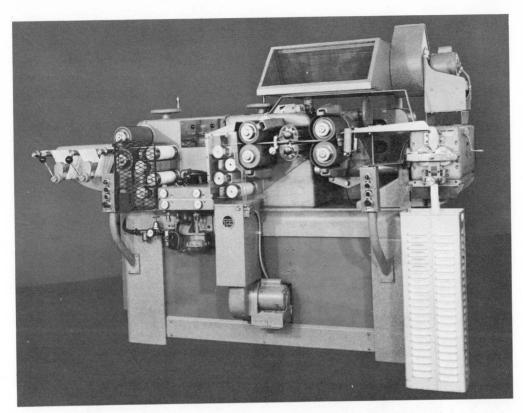

Fig. 4:36. The Turbo Stapler. (Courtesy of the Turbo Machine Company.)

tow nine inches wide (180,000 denier or more) enters the machine through leveling rolls and then passes between two sets of nip rolls which apply the breaking tension. Breaker bars between the sets of rolls control the length of the staple. As the tow travels through the breaking zone, tension is applied suddenly and the fibers break in the breaker bar area. This is then repeated as more tow enters the breaking zone. The fiber strand moves on through another set of rolls into a crimping box and emerges as crimped *sliver*. The rest of the yarn making process is completed on conventional spinning machinery.

The *Turbo Stapler*, Figure 4:36, is a Perlock heavy tow machine with a heating plate attachment for processing thermoplastic fibers to make hi-bulk yarns. The sheet of the thermoplastic fibers passes between the heater plates (draw zone) and the fibers are heat-stretched by tension from two sets of nip rolls before entering the breaking zone. This gives the fibers high shrinkage properties. Acrylics will shrink 20% or more when they are subsequently relaxed by a heat treatment.

After heat-stretching, the tow is broken and crimped. A portion of the sliver produced on the Turbo Stapler is sent in louvered cans to a Fiber-Setter. Steam enters the can through the slot openings and relaxes the fiber from the strains of heat-stretching. This shrinks it so that it loses its high shrinkage properties. It then rejoins the portion that was not heat relaxed, and the combined sliver is finished as described on page 114 to make hi-bulk yarn.

The *Pacific Converter*,[4] Figure 4:37, was invented in 1939. It is a diagonal-cut stapling machine which changes filament tow into staple of equal or variable lengths, and forms it into a crimped sliver ready for further drawing, blending, and spinning operations.

[4] The Greenfield Top and N. Stuart Campbell machines are similar.

The filament tow enters the machine through a series of leveling rolls which spread the fibers out into a sheet about fourteen inches wide.

The Pacific Converter operates like a lawn mower. A helical cutting blade cuts the fiber band in diagonal strips while they are carried along on a conveyor belt thus preventing disruption of the parallelism of the fibers. The cut fibers are flexed to break open any sections that might have fused together and are drawn lengthwise to make them into a thinner sheet.

Fig. 4:37. The Pacific Converter. (Courtesy of the Warner & Swasey Company.)

They are moved by serpentine action between fluted rolls which cause further separation. The thin sheet is then rolled into a continuous sliver and a slight crimp is imparted to the fibers by the crimping unit. The sliver is collected and coiled in a can ready to be taken to a conventional drawing or roving machine.

Hi-bulk yarns can be made on the Pacific Converter in one of two ways. First, the filament tow may be purchased as high shrinkage and low shrinkage types and then blended and cut on the Converter. Second, a heat-stretch attachment may be added. (*See* Fig. 4:38.) Part of the tow then goes through the heat-stretching attachment and the remainder passes over the heating unit. The two parts of the tow are combined before entering the cutter. See page 115 for a discussion of the finishing of and uses for hi-bulk yarns.

Natural fibers are not processed on the Pacific Converter except when wool top is to be added for a blend. Then a blending attachment is used with the converter.

Hi-Bulk Yarns

Bulk is desirable for warmth, texture and cover. Bulking characteristics result when the curl or crimp of the fibers prevents orderly arrangement and creates air spaces within the yarn.

Hi-bulk yarns are made from a blend of heat relaxed fibers and unrelaxed fibers. This blend is made on either the Turbo Stapler or

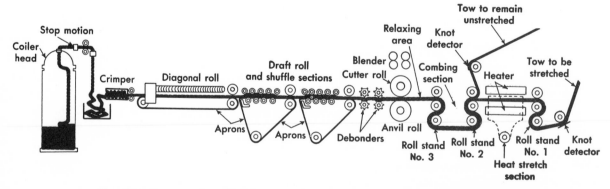

Fig. 4:38. Diagram of Pacific Converter. (Courtesy of the Warner & Swasey Company.)

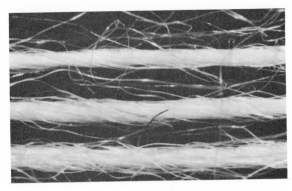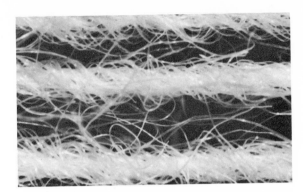

Fig. 4:39. Hi-bulk yarn before (left) and after (right) steaming.

the Pacific Converter as discussed on pages 113 and 114. The spinning of the yarn is done on conventional spinning machinery. The yarn at this stage is similar to other staple fiber yarns since the bulk has not yet been developed. The bulk is developed by subjecting the yarn to high temperature, usually in the dyeing process. This may occur at either the yarn, fabric, or garment stage. The heat causes the unrelaxed fibers to shrink (*see* Figure 4:39), and as they shorten, they force the relaxed fibers to bend and thus create bulk.

Most of the yarn is made from acrylic fibers which can be heat stretched to shrinkage of 20% or more. The yarn usually consists of

Fig. 4:40. Hi-bulk yarns before (above) and after (below) heat treatment.

40% non-relaxed and 60% heat relaxed fibers, but other percentages may be used.

Much hi-bulk yarn has gone into the knit apparel trade, especially sweaters. It does, however, have good potential for woven fabric uses.

Yarn Twist

If a yarn is alike in all of its parts, it is called a *simple* yarn. The yarns shown below are examples. If a yarn has unlike parts or irregularities, it is a *novelty* or *complex* yarn. These are discussed on page 120.

The number of twisting operations, the method of twisting, and the direction and degree of twist are important in the determination of the classification and properties of the yarn.

Twist is defined as the spiral arrangement of the fibers around the axis of the yarn which binds them together and gives strength to the yarn. It is expressed in turns per inch (t.p.i.). Twist is produced by revolving one end of a fiber strand while the other end is held stationary.

SIMPLE YARNS CLASSIFIED BY NUMBER OF TWISTING OPERATIONS

The *single* yarn (Figure 4:41) is the product of the first twisting operation which is performed by the spinning frame.

Fig. 4:41. Single yarn.

A *ply* yarn (Figure 4:42) is made by a second twisting operation which combines two or more singles to increase the diameter, strength, or quality. Each part of the yarn is called a ply. The twist is inserted by a machine called a *twister*.

Fig. 4:42. Two-ply yarn.

A *cord* (Figure 4:43) is made by a third twisting operation which twists ply yarns together. Some types of sewing thread belong in this class. (*See* page 123.)

Fig. 4:43. Cord yarn.

Plying tends to offset unevenness and give a more uniform yarn. Ply yarns are usually 10% stronger than the combined strength of the single strands. Increasing the twist up to a certain point will increase the strength of the yarn. Too much twist places the fibers at right angles to the axis of the yarn (*see* Figure 4:44), so that tension on the yarn will cause a shearing action between the fibers.

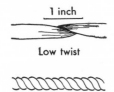

Fig. 4:44. Diagram showing low twist and high twist.

Most ply yarns are twisted in the opposite direction to the twist of the singles, hence the first few revolutions tend to untwist the singles and give a yarn in which many of the fibers are straightened somewhat from their spiral position. The yarn also becomes softer and smoother.

The direction of twist is described as S-twist or Z-twist. These terms have largely replaced the terms "regular" and "reverse," and "right" and "left," which are used with opposite meanings by the various segments of the textile industry.

A yarn or cord has S-twist [5] if, when held in vertical position, the spirals conform to the direction of the slope of the central portion of the letter S, and Z-twist if the spirals conform to the direction of slope of the central portion of the letter Z. Z-twist is the standard twist of the trade. (*See* Fig. 4:45.)

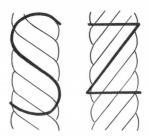

Fig. 4:45. S and Z twist.

The amount of twist varies with the length of the fibers, the size of the yarn, and the uses to which it will be put. Yarns with long staple fibers do not require as much twist as those with short staple fibers since they establish more points of contact per fiber and give a stronger yarn for the same amount of twist.

Fine yarns require more twist than coarse yarns. Warp yarns need more strength than filling yarns, and so have more twist. The lower twist of the filling yarns make them softer and less apt to kink. Low twist yarns are used for fabrics which are to be napped. (*See* page 179.)

Knitting yarns have less twist than filling yarns. Voile and crepe yarns have more twist than warp yarns. In general warp yarns have the amount that gives maximum strength; this amount is referred to as standard warp twist.

Three factors limit the amount of twist that is put in a yarn. Beyond a certain amount:

The yarn will lose strength.

[5] A.S.T.M. definitions.

The diameter will increase rather than decrease.

The yarn cannot be twist-set for satisfactory handling in manufacture.

Twist-setting is a yarn finish which sets the twist with heat or moisture to prevent any tendency to untwist and cause kinking or tangling. In the chart below are some examples of different amounts of twist.

Amount	*Example*
Low twist	Filament yarns; 2 to 3 t.p.i. is normal
Napping twist	Blanket warp; 12 t.p.i. Filling; 6 to 8 t.p.i.
Average twist	Percale warp; 25 t.p.i. Filling; 20 t.p.i. Nylon hosiery; 25 to 30 t.p.i.
Voile twist	Hard twist singles; 40 t.p.i. Plied with 16 to 18 t.p.i.
Crepe twist	Singles; 40 to 60 or more t.p.i. Plied with 2 to 5 t.p.i.

IMPORTANCE OF YARN TWIST

The outstanding characteristics of a fabric are sometimes directly attributable to yarn twist. *Strex* elastic fabric is a good example of this fact. The yarn in this fabric has been *engineered* to completely neutralize an undesirable fiber property. Although cotton fiber is naturally low in resiliency and elasticity, the coiled construction of the yarn, Figure 4:46,

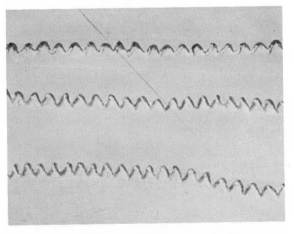

Fig. 4:46. Coil spring twisted cotton yarn (Strex).

gives the fabric the ability to stretch 100% and recover. Strex has largely replaced the rubber-core-yarn, elastic bandage fabric formerly used. It has a lower degree of tension, and so is more comfortable and interferes less with blood circulation.

Another example of the importance of the yarn is shown by a comparison of Strex elastic fabric and cotton duck, Figure 4:47. Both are

Fig. 4:47. Comparison of yarn properties as shown by the limpness of the elastic fabric above and the stiffness of duck below.

all cotton, unfinished fabrics made in plain weave. Duck is stiff and boardy whereas the elastic fabric is soft, limp and flexible. The difference is due to the yarn construction.

FABRICS CHARACTERIZED BY TWIST: TRUE CREPES [6]

The oldest twist effect is creping. Crepe is a French word meaning crinkle.

Any fiber that can be given high twist and have that twist set by moisture is suitable for use in crepe fabrics. Cotton, flax, wool, and silk have all been used. Viscose rayon, however, is the most widely used. Viscose crepe

[6] Crepe effect fabrics are discussed on pages 149 and 150.

yarns were first developed in 1927 and became popular during the depression of the 1930's when they had a cost advantage over silk in competition for fashion fabrics. It is easy for the throwster to twist rayon and the twist can be set with water to control the "liveliness" of the yarn during weaving.

The heat-sensitive fibers can be given a high twist, but the liveliness cannot be set by moisture and twist-setting by heat permanently deadens the liveliness so the finished fabric is not crepey.

Combination rayon-acetate ply yarns produce a superior crepe fabric. The crepe twist rayon ply gives shrinkage to create the crinkle and the lower twist acetate ply gives body and softness.

Crepe yarns are made by a throwster which inserts a high number (40 to 80) of turns per inch. The yarn is first twist-set for weaving. When the fabric is wet in finishing, the twist tends to uncoil itself causing shrinkage and the crinkle characteristic of crepe. Increasing the amount of twist or alternating crepe twist yarns of different direction of twist will increase the amount of crinkle. For example, 6S and 6Z will give a more prominent crinkle than 2S and 2Z.

Weaving of crepe fabrics is done on a loom with a box attachment which can insert alternating groups of S- and Z-twist yarns in the filling direction. The weave is usually plain weave with fewer yarns in the filling to give freedom of movement for the development of crinkle.

Crepes are woven wide and then shrunk to develop the crinkle. Rayon crepes are woven 47 inches wide, shrunk to 30 or 33 inches and finished 39 to 40 inches wide. They have, therefore, a large amount of potential shrinkage. The higher the twist the more potential shrinkage the fabric will have.

Crepes which are designed for washable garments do not have exceedingly high twist yarns. They usually have a flatter surface since they must be ironed.

French crepe, the smoothest, most lustrous of the washable crepes, is made with voile twist yarns of 30 to 40 t.p.i. It has a higher warp than filling count and a higher number of filaments in each warp yarn to give softness to the fabric.

When sewing with crepe it is *not advisable to pre-shrink* it with the hope that it will then be completely relaxed. If crepes are completely relaxed, they will stretch too much during pressing and use. True crepes present some problems in pressing, but the secret is to work quickly with as little pressure and moisture as is necessary to obtain good results.

It is best to dry clean crepes which have enough crinkle to present a shrinkage or pressing problem.

To identify crepe yarns, ravel adjacent sides to obtain a fringe on each of the two edges. Test the yarns that are removed by pulling on the yarn and then letting one end go. The yarn will "kink up" as shown in Figure 4:48. (Do not confuse kink with yarn crimp.) Ex-

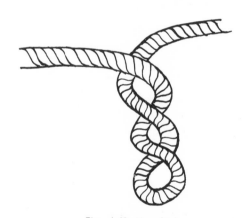

Fig. 4:48. Yarn kink.

amine the fringe on the fabric. If yarns other than crepe yarns are used in the fabric, they will probably be of very low twist. The majority of the crepe fabrics have crepe yarns in the crosswise direction, although some are in the lengthwise direction and some have crepe yarns in both directions. (*See* chart, page 119.)

True crepe fabrics are classified by the position of the crepe yarn. (*See* Fig. 4:49.) Crepe effect fabrics are discussed in the sec-

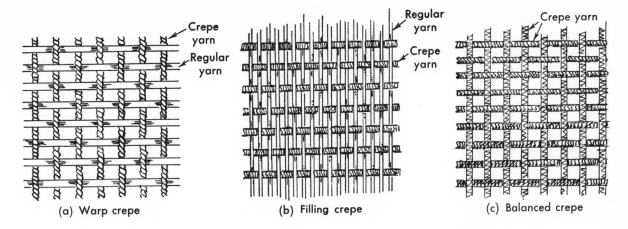

(a) Warp crepe   (b) Filling crepe   (c) Balanced crepe

Fig. 4:49. Drawings showing the use of crepe yarns in plain woven fabrics.

tion on weaves and in the section on finishes. A description of the less commonly used crepe fabrics is found in the glossary (crepe de Chine, canton crepe, crepon, bark crepe, chiffon, crepe romaine, georgette, alpaca).

A. Warp crepes are made with crepe yarns in the warp and regular yarns in the filling direction. There are very few warp crepes on the market, possibly because they tend to shrink more in the warp direction and it is, therefore, difficult to keep an even hemline in washable fabrics. Bemberg sheer and some wool crepes belong in this group.

B. Filling crepes are made with crepe yarns in the crosswise direction only. This is the largest group of true crepe fabrics. They usually have many more warp than filling yarns per inch, giving a crosswise rib effect in the fabric. *Flat crepe* is the most widely used of the fabrics in this group. It has a duller, crepier surface than French crepe (discussed on page 118), but is washable if the colors are fast. It is used in blouses, dresses, lingerie, and coat and suit linings. A typical flat crepe thread count would be 150 warp by 76 filling yarns. It has 50 t.p.i. and the filling yarns alternate 2S and 2Z twist. The fiber content is usually rayon and acetate.

C. Balanced crepes have crepe yarns in both directions and are usually balanced in thread count. They are often made in sheers and the crepiness of the yarns in both directions helps to prevent yarn slippage.

FABRICS CHARACTERIZED BY TWIST: PUCKERED FABRICS AND VOILE

True Crepe Puckered Fabrics

Puckered rayons (seersucker) are made in plain weave with alternate groups of regular and crepe yarns in the filling. (*See* Fig. 4:50.) When the fabric is wet during fabric finishing, the crepe yarns shrink, creating crosswise crinkle stripes where the regular yarn areas are puckered.

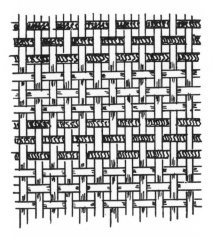

Fig. 4:50. Puckered rayon made with groups of crepe filling yarns alternating with regular filling yarns.

Matelassé is a double cloth construction with three or four sets of yarns. One set of regular warp and filling are woven together criss-crossing at intervals with a set of crepe warp and filling yarns which are also woven

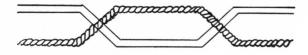

Fig. 4:51. Matelassé double cloth construction showing crepe and regular yarns crisscrossing.

together. It is as if two fabrics interlaced with each other. During wet finishing the crepe yarns shrink creating puffy areas in the areas made with regular yarns. Most of these fabrics are a rayon and acetate combination.

Voile

Voile is a sheer cotton fabric characterized by an open weave and a sandpapery feel which is created by the use of high-twist, hard-twist yarns, 35 to 40 t.p.i. These yarns are called *voile-twist* yarns. The hardness of the yarn results when twist brings the fibers closer together and makes the yarns more compact. The effect is more pronounced when a twist-on-twist ply voile-yarn is used.

Fig. 4:52. Twist-on-twist yarn.

Twist-on-twist means that the twist of the ply is the same in direction as the twist of the singles with a resulting increase of total twist.

Single hard-twist yarns are used in less expensive voile fabrics and a wash-and-wear finish is used on this quality to increase resiliency.

The twist-on-twist yarns are used in better quality fabrics. These voiles have exceptionally good resiliency. The fabric has a soft drape comparable to crepe. Voile is made with yarns of similar size (yarn count) as those used in other sheer cotton fabrics but there are usually fewer of them.

Fabric	Thread Count	Yarn Count (Size)
Lawn	88 x 88	70's x 100
Voile		
Twist-on-twist	74 x 76	180/2 x 180/2
High-twist	68 x 70	70's x 70's

All voile has wide tape selvages and the yarns are gassed or singed to remove fuzzy ends and to emphasize the open effect. The removal of fuzzy ends permits movement of air and makes voile one of the coolest summer fabrics.

Novelty Yarns

Novelty yarns have regular cycles of uneven arrangement and may be unlike in all parts. They are made on spinning machines with special attachments for giving different tensions and rates of delivery to the different ply and thus allow loose, curled, twisted, or looped areas in the yarn. Slubs and flakes are also introduced into the yarn by special attachments. The durability of novelty yarn fabrics is dependent on the size of the novelty effect, how well the novelty effect is held in the yarn, and on the firmness of the weave of the fabric. Generally speaking, the smaller the novelty effect the more durable the fabric, since the yarns are less affected by abrasion and do not tend to catch and pull out so readily.

A typical novelty yarn has three basic parts: the ground or foundation, the fancy or effect, and the binder. (See Fig. 4:53.)

Ratiné is a typical novelty yarn. The effect ply is twisted in a somewhat spiral arrangement around the ground but at intervals a longer loop is thrown out, kinks back on itself and is held in place by the binder.

The *spiral or corkscrew* yarn is made by twisting together two plies that differ in size or in twist. (See Fig. 4:54a.) These two parts may be delivered to the twister at different rates of speed.

The *knot, spot, nub, knop* yarn is made by twisting the effect ply many times in the same place. (See Fig. 4:54c.) Two effect plies of different colors may be used and the knots arranged so the colors are alternated along the length of the yarn. A binder is added in a second twisting operation.

In the *spike or snarl* the effect yarn forms alternating unclosed loops along both sides of the yarn. (See Fig. 4:54d.)

Fig. 4:53. Novelty yarn.

The *loop, curl,* or *bouclé* yarn has closed loops at regular intervals along the yarn. (*See* Fig. 4:54e.) These yarns are used in woven or knit fabrics to create a looped pile that resembles caracul lambskin and is called an *astrakhan cloth.* They are used to give textured effects to other coating and dress fabrics.

Slub effects are achieved in two ways. (*See* Fig. 4:54f.) True slubs are made by varying the tightness of the twist at regular intervals. Intermittently spun flake or slub effects are made by incorporating soft, thick, elongated tufts of fiber into the yarn at regular intervals. A core or binder is needed with these yarns.

SPECIAL NOVELTY YARNS

Metallic Yarns

Metallic yarns have been used for thousands of years. The older yarns were made of pure metal (lamé) and were heavy, brittle, expensive, and had the disadvantage of tarnishing.

The new metallic yarns (1946) are made by laminating a layer of aluminun foil between two sheets of plastic film. This laminate is then split into strips that range from $\frac{1}{120}$ of an inch to $\frac{1}{8}$ of an inch. The sheets of film may be colorless, giving the yarn the natural aluminum color; or the film or adhesive may be colored before the laminating process. The colors used are gold, silver, copper, and pastel or "porcelain" colors. (*See* Fig. 4:55.)

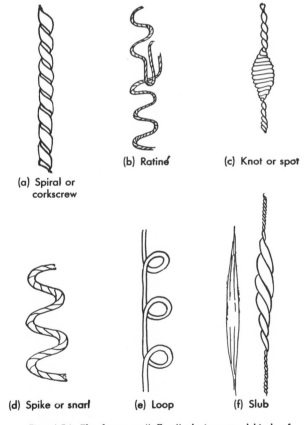

(a) Spiral or corkscrew

(b) Ratiné

(c) Knot or spot

(d) Spike or snarl

(e) Loop

(f) Slub

Fig. 4:54. The fancy or "effect" ply in several kinds of novelty yarns.

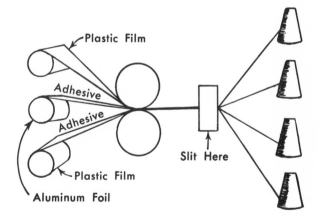

Fig. 4:55. Laminating metallic yarn.

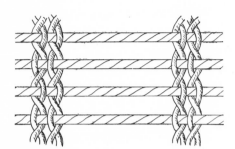

Fig. 4:56. Fabric from which chenille yarn is made.

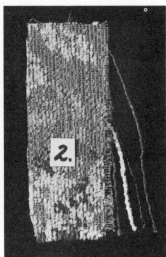

Fig. 4:57. (1) Chenille yarn is made by cutting a specially woven fabric into strips. (2) Fabric made from chenille yarns.

The first plastic film to be used was cellulose acetate. In 1954, Mylar, a polyester film, was produced by Du Pont. It was stronger, more flexible and more washable than the acetate.

In 1957 a metalizing process was developed. Aluminum, vaporized under high vacuum, was deposited on the Mylar film. This process required a very small amount of metal to produce a silver color. No foil was needed but instead the metalized Mylar could be laminated between two layers of clear film or it could be used with only one other layer of film. The three layer laminate could be colored as before but the two layer laminate could be produced only in silver color.

The metalized Mylar is stronger and more flexible than the foil laminate and can be used in a wider variety of products such as upholstery and knitwear, two areas where metallic yarns had not previously been used.

The new metallic yarns are washable, nonirritating and do not tarnish. Fabrics containing a large amount of metallic yarn can be embossed. Ironing is a problem when metallic yarns are combined with cotton. A temperature high enough to remove the wrinkles will melt the plastic. The best way to remove wrinkles in the metallic yarns is to tip the iron on its side and draw the edge of the sole of the iron across the fabric.

Chenille Yarn

Chenille yarn is made by cutting a specially woven ladder-like fabric into warp-wise strips. (*See* Figs. 4:56 and 4:57.) The cut ends of the softly twisted yarns loosen and form a pile-like fringe. This fringed yarn may be woven to make a fabric with pile on one or both sides. If the pile is on one side only, the yarn must be folded before it is woven. The yarn is sometimes referred to as a "caterpillar" yarn.

Sewing Thread

Cotton thread is made from long staple Egyptian or Supima cotton. The average spool contains 50 yards and large spools contain 400 yards. Some 900 yard spools are available from tailoring supply houses. Since the average dress requires 135 yards of thread it is often more economical to buy large spools.

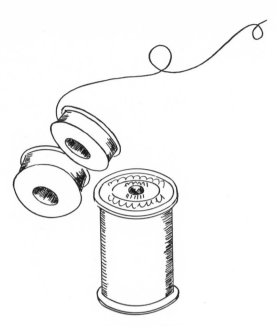

Fig. 4:58. Cotton sewing thread.

The following types of cotton thread are available on the market:

1. Six cord cotton thread (6 ply SZS twist) in black and white in a range of sizes.

2. Mercerized cotton thread, with three ply (usually referred to as 3 cord) size A or 50. Recommended for use where laundering includes the use of strong bleaches and high temperature.

3. Heavy duty thread—a mercerized 3 ply thread is recommended for use on heavy fabrics and wool.

Thread should be chosen according to the color (slightly darker), and size of yarns in the fabric. Needles are chosen by thread size—fine needles for fine thread.

Cotton Thread Size (Medium)	Hand Needle Size (Medium)	Machine Needle Size (Medium)
40–60	7–9	14 (14 stitches to inch)

Silk thread—size A for sewing and buttonhole twist—is lint free and stronger and smoother than cotton. Because it is elastic, lower machine tension should be used. Many heat-sensitive fibers have been used for thread: nylon, Dacron, Orlon. Nylon, the one most often used for home sewing presented problems of puckering and melting. Nylon thread has been made in three constructions: conventional twisted, twistless Nymo, and Taslan. (*See* page 101.) In 1960, Coats and Clark Co. announced that their future production would be Taslan thread only and they were discontinuing conventional nylon and Dacron thread. Taslan is softer and easier to handle. It was developed especially for the wash-and-wear man-made fabrics, and blends of cotton and man-made fibers.

When heat-sensitive thread is used on a heat-resistant fabric, such as cotton, *the temperature of the iron must be kept below the melting point of the thread.*

Yarn (Count) Number

The number, count, or size of a yarn is based on its weight and length.

In the *cotton system*, the unit of *weight* remains constant. This is an *indirect* numbering system, since the finer the yarn the larger its number. The cotton system is used for yarn size of cotton weaving yarns and of sewing thread.

No. 1, one hank	840 yds., weight: one lb.
No. 2, two hanks	1680 yds., weight: one lb.

Denier (pronounced den—yer) is the system used for filament yarns and fiber. In this system the unit of *length* remains constant. It is a direct numbering system, since the finer the yarn the smaller the number.

1 denier	9000 meters weigh 1 gram
2 denier	9000 meters weigh 2 grams

The TEX system of yarn numbering has been adopted by the International Organization for Standardization. (One tex = one gram per thousand meters.) In 1960 conversion tables were completed so it is possible to convert quickly from one system to another.

FIBER BLENDS

A blend is an intimate mixture of staple fibers of different composition, length, diameter, or color spun together into a yarn.

Yarns of unlike fiber content are also used in fabrics, usually one fiber content yarn in the warp and the other in the filling. These are called *mixtures*. Two unlike fiber strands may be twisted together as a ply making a *combination* yarn. Mixtures, combinations, and blends give properties to fabrics that are different from those obtained with one fiber only. The following discussion relates to blends, although most of the facts are true for mixtures and combinations as well.

In the last ten years, blends have become very important, but they are not new. *Viyella flannel*, a 55% cotton, 45% wool fabric, has been woven in England for years. It feels like a light weight wool but does not felt and is washable. Long Johns are made from a combination of wool and cotton. Covert, a fabric specially designed for hunting, is also a blend of cotton and wool. Today it is possible to obtain all basic fabrics in fiber blends. In promotion of these fabrics, the traditional fabric name may be used or a new name may be coined, for example—Cotdel is a blend of 50/50 cotton and Kodel, and Dacton is a blend of Dacron and cotton. Bondyne refers to a mixture of wool or cotton warp yarns and Dynel filling yarns.

There is no perfect fiber. All fibers have good, fair, and poor characteristics. Blending enables the technician to combine fibers, so the good qualities are emphasized and the poor qualities minimized. Blending requires knowledge in both science and art.

For a specific end-use, a blend of fibers that complement each other will give more satisfactory all-around performance than a 100% fiber fabric.

M. J. Caplan, in his article "Fiber Translation in Blends," used the following example to show that a blend will yield a fabric with intermediate values. He took two fibers, A and B, each of which could be used to make a similar fabric, measured five performance properties of each of these 100% fabrics, and then predicted the performance of a blended fabric 50/50 A and B by averaging the values of each fabric in the blend.

Property	Known Values		Predicted Values
	A	B	50/50 A and B
1	12	4	8
2	9	12	10.5
3	15	2	8.5
4	7	9	8
5	12	8	10

Notice that the predicted value for the blend is lower than the high value of one fabric, and is greater than the low value of the other 100% fabric. By blending them, a fabric with intermediate values is obtained. Unfortunately, the real values do not come out in the same proportion as the respective percentage in a blend.

Much research has been done by the fiber manufacturers to determine just how much of each fiber is necessary in the various fiber constructions. It is very difficult to generalize about percentages because the percentage varies with the kind of fiber, the fiber construction, and the expected performance. For example, a very small amount of nylon (15%) improves the strength of wool, but 60% nylon is needed to improve the strength of rayon. For stability, 50% Orlon blended with wool in a woven fabric is satisfactory, but 75% Orlon is necessary in knitted fabrics.

As more research is done in this area, there will, no doubt, be standards set up or agreed upon so consumers will have a good way of judging blended fabrics. At the present time, one must have faith in the producer of the garment that the fabric will perform as stated on the label, or assume that a 50/50 blend will have somewhat good properties of both fibers, or assume that 10% or less fiber in a blend is added for aesthetic reasons or as a "sales gimmick."

BLENDING METHODS

Blending can be done at any stage prior to the spinning operation. Blending can be done during opening-picking, drawing, and roving. One of the disadvantages of direct spinning is that blending cannot be done before the sliver is formed.

The earlier the fibers are blended in processing, the better the blend. The drawing below shows a cross-section of a yarn A, in which the fibers were blended in opening, and yarn B, a yarn in which the fibers were blended at the roving stage.

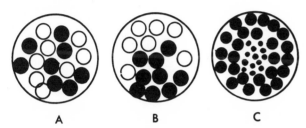

Fig. 4:59. Cross sections of blended fiber yarns.

Variations occur from spot to spot in the yarn and also from inside to outside. Long, fine fibers tend to move to the center of a yarn, while coarse, shorter fibers migrate to the periphery of the yarn—C, in Figure 4:59.

The older methods of blending involve much hand labor.

Opening-Picking. In one method several bales of fiber are laid around the picker and an armful from each bale is fed alternately into the machine. Another method is called sandwich blending. The desired amounts of

Fig. 4:60. Sandwich blending.

each fiber are weighed out and a layer of each is spread over the preceding layer to build up a sandwich composed of many layers. Vertical sections are then taken through the sandwich and fed into the picker.

Feeder blending is an automatic process in which each type fiber is fed to a mixing apron from individual hoppers.

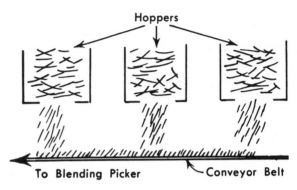

Fig. 4:61. Feeder blending.

Blending on the Drawing Frame. When the physical properties of two fibers differ, it is not always practical to blend them before carding, so they are picked and carded separately and then blended on the drawing frame. The problem of mixed wastes is eliminated with this process.

Blending on the Roving and Spinning Frame. Both of these operations combine fiber strands to reduce size and increase amount of twist until the final size and twist are achieved. Blending colors is the primary purpose at this stage.

Blending is a complicated and expensive process, but it makes it possible to build in a combination of properties which are permanent. Not only are blends used for better functionality of fabrics, but they are also used for beauty of appearance and hand.

Polymer blends are a new approach to the problem of blending. The raw materials for Orlon and acetate have been dissolved together as a single solution to make a fiber. Polymer blending creates the possibility of a whole new field of fibers.

REASONS FOR BLENDING

Blending is done for several reasons:

1. To obtain cross-dyed effects or create new color combinations. Special fiber types, called dye resist, are developed for cross-dyeing. For example, Orlon 44 was developed to be used with regular Orlon Type 42 for cross-dyeing. Piece dyeing is cheaper than fiber dyeing and heather effects are obtained when fibers with unlike dye affinity are blended together and then piece dyed. Special color effects are obtained by blending different proportions of stock dyed fibers.

2. To improve spinning, weaving, and finishing efficiency or uniformity of product. Blending of this sort, called self-blends, is done with the natural fibers which are never uniform in length or diameter. The consumer is not aware of this blending.

3. To obtain better texture, hand, or fabric appearance. A small amount of a specialty wool may be used to give a buttery or slick hand to wool fabrics or a small amount of rayon may give luster and softness to a cotton fabric. Fibers with different shrinkage properties are blended to produce bulky and lofty fabrics or fur-like fabrics with guard hairs.

4. For economic reasons. Expensive fibers can be extended by blending them with more plentiful fibers. This use is sometimes unfair to the consumer, especially when the expensive fiber is used in small amounts but advertised in large print; for example, CASHMERE and wool.

5. To produce fabrics with better performance.

The chart below lists some fiber properties which are important in apparel with the ratings of the most commonly used fibers in the group.

REFERENCES

1. Press, J. J., ed., *Man-Made Textiles Encyclopedia*, New York: Textile Book Publishers, Inc., 1959, pp. 562–583.
2. Du Pont de Nemours, E. I. and Co., "Properties of Blended Fabrics" (Bulletin X-21), Wilmington, Del.: Du Pont, no date.
3. Graybarn, Dr. A., "Combination of Fibres and Fibre Blends," *Canadian Textile Journal*, 73:53 (Nov. 1956).
4. Goldberg, Jules, "The Whys and Wherefores of Blends," *Canadian Textile Journal*, 73:67 (Jan. 1954).
5. "Polymer Blending," *Modern Textiles Magazine*, 35:56 (Jan. 1954).
6. Westbrook, W. C., "Fiber Blending Systems," *Textile World*, 106:122 (May 1956).
7. Caplan, M. J., "Fiber Translation in Blends," *Modern Textiles Magazine*, 40:39 (July 1959).
8. Fiori, L. A., and Louis, G. L., "Blending for Quality," *Textile Industries*, 126:110 (Apr. 1962).

Properties	Cotton	Rayon	Wool	Acetate	Nylon	Polyester	Acrylic	Modacrylic	Nytril	Olefin
Bulk and loft	−	−	+++		−	−	+++	+++	+++	
Wrinkle recovery	−	−	+++	++	++	+++	++	++	++	++
Press (wet) retention	−	−	−	+	++	+++	+			
Absorbency	+++	+++	+++	+	−	−	−	−	−	−
Static resistance	+++	+++	++	+	+	−	+	+	+	++
Resistance to pilling	+++	+++	+	+++	+					++
Strength	++	+	+	+	+++	+++	+	+	+	+++
Abrasion resistance	+	−	++	−	+++	+++	+	+	+	+++
Stability	++	−	−	+++	+++	+++	+++	+++	+++	+++
Resistance to heat	+++	+++	+++	++	+	+	++	−	+	−
	+++ Excellent		++ Good		+ Fair		− Deficient			

V. FABRIC
CONSTRUCTION

Fabrics are constructed from yarns; directly from fibers; or from plastic materials.

Weaves, knits, braids, and laces are made from yarns and are distinguished from one another by the way the yarns are arranged.

Woven fabrics have yarns that interlace at right angles. They are usually flat fabrics although some, such as pillow cases, may be tubular. In 1960, a process for weaving shape into a garment was developed. It has been predicted that by 1975 garments would be woven in finished shape ready to be worn.

The majority of fabrics produced are made by weaving since it is a firm, durable construction. A fabric can be identified as a woven fabric if yarns can be raveled from adjacent sides. The right angle yarn arrangement of woven fabrics is shown at right.

Knit fabrics are made by interlocking one loop of yarn into another. Knit fabrics can be made either flat or tubular and it has always

been possible to "fashion" garments during the knitting process.

Knit fabrics rank second to woven fabrics in quantity of fabric made and the amount is increasing since knits are wrinkle resistant,

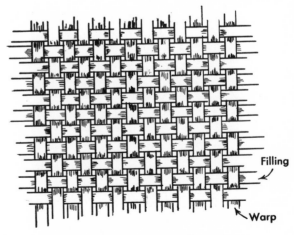

Fig. 5:1. Yarn arrangement in weaving.

127

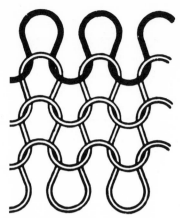

Fig. 5:2. Yarn arrangement in knitting. (Courtesy of American Bemberg.)

stretchy, and comfortable to wear. Interlocking knitting loops are shown in Figure 5:2.

Braid is made by diagonal interlacing of yarns which come from the same source. Braid is a narrow fabric used for trimmings. It is very stretchy and difficult for the home sewer to apply evenly. A diagram of the arrangement of yarns in braid is shown in Figure 5:3.

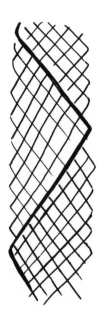

Fig. 5:3. Yarn arrangement in braid.

Lace and net are made by knotting or twisting yarns. They are used for decorative edgings, curtains, and dresses. (*See* Fig. 5:4.)

Felts and non-wovens are made directly from fibers; *plastic fabrics* are made directly from solutions.

WEAVING

New England was the center of the weaving industry in the United States until the 1950's when mills began to move south where wages were lower and labor was less unionized. By 1960, 77% of the weaving was done in the southeastern states.

Weaving is one of the oldest arts. All of the types of weaves used today were made in ancient times. The loom, on which fabrics are made, has not changed in principle since man first began weaving true cloth.

Power driven looms were perfected in the early part of the 19th century. The Jacquard loom, invented 150 years ago, was one of the first developments in automation. The warp yarns in the Jacquard loom are controlled by punch cards. (*See* Fig. 5:5.)

Most of the recent developments have been concerned with the developments of a loom that does not need a shuttle. The Draper shuttleless loom uses two finger-like arms, one of which takes the yarn half way across and the other reaches in to receive it. An air jet loom, now in use in Europe uses a blast of air to carry the yarn from one side to the other.

In the 1950's and 60's, many mills modernized obsolete equipment and installed wider looms. The width of the loom deter-

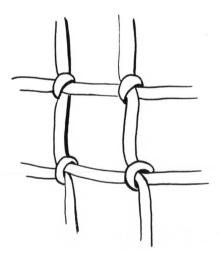

Fig. 5:4. Yarn arrangement in lace.

mines the width of the fabric. Hand woven fabrics were usually 27 to 36 inches wide, and before the 1950's, machine woven cottons were traditionally 36 inches wide. However, wider fabrics are more economical to weave and the garment cutter can lay out patterns to better advantage. The new looms weave cotton 45 inches wide. Wool fabrics are 54 to 60 inches and silk type fabrics are 40 to 45 inches wide.

Most fabrics are woven on a simple loom. This is described on this page. Loom attachments or more complex looms are used for weaves or designs more complicated than those that can be made on a simple loom. These are listed below.

1. A dobby attachment (Figure 5:6) makes possible many more arrangements of the warp threads and is used to make fabrics with small woven-in designs, for some gabardines, and satin-striped fabrics.

2. A swivel attachment is used for weaving in yarn dots.

3. A doup attachment is used to shift the warp threads across as well as up and down in making marquisette.

4. The Jacquard loom (*see* Figure 5:5), in

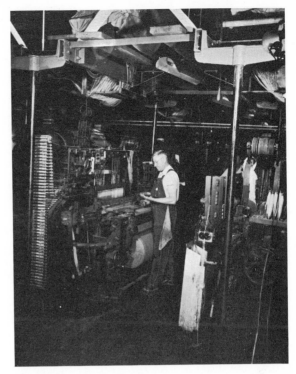

Fig. 5:6. Loom with dobby attachment. (Courtesy of *Textile World*.)

which each warp thread is controlled separately, is used for large figures as found in damask, brocade, and tapestry.

The Simple Loom

A knowledge of the loom and the weaving process is important because it helps develop an understanding of the cost, the characteristics, and the limitations of woven fabrics. Some of the vocabulary used to describe fabrics comes from terms associated with the weaving process; for example, end-and-end chambray and skipped-dent dimity. Weaving consists of three steps:

Shedding—the raising of one or more harnesses to separate the warp yarns and form a shed.
Picking—passing the shuttle through the shed to insert the filling.
Beating up—the reed pushes the filling yarn back into place in the cloth.

The weaves that can be made on the simple loom are plain, rib, satin, basket, and some twills.

Fig. 5:5. Jacquard loom. (Courtesy of *Textile World*.)

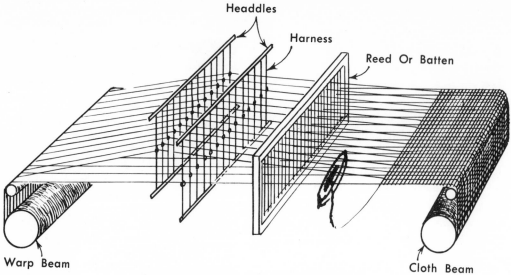

Fig. 5:7. Simplified diagram of two-harness loom.

The simplified drawing above shows a two harness loom. The simple loom may have six or seven harnesses. For more intricate pattern arrangements of the warp yarn, loom attachments and more complicated looms are used. These are discussed on page 129. However, all looms have the same basic parts as shown in Figure 5:7.

THE PARTS OF THE LOOM

The *warp beam* holds the warp or lengthwise yarns of the cloth. The warp beam is prepared by winding yarn from a large number of spools held on a creel. (*See* page 110.) This may be done at the yarn spinning mill or at the weaving mill.

The *harness*, a frame containing a number of heddles, is used to raise some of the warp yarns and thus form the shed through which the filling is inserted.

A *heddle* is a wire with a hole in the center. It controls the action of the warp yarn which is threaded through it. There are as many heddles as there are warp yarns.

The *reed* is a frame containing as many wires per inch as there are warp threads. The warp threads are placed between the wires in the reed. These spaces are called *dents*. After each filling is inserted, the reed beats it back into the cloth.

The *shuttle* is a boat-like object that carries the filling back and forth across the warp.

The filling yarn is wound on *quills* which are placed in the shuttle. The filling is the cross-wise yarn in the fabric.

The *cloth beam* holds the finished fabric.

SELVAGES

The yarns that run length-wise in a fabric are called *warp yarns* or *ends*.

The yarns that run from selvage to selvage across a fabric are called the *filling yarns*. *Woof*, *weft*, and *picks* are other names sometimes used for filling yarns.

Observe, in the picture of the loom, that the filling yarn turns at the edge of the cloth, enters the next "shed" and is carried back across the cloth. This forms a self-finish along the lengthwise edges of the cloth that is called a *selvage*.

The selvage is made firmer and stronger than the rest of the fabric by using more yarns, coarser yarns, or a different weave. The width of the selvage varies from 18 to 30 threads. Wider selvages are often used on thinner fabrics, such as voile.

There are several different kinds of selvages.

Plain selvages are made with the same size yarns as the rest of the fabric but there are more of them. Plain selvages do not shrink and can be used as seam edges in garment construction. Examples are selvages on percale and gingham.

Tape selvages are made of larger yarns or ply yarns to give strength. Basket weave is often used in this selvage to make a flatter edge. Examples are the selvages on sheets.

A *split selvage* is used on some narrow width fabrics which have been woven twice the finished width with two selvages in the center and the fabric then cut between the two. These cut edges are finished by a small hem or by a machine chain stitch along the edge. In towels made this way the machine stitch finish frequently outwears the rest of the towel.

Fused selvages are now possible on fabrics made from the heat-sensitive fibers (acetate, nylon). Heat is used to seal the fibers together at the edges when a wide fabric is split into numerous narrow widths. Ribbon is often made this way. Fused selvages on the edges of nylon jersey prevent rolling of the edge.

RECOGNITION OF WARP AND FILLING

Warp yarns have relatively high twist, and are made from better quality fibers. They are constructed to resist the high tension put on them in weaving.

It is very important to be able to recognize the warp direction (and filling direction) of a fabric.

Some reasons are:

The fabric will shrink more in this direction.

The fabric is stronger in this direction and it usually stretches less in this direction.

Fabrics are often stiffer in this direction because the warp yarns, to be stronger, must have more twist.

Because fabrics are stiffer in this direction they *drape* differently.

It is difficult to recognize a difference in the warp and filling direction of plain woven fabrics. A trained eye can see the difference but training requires practice.

Except for the first method given here, no one method fits all fabrics. Many of these will be more easily understood as fabrics are

studied so reference should be made to this list from time to time.

1. The selvage always runs warp way (lengthwise) of the fabric.
2. Most fabrics stretch less in the warp direction.
3. Warp yarns usually appear to be straighter in position in the fabric. (This is a result of the tension on the yarns during weaving.)
4. Warp yarns are usually the regular yarns, while filling yarns may be decorative or functional yarns. (Regular yarns are the ordinary weaving yarns, of medium size and medium twist and of uniform construction. Example: the yarns in a percale fabric.)
5. Many fabrics have certain characteristics that indicate the warp or filling direction. For example, poplin always has a filling rib, satin always has warp floats, and flat crepe has crepe yarns in the filling and regular yarns in the warp.

GRAIN

Grain is a term used to indicate the warp and filling yarns of the fabric. The warp yarns are the *lengthwise* grain and the filling yarns are the *crosswise* grain.

Any position that does not follow the threads of the fabric is a bias position. Observe in the picture, Figure 5:8, the position of the warp and filling threads in the cut edge of the fabric at the right. This edge is *true bias*. True bias is the diagonal of a square. The other fabric edge is a garment bias. *Garment bias* is any position between true bias and straight grain. Analysis of the picture will show why this edge will ravel more than any of the others.

Fig. 5:8. Grain position of cut edges: (1) garment bias; (2) true bias.

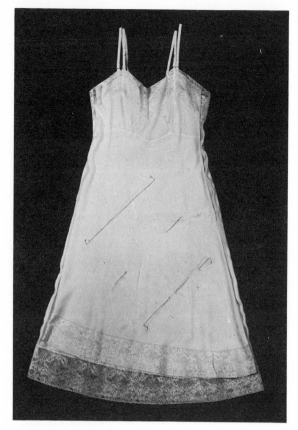

Fig. 5:9. Shrinkage in crepe slips. The warp shrank more than the filling.

The ability to recognize grain and to understand its influence on fabric performance is essential to every consumer.

Lengthwise grain stretches the least and shrinks the most. It is the most difficult to "ease" in sewing. Lengthwise yarns bend less easily than filling yarns because they have more twist and often have more sizing so fabrics are usually stiffer in the lengthwise direction. This is a factor in the way pleated skirts hang, the bouffant effect in gathers, etc.

True bias is the stretchiest position on the cloth. Bias seams will stretch from the weight of the cloth and cause sagging hemlines. Garments *properly* cut on the bias are often more comfortable because of the "give" in the fabric. If garments are *improperly* cut so that an edge, which should be on straight grain, is "off-grain," discomfort, twisting, and wrinkles will result.

The picture of the bias cut slip, Figure 5:9, illustrates the difference between the shrinkage of the warp and the filling yarns. This same difficulty is often encountered in skirts made from a circular pattern. Grainlines are an important marking on each commercial pattern piece since they are the guide to the position of the pattern piece on the fabric. Figure 5:10 shows a lengthwise grainline on a skirt pattern. This line is usually labeled "straight of the material" or "lengthwise of the goods."

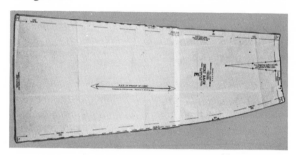

Fig. 5:10. Grainline on a commercial pattern.

INTERLACING

An *interlacing* is the point at which a yarn changes its position from the surface of a fabric to the underside or vice versa, by passing over or under one or more yarns. Plain weave has more interlacings than any other weave with the same number of yarns per square inch. (*See* Fig. 5:11.) High count fabrics have more interlacings than low count fabrics.

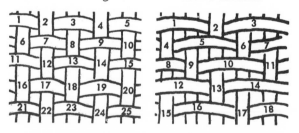

Fig. 5:11. Diagrams showing number of interlacings of plain weave on the left and twill weave on the right.

Recognition of the number of interlacings is important in predicting care needed during garment construction and in predicting durability and care required during use.

The greater the number of interlacings in a fabric, the more it will wrinkle, the less it will ravel, the less slippage of yarns will occur at points of strain, the firmer the fabric will be and the less absorbent it will be.

A *float* is that portion of a yarn which goes over two or more yarns from the opposite direction. (*See* Fig. 5:11.) In this fabric the floats are in the filling direction, and the fabric is, therefore, a *filling faced* fabric.

Floats in a fabric result in fewer interlacings per square inch and thus permit higher thread count. Long floats are apt to snag or abrade readily. Long floats reflect more light and aid in making smooth lustrous fabrics. If low twist yarns are used, the long floats are more absorbent. Woven designs, figures, satin stripes are made by changing the direction of the floats in the figure or stripe from that of the background.

Fractions are used as symbols to indicate the interlacing pattern of the yarns in the fabric. This is discussed on page 144.

RAVELING

Raveling is the fraying of yarns at the cut or torn edge of the fabric. Excessive raveling of a seam edge is one of the reasons for unsuccessful performance of a garment.

Washing causes much more raveling than dry cleaning. Unfinished seams in a garment to be dry cleaned might be successful, but if the garment were to be washed, some kind of finish might be needed.

Washable cotton fabrics show wide variation in the amount of ravel. Sheer fabrics, loose weaves, and large yarns ravel the most.

The position of the seam on the fabric is an important factor in ravel. Garment bias seams ravel much more than straight grain or true bias seam edges. Therefore, it may be necessary to finish only the garment bias seams in a garment.

The kind of finish used to prevent ravel gives varying degrees of success as shown in Figure 5:12.

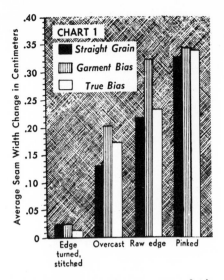

Fig. 5:12. Effectiveness of various seam finishes in the prevention of ravel.

THREAD COUNT

Thread or cloth count is the number of warp and filling yarns in one square inch of a gray goods fabric as it comes from the loom. This may be changed by shrinkage during dyeing and finishing. Thread count is written as, for example, 80 x 76, with the warp number given first; or it may be given as the total of the two, as 156. (Thread count should not be confused with yarn count or number, which is a measure of yarn size.) (*See* the discussion on page 123.)

Thread count is an indication of the closeness of the weave and can be used in judging quality, shrinkage, raveling, and durability. The higher the count, the better the quality for any one fabric. Higher count also means less potential shrinkage and less raveling of seams.

Thread count is sometimes printed on the selvage of percale. Sheets usually have the count given on the label. Mail-order houses frequently give the thread count since the customer must judge the quality from printed information rather than from the fabric itself. Some familiarity with the count of standard fabrics will help the consumer in judging the count of other fabrics.

A standard method of making a thread count may be found in the A.S.T.M., American Standards for Testing Materials. The count is made with a thread counting instrument. (*See* Fig. 5:13.) It is possible to use a "hand" method by which the area is measured by a ruler and counted by sight or yarns raveled off and counted.

Fig. 5:13. Thread counter. (Courtesy of the Alfred Suter Company.)

Percale fabrics have, in the past, had a standard thread count of 80 x 80 and were called 80-square fabrics. In February 1960, the *Women's Wear Daily* announced that, due to cost factors, a 78 x 78 fabric would now be the basic print cloth used. (Print cloth is the percale fabric as it comes from the loom before any finishing has been done.)

Balance is the ratio of warp yarns to filling yarns. For example, a dress percale with 78 warp yarns and 78 filling yarns in each square inch of fabric will have a ratio of one to one. This fabric is balanced. Cotton broadcloth has a count of 144 x 76, or a ratio of 2:1. This fabric is unbalanced.

Balance is helpful in recognizing and naming fabrics and in distinguishing the warp direction.

Balance is not always related to the quality of fabric. When the ratio is 2 to 1 or 3 to 1, the filling yarns are completely covered by the warp yarns, so the wear is on the warp yarns only. High warp count will give durability if the warp yarns have sufficient twist and are smooth and uniform.

In unbalanced fabrics, the filling yarns may not be as good quality as the warp yarns, but since there are many more warp threads, the fabric will be durable. In balanced fabrics, however, the same amount of filling and warp threads appear on the surface of the fabric and will be exposed to the same amount of abrasion and for this reason the filling threads should be as good as the warp threads. In balanced fabrics the more nearly the ratio is one to one, the better the quality. Balance plus thread count is important in predicting slippage. If the count is low, there seems to be more slippage in unbalanced fabrics than in balanced fabrics—for example, ribbed fabrics, satin, and sateen fabrics in low count pull out at the seams or the yarns shift from abrasion and strain. (*See* page 141.)

Plain Weave

PLAIN WEAVE FABRICS

Balanced	Unbalanced
Sheers	Ribbed fabrics—cotton
Dress weight	Ribbed fabrics—man-made fibers
Suiting weight	

Plain Weave Balanced Fabrics

Plain weave balanced fabrics are the largest group of woven fabrics. Plain weave is used in all weights from very sheer fabrics to very heavy fabrics and it has a wider range of end-uses than any of the other weaves.

Plain weave is formed by yarns at right angles passing alternately over and under each other. This is referred to as a 1/1 weave (one warp up and the next warp down when the shed is formed on the loom). Figure 5:14a shows the interlacing of yarns. At the weaving mill, the weave would be represented by the checkerboard design. (*See* Fig. 5:14b.) The dark squares are the warp yarns.

Fig. 5:14(a). Plain weave fabric.

Fig. 5:14(b). Checkerboard design of plain weave.

Fig. 5:14(c). Cross-sectional view of plain weave.

The weave may be also represented by the cross-sectional view. (*See* Fig. 5:14c.)

CHARACTERISTICS

Plain weave requires only a two harness loom and is the least expensive to produce. Unless it is printed or has a surface finish, there is no right or wrong side. The plain uninteresting surface serves as a good background for printed and embossed designs, puckered finishes, and glazed finishes.

Interesting effects can be achieved by using yarns of different size, color, or texture (novelty yarns for example). Two or more yarns can be woven as one or yarns can be omitted at regular intervals to give an open work effect.

Sheer Fabrics

Sheer fabrics are very thin, light weight fabrics that are transparent or semi-transparent. They are classified according to the thread count and the size of the yarns. (*See* page 136.)

SOME PROBLEMS WITH SHEER FABRICS

Sheer fabrics ravel enough to make it advisable to use enclosed seams. Since most seams show through, they should be made carefully so they are uniform in size. Seam-thin zippers should be used. With soft sheers, it is often desirable to use an interfacing in collars and cuffs to give more character to the design. Interfacings in a front or back opening give enough reinforcement to prevent buttons and buttonholes from pulling out readily. When using an interfacing, there is always the problem of color. Often a white fabric under the sheer is not pleasing and self-fabric, if printed, creates a distracting pattern.

Sheer fabrics also require special attention in washing and ironing. They are delicate fabrics and should be washed by hand or by machine in a special nylon mesh laundry bag. When clothes are washed in these bags they do not receive as much swirling in the machine and are not so apt to pull out at the seams. Nylon and rayon sheers often pull out even though the seams are finished, unless they are carefully handled. Sheer fabrics dry out faster than heavier weight fabrics and may need to be re-dampened during ironing. They also scorch readily unless a lower ironing temperature is used.

Sheers require suitable undergarments. Straps that do not match, slips so sheer that bra and girdle show, lace and embroidery not in keeping with the dress or blouse design, and slips too short or uneven at the lower edge all detract from the beauty of a sheer garment.

Sheers look cool but if many layers of undergarments are needed, they may not be as comfortable as a heavier garment worn with fewer layers of undergarments.

Low count sheers are balanced fabrics characterized by open spaces between the yarns. Since the yarns are similar to those used in dress weight fabrics, the sheerness is due to spacing rather than yarn size. These fabrics are made with carded yarns giving them a "clothy" look. They are neither strong nor durable, but are satisfactory for many uses. They are seldom printed. The fabrics differ in the way they are finished.

Fabric	Range in Thread Count	Yarn Size Warp	Filling
Cheesecloth	10 x 12 to 48 x 44	28s*	39s
Crinoline	Same as above	30s	42s

* The "s" after the number means that the yarn is a single thread. If ply yarn is used in the fabric, it will be indicated by writing the number as 38/2 or 44/3, etc.

Cheesecloth is a sleazy cotton fabric with a soft texture. Observe the range in count of the fabrics given in the chart above. Cheesecloth may be natural color, bleached, or dyed. It is used for interlinings, dust cloths, bandages, flag buntings, and sign cloths. Cheesecloth of very low count is used for covering tobacco plants which must be grown in the shade, so it is called tobacco cloth.

Crinoline is a cheesecloth that has been sized with starches and glue or resin to make it very stiff. Of these sizings only the resin is durable; the others wash out leaving a soft, sleazy fabric. Crinoline is usually black or white; if used for costumes, it may be colored. The dyes used in crinoline are seldom fast color. Some crinoline has a bonded material pressed on the back to make it more comfortable to wear. Crinoline petticoats need to be lined—otherwise, they snag hose or scratch the legs. Crinoline is used for costumes, interlinings, and hat frames.

Medium to high count sheers are more closely woven than the fabrics of the preceding group. Their transparency is due to the fineness of the yarns. The *cotton sheers*, lawn, organdy, and batiste, are made from the same gray goods lawn. (*See* page 117.) They differ from one another in the way they are finished. The gray goods may be made of either carded yarns or combed yarns. The better quality has combed yarns and the chart below gives a typical thread count and yarn number.

Fabric	Typical Thread Count	Yarn Size Warp	Filling
Lawn	88 x 80	70s	100s
Organdy	Similar to above	Similar to above	
Batiste	Similar to above	Similar to above	

Organdy is the sheerest cotton cloth made and has more crispness than lawn or batiste. (Organdy finishes are discussed on page 198.) Because of its stiffness, it wrinkles badly so is not suitable for baby clothes and handkerchiefs.

Lawn has a starched finish and is often printed. It may be given a durable finish. (*See* page 173.)

Batiste is the softest of the three. It is highly mercerized and is usually used in white or pastels. It is never starched or given a crisp finish.

(Voile is a cotton sheer made with special yarns and is discussed on page 120.)

Dacron-cotton batiste is similar to cotton batiste but is crease resistant so is suitable for wash-and-wear garments.

100% Dacron batiste is not as soft or opaque as Dacron-cotton batiste.

Filament yarn sheers are similar in sheerness to cotton organdy. Georgette has a texture similar to that of voile. Chiffon is a smooth sheer fabric. These sheers are designated by fiber content as nylon chiffon, etc.

Tissue gingham and chambray are yarn dyed sheers.

Dress-Weight Fabrics

The largest quantity of plain weave fabrics belongs in this group since a medium weight fabric has more uses than either a light weight or a heavy weight fabric.

CONVERTED FABRICS

Cotton	Other Fiber Contents *
Percale	Pigment taffeta
Muslin	Rayon challis
Plissé **	Wool challis
Resin-treated cottons **	Dress linen

Range in Thread Count for Cotton Fabrics		Yarn Size	
		Warp	Filling
Carded cottons	80 x 80 to 44 x 48	30s	42s
Combed cottons	96 x 80	40s	50s

* See Glossary.
** Discussed in section on finishes.

Print cloth is the gray goods name for cotton fabrics in this group.

Muslin is a general name applied to any plain-woven, balanced fabric which ranges in weight from lawn to heavy bed sheeting. Muslin is also a specific name used for medium weight fabrics which are starched or given a slightly crisp finish. They may be white, colored, or printed, but the name is most frequently used for the white or unbleached fabrics.

Percale is a smooth-finished cotton fabric which is slightly starched and may be printed or solid color. Carded yarns are used in counts ranging from 48 x 48 to 80 x 80. Combed yarns are used in higher count fabrics. Percale is used for dresses, aprons, and pajamas. *Calico* is an old name used for percale with a quaint printed design. Its popularity is dependent on fashion cycles while other percale designs are more standard. *Chintz* is a percale printed with flowers or other designs in a number of different colors. The name "chintz" comes from the Hindu word meaning "spotted." The designs used in chintz are similar to those used in cretonne but the fabrics differ in weight. Cretonne is a heavier fabric. Chintz is usually given a glazed finish. It may be made in plain colors.

Printed percales may be made in designs that resemble but are not true gingham. These should not be called gingham. The consumer can easily identify those fabrics since they have a right and wrong side while the true ginghams are the same on both sides.

YARN-DYED FABRICS

Cotton	Other Fiber Content *
Chambray	Silk gingham
Gingham	Rayon gingham
	Rayon taffeta

Gingham	
84 x 76 combed	64 x 50 standard carded
88 x 84 combed	48 x 44 low quality carded

* See Glossary, *gingham* and *taffeta*.

Gingham and chambrays are yarn-dyed. Ginghams are made with solid colors, plaids, and checks. Chambrays are plain colored or striped with white filling and colored warp. *Iridescent chambray* is made with yarns of two different colors—the darker yarns in the warp direction and the light yarns in the filling. Ginghams and chambrays are made with either carded or combed yarns and they vary in thread count and yarn size. Good quality fabrics are made with combed yarns and high count. Most ginghams are balanced fabrics,

Fig. 5:15. Balanced plaid—gingham.

Fig. 5:16. Unbalanced plaid—gingham.

but some are made with many more warp than filling (a rib construction) giving a solid color to chambray and solid color stripes to gingham.

Medium quality ginghams and chambrays are often given a resin finish for crease recovery or for smooth, polished appearance.

Ginghams are usually made of cotton but similar fabrics of other fiber contents could be called gingham. In this case, the fiber content is included in the name; for example, silk gingham, rayon gingham. In filament rayon, these fabrics are given a crisp finish and called taffeta. In wool, similar fabrics are called wool checks, wool plaids, and shepherd's checks.

The construction of ginghams is a more costly process than making printed or piece-dyed fabrics, because the loom must be re-threaded for each new design and threading a loom for "woven in" designs requires more skill than threading it with undyed yarns. It is also necessary for the manufacturer to keep a large supply of threaded warp beams ready to weave fabrics to fill orders as they come in.

SUGGESTIONS FOR SEWING WITH GINGHAM

Stripes, plaids, and checks present problems that are not present with plain colored fabrics. The selection of the pattern is important. Few pieces are easier to work with than many. Cutting and sewing should be done so design lines match perfectly. Ginghams may

have an up and down, a right or left, or both. Figure 5:15 shows a balanced plaid with no up or down or right or left. Figure 5:16 also shows an unbalanced plaid which would be the more complicated pattern-cutting problem. Plaids in inexpensive gingham dresses seldom match except at center front and center back seams, places where failure to match would be most noticeable. Matching of plaids is somtimes difficult since they are not always woven the same size.

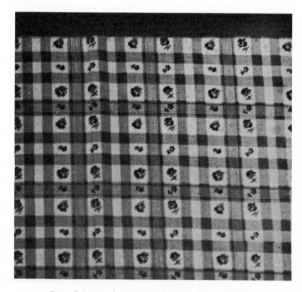

Fig. 5:17. Fabric printed on grain—percale.

Printed geometric designs may resemble gingham. There is, however, a right and wrong side whereas plain-woven gingham is the same on both sides. Printed warp stripes are usually on grain but designs in the filling direction are often off grain. Figure 5:17 shows a geometric design printed on grain. Notice how it follows the torn edge. Figure 5:18 shows a design printed very much off grain.

Sheets and Pillow Cases

Sheets and pillow cases are comparable in weight to the dress-weight fabrics. Sheets are, however, woven in much wider widths and pillow cases are often woven tubular.

Fig. 5:18. Fabric printed off grain—percale.

	TYPES AND CHARACTERISTICS OF SHEETS				
Muslin				*Percale*	
Lightweight Type 128	Heavy-weight Type 140		Utility Type 180 Carded	Combed Type 180 Long staple	Supercale Type 200 Fine, smooth
Grade B muslin Carded yarns Widely used Medium priced	Grade A Carded yarns Strong, most durable		Smooth, lighter weight than muslin Wrinkles more than muslin		

The purchase of sheets is relatively simple because government specifications set a minimum thread count for the different grades of sheets. The term *Type,* which is used in the chart above, refers to this minimum thread count.

Back-filled muslin sheeting (Type 112) is sometimes available. It is less durable and less expensive than the muslin sheetings given above.

Carded percale and heavy-weight muslin are similar in price. Heavy-weight muslin is more durable but carded percale is sold in the largest volume, possibly because the name "percale" is associated with quality by the average consumer. Carded percale does not wear as well as the combed percale.

Standard sizes for sheets are:

Width—single bed, 54 inches; twin bed, 63 or 72 inches; double, 81 or 90 inches.

Lengths—99, 108, and 113 inches. Length is measured as torn length before hemming.

(Extra length and width sheets are available.)

The hems on muslin sheets require five inches—three inches for the top, one inch for the bottom, and one inch for the double turn; on percale the top hem is four inches. Shrinkage reduces the length of the sheet about 6 per cent in muslin and a little less in percale, or by approximately five inches. A 108-inch sheet thus will measure 98 inches after hemming and washing.

Contour sheets are tailored to fit the mattress so they are held firmly on the bed and do not wrinkle. It is important that they be Sanforized to minimize shrinkage.

Until 1952, when nylon sheets were introduced, buying did not involve a choice of fiber content or weave. All sheets are plain-weave balanced fabrics except for nylon fitted sheets, and they are knitted.

The comparative cost of laundering muslin and percale is no longer a problem, since laundries usually charge by the sheet, not by the pound. When washing at home, it may be a little easier to lift lighter weight percale sheets than the heavier muslin sheets.

Pillow cases are made to match sheets. They should be ten inches longer than the pillow and about two inches larger around. Pillow slips are woven tubular or flat. Flat fabric must be sewed along the side. The length of pillow cases is quoted as length before hemming:

Standard pillow size is 21 x 27 inches and the size of the case should be 45 x 36 inches.

REFERENCE

Hoye, John, *Staple Cotton Fabrics*, New York: McGraw, 1942, p. 58.

Suiting and Heavy Fabrics

Any fabric which is heavy enough to tailor well can be called suiting. These fabrics have coarse yarns and a medium count. Filling yarns are usually larger than warp yarns due to slightly lower twist.

Fabrics in the heavy-weight group are all referred to as duck or canvas. They are the heaviest and strongest fabrics made. They have many industrial uses and are used for tents, army cots, sails, golf bags, tarpaulins, conveyor belts, water hoses, sneakers, etc.

SUITING WEIGHT FABRICS

Fabric	Typical Count	Typical Yarn Size
Cotton suiting	48 x 48	13s to 20s
	66 x 76	
Tropical worsted		
Linen suitings		
Cretonne		
Crash		
Butcher rayon		
Flannel *		
Tweed		
Sailcloth **		
Homespun **		

* *See* page 182.
** *See* Glossary.

Cotton suiting is used for sportswear, luncheon cloths and place mats, draperies, and slip covers. Indian Head is a well-known trade name.

Tropical suiting is a lightweight summer suiting fabric made with worsted yarns. Other fiber contents and blends of fibers are also used in fabrics of this kind. *Linen suiting* is often called dress linen.

Crash differs from cotton suiting and cretonne in the construction of the yarns. Crash yarns always have thick and thin areas. This gives an uneven, nubby look to the fabric, and wrinkles show less than they would on a plain surface.

Cretonne is similar to cotton suiting except that it is printed in floral designs. It is used for slip covers and draperies.

Butcher rayon is a crash-like fabric that is made in various weights. All kinds of names are given to this fabric. In heavier weights it looks like linen suiting. Butcher rayon may be an acetate and rayon blend or it may be 100 per cent rayon. It is often given a crease-resistant finish. A recent Federal Trade Commission ruling prohibits the use of the word "linen" for this type of fabric.

Tweed is the name for a large range of fabrics with mixed color effects made of any fiber or mixture of fibers. The name comes from the Tweed river in Scotland where the fabrics were first woven. Harris tweed is a hand woven fabric from the Outer Hebrides. Donegal tweed is a hand woven tweed from Donegal County, Ireland.

HEAVY FABRICS

Fabric	Thread Count	Yarn Size	
		Warp	Filling
Duck	54 x 40	8/2	14/2
	72 x 40	12/2	15/2

Duck or canvas is the heaviest and strongest of all the cotton fabrics. Most duck is made with ply yarns in both directions. The fabric is either plain weave or is a variation of basket weave in which the warp yarns are used in pairs. The latter is called *flat duck* and is used in draperies and slip covers. Duck fabrics are often used in natural colors. Duck may be either printed or plain. Very little duck is used for clothing purposes.

Plain-Weave Unbalanced Fabrics

Ribbed fabrics are made with a plain weave with many more warp than filling yarns. The result is a crosswise rib or ridge. The warp yarns completely cover the filling yarns, forming a warp-surface fabric. This can readily be seen when the color of the warp differs from the color of filling yarns. Then the only color on the surface will be that of the warp yarns. Ribbed fabrics may have the same size yarn in warp and filling or may have larger yarns in the filling direction. Ribbed fabrics always are unbalanced, having a ratio of 2:1 or greater. In the fine fabrics the rib is not so obvious, but a ribbed fabric can always be recognized by ravelling adjacent sides and examining the fringe.

Ribbed fabrics have more body because there are more interlacings per square inch than in balanced plain-weave fabrics. The heavier the fabric the more body it will have and the less drapability. These heavy fabrics are especially good where a bouffant rather than a clinging silhouette is desired. The exceptions are fine, mercerized ribbed fabrics, such as broadcloth which are softer and drape better than percale.

In a warp surface fabric of this type, warp yarns wear out first, resulting in cross-wise breaks. In a balanced fabric, both sets of yarns wear equally and give out at the same time, forming holes rather than slits. Because of their warp count, ribbed fabrics tear more easily in the length-wise direction. Fabrics with large filling yarns would be exceptions. Slippage (*see* Figure 5:19) of the warp yarns across the filling may occur in filament fabrics of medium or low quality. Buttonholes and seams will pull out if under strain. Examination of the fabric for closeness of weave will give the consumer some indication of the possibility of slippage.

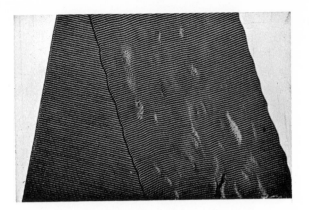

Fig. 5:19. Slippage of yarns in a ribbed fabric.

COTTON

Fabric	Count	Yarn Size Warp	Filling
		60s	60s
Combed broadcloth	144 x 76	100/2	100/2
Carded broadcloth	100 x 60	40s	40s
Combed poplin	102 x 50	50/2	28s
Carded poplin	100 x 44	30s	24s
Rep	88 x 31	30/2	5s

Broadcloth has the finest crosswise rib. It is an American name for fine poplin. Unless examined closely, it may be mistaken for percale. The best qualities are made of long staple cotton and ply yarns. The same size yarns are used in both warp and filling. On the label "Pima Broadcloth," the word "Pima" refers to a variety of long staple cotton. Broadcloth is usually mercerized to increase the luster. Best qualities are very silky in appearance. The warp yarns have soft twist since high twist reduces luster. This is one reason broadcloth is softer and more drapable than percale. Ply yarns, when used, give increased strength to compensate for lower twist. Carded yarns, usually in the filling, are used in lower quality broadcloth. Variation in quality may give variation in price of more than a dollar a yard. Durability tests have shown that broadcloth does not wear as long as percale.

Slub broadcloth is a broadcloth made with yarns containing definite slubs at regular intervals. The slubs are usually an inch or so in length and somewhat spindle-shaped.

Poplin is similar to broadcloth but has a heavier crosswise rib. The filling threads are heavier than the warp but the difference is too slight to be noticeable when adjacent sides are raveled and the fringe examined.

Rep is a heavy, coarse cotton fabric with a pronounced rib effect.

OTHER FIBERS

Fabric	Count	Yarn Size	
		Warp	*Filling*
Viscose taffeta	60 x 15	10/2	3s
Acetate taffeta	140 x 64	75 denier	150 denier
Faille	200 x 64	75 denier	200 denier
Bengaline	92 x 40	150 denier	15s spun
Shantung	140 x 44	150 denier	30/2 cotton

Taffeta has a crosswise rib flatter than other rib fabrics. It has crispness or body which is obtained by weave and fiber in acetate and by weave and finish in rayon. It is made of filaments and varies in weight from a fine, lightweight (tissue) to a medium-weight fabric. The word "taffeta" is a little confusing, since it is used for both a balanced plain-weave fabric as well as a ribbed fabric.

Moiré taffeta is produced by embossing a watered or waved design on faille taffeta (page 176). Acetate holds the pattern permanently. Figure 5:20 shows a "before and after" view of viscose moiré. Viscose does not hold the design permanently and in the fabric on the right, the watered design has disappeared completely.

Faille (pronounced, file, and less commonly, fale) is usually made of rayon. It is similar to poplin in weight. Faille has filament warp of viscose or acetate and filling of spun viscose. Faille could also be called rayon poplin.

Bengaline is similar to faille and is often made with rayon warp and cotton filling. It is sometimes woven two warps at a time to emphasize the rib.

Grosgrain (pronounced grow-grane) has a crosswise rib rounder than faille. Grosgrain ribbon frequently shrinks as much as two inches a yard.

Shantung has an irregular rib surface produced by irregularities in the filling yarn.

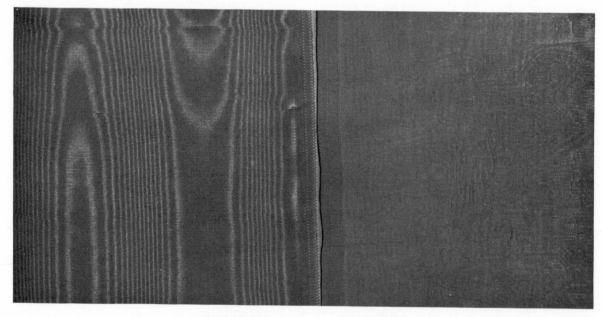

Fig. 5:20. Moiré before and after washing.

Basket Weave—Plain Weave Derivative

FLAT SURFACE FABRICS

Basket weaves are made with two or more adjacent warp yarns woven as one and with two or more filling yarns placed in the same shed. The most common basket weaves are 2 x 2 and 4 x 4 arrangements, but other combinations are made, as 2 x 1, 3 x 3, 6 x 6, etc. With this weave it is possible to pack the yarns closely together because there are fewer interlacings per square inch. The fabrics have a flatter appearance than 1 x 1 plain weaves and if the count is not high the fabrics are porous and very pliable. Arrangements such as 3 x 3, 4 x 4, 6 x 6 snag easily, especially if the count is medium or low.

Monk's cloth is one of the oldest homespun type fabrics. It is also called friar's cloth, bishop's cloth, Druid's cloth, mission cloth. It is a heavy coarse fabric in a 2 x 2 or 4 x 3 basket weave. It is usually brownish-white or oatmeal color, but it may be white or piece dyed. (The oatmeal color is obtained with ply yarns, one unbleached cotton and the other brown, or with a blend of natural and dyed cotton fibers.) The yarns are carded, soft spun in sizes 7/2 to 10/2 or 3s to 5s. Monk's cloth is used

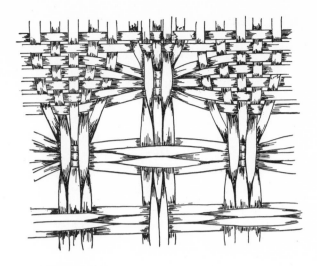

Fig. 5:22. Novelty basket weave; window-pane effect.

for draperies, wall or bulletin-board coverings, bedspreads, and dresser scarves.

Hopsacking is an open basket weave fabric made of cotton, linen, or wool. It is primarily used for coats and suits. It derives its name from sacks used to gather hops.

Variations of basket weaves are made by using two yarns in the warp direction and one in the filling direction. This combination is often called Oxford weave because it is so widely used in Oxford cloth.

Oxford is a 2 x 1 shirting fabric made with combed cotton yarns in which the warp yarns are much finer than the filling yarns. It has a flat look because the two warp yarns occupy as much space as the one filling yarn. It is porous and rather lustrous.

Shirley cloth, developed at the Shirley Institute in England, is a 2 x 1 Oxford cloth used for rainwear. Combed cotton 3-ply yarns with low twist are used and the yarns are packed so closely together that a water-repellent finish is not necessary. (For flat duck, *see* page 141.)

Novelty open work effects or square effect designs are used by alternating an area of plain weave with an area of basket weave. The one shown in Figure 5:22 is called a windowpane effect because it has been used to give a cooler, more comfortable fabric. This was the method used to make some of the first nylon fabrics more comfortable.

Fig. 5:21. Basket weave.

Twill Weave

A twill weave is one in which each filling yarn floats across two or more warp yarns with a progression of interlacings of one or more to the right or left to form a distinct diagonal line or *wale*. In the checkerboard design below, the progression (from lower to upper part of the diagram) of interlacings is to the left.

Twill fabrics vary in the number of harnesses used, the prominence of the wales, the direction of twill line, the degree of angle, and the kind of floats on the surface of the cloth. (A float is that portion of a yarn which goes over two or more yarns from the other direction.)

The simplest twill requires three harnesses. Figure 5:23 shows a 3 harness twill. This is designated as a 2/1 twill, i.e., two warp up and one warp down when the weaving shed is formed. The floats on the surface are warp yarns making it a warp surface (warp face) twill.

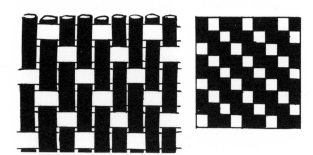

Fig. 5:23. 2/1 twill weave.

Fig. 5:24. 2/1 twill weave.

The more complex twills may have as many as 15 to 18 harnesses and are woven on a loom with a dobby attachment.

The *prominence of a twill wale* may be increased by the use of long floats, combed yarns, and ply yarns, high count yarns, hard twist yarns, and twist of yarn opposite to the twill line.

The direction of twill wale goes up to the right in wool fabrics, while in cotton fabrics the twill line goes up to the left. This fact is important only in that it is one way to tell the right and wrong sides of a fabric. In some fabrics made with white and colored yarns, and a very prominent twill line, it is not possible to make both lapels on a suit or coat look the same; this gives a disturbing design effect and should be avoided. (*See* Fig. 5:25.)

Fig. 5.25. Twill wales in lapel look unbalanced.

The degree of angle depends on the balance of the cloth. Fabrics are steep twills, reclining twills, or regular twills. In Figure 5:26 the same number of filling yarns is used in each fabric but the number of warp yarns vary. The greater the difference between warp and filling, the steeper the twill line. The importance of the angle, then, is in determining comparative strength of fabrics. Steep twill fabrics have a higher warp count and are therefore stronger in the warp direction.

Characteristics

Twill fabrics have a right and wrong side. If there are warp floats on the right side there will be filling floats on the wrong side. If the

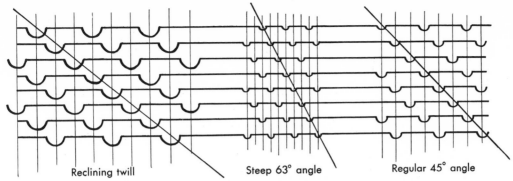

Reclining twill   Steep 63° angle   Regular 45° angle

Fig. 5:26. Twill angle depends on warp count.

twill wale goes up to the left on one side it will go to the right on the other side.

Twill fabrics do not have an up-and-down except for fabrics that are highly napped. This can be verified by turning the fabric upside down and examining the direction of the twill line.

Printed designs are seldom used on twills because the surface has interesting texture and design as a result of the wales. Silk and some lightweight twills are exceptions.

Sheer fabrics are seldom made with a twill weave.

Soil shows less on twills than on smooth fabrics and they probably soil less easily because the twill ridge prevents the entire surface from coming in contact with soil.

Fewer interlacings give a fabric more softness, pliability, and wrinkle recovery than a comparable plain weave fabric has because the yarns can move more freely. They also permit the yarns to be packed closer together to produce added weight and durability. It is possible to obtain higher count in twill weave than in plain weave because of fewer interlacings.

If plain weave and twill weave are made with the same kind and number of yarns, the plain weave fabric will be stronger because it has more interlacings.

Pressing and Care

Prominent wales, shown in the cross-section view of gabardine, may easily be pressed

Fig. 5:27. Cross-sectional view of gabardine.

flat in use thus causing a very shiny surface, especially in dark colors. The ridges may also wear flat with the same result. If they have been flattened by pressure, steaming the fabric will raise them to remove the shine but if the ridges are worn off nothing can be done.

Classification of Twills

Filling-faced twills are not often made today. At one time they were widely used as lining fabrics. Some printed dress twills are made in this manner to obtain luster and softness and to give a smoother surface for printing.

Even-sided or *reversible* twills have the same amount of warp and filling yarns on both sides of the fabric. They are 2/2 twills and of all twill weaves they have the best balance.

Fig. 5:28. 2/2 reversible twill.

Better quality filling yarns must be used in these fabrics than with the warp-faced twill since the wear is on both the warp and the filling yarns. They are often called reversible twills because they look the same on both sides except for the direction of the twill line.

Warp-faced twills have a predominance of warp yarn on the right side of the cloth. Since warp yarns are made with higher twist, they are stronger and more resistant to abrasion; thus, warp-faced fabrics should be more durable than comparable filling-faced fabrics. They are widely used in utility garments.

Fig. 5:29. 2/1 warp-faced twill.

Twill Weave Fabrics

EVEN-SIDED TWILLS *

Fabric	Thread Count	Range in Yarn Size Warp	Filling
Serge	48 x 34 to 62 x 58	Vary with fiber content	
Flannel	56 x 30 to 86 x 52	Vary with fiber content	
Surah			

* See Glossary for other twill fabrics.

Serge, a 2/2 twill, is a smooth fabric in which the twill line is quite apparent. Cotton serge, of fine yarn, high count is often given a water-repellent finish and used for jackets, snow suits, and raincoats. Heavy yarn cotton serge is used for work pants.

Wool serge gets shiny from abrasion and repeated pressing but is not subject to flattening of the twill line as is gabardine. The luster comes from smoothness of yarns. Quality is determined by fiber, kind of yarn and count. Good quality serge is made from fine wool, 2-ply worsted yarns, and has a high thread count. Serge comes in various weights.

Twill flannel is similar to serge in construction but differs in appearance. Flannel has a napped surface which gives it a soft fuzzy texture. The filling yarns are larger, low twist yarns suitable for napping.

Some flannels are a 2/1 construction. Flannels may be either woolen or worsted. Worsted flannels, frequently used in tailored suits, are easy to press and will take and hold a sharp crease. They usually have less nap than woolen flannels and are less apt to show wear at the edges of sleeves and lapels and at the elbows. Low count flannels tend to get "baggy" in areas of strain because there are fewer points of contact between fibers in low twist yarns and the fibers tend to pull past one another.

Surah is a printed filament twill fabric of 2/2 construction which is used for dresses, linings, ties and scarves.

WARP-FACED TWILLS

Fabric	Thread Count	Range in Yarn Size Warp	Filling
Drill	60 x 36 to 80 x 48	12s–20s	10s–22s
Jean	84 x 56 to 100 x 64	21s–24s	24s–30s
Denim (work)	60 x 36 to 72 x 44	7s–16s	8s–23s
Gabardine	110 x 76 to 130 x 80	15s–39/2	15s–26s

Drill is a fairly heavy cotton fabric used for work clothing, uniforms, and ticking. It is piece dyed. It is also often used in the gray.

Jean is lighter in weight than drill. It is used for children's play clothes, draperies, slipcovers, and work shirts. Jean is not used for "blue jeans." Blue jeans, levis, dungarees, and overalls refer to the cut of the trousers. They are all made of denim.

Denim comes in two weights. Overall denim is made of heavier yarns than drill, usually blue yarns in the warp and natural yarns in the filling. Sports wear denim is similar to drill in weight and is used for sportswear, slipcovers, etc. It is always yarn dyed and may have stripes, plaids or appear to be a solid color.

Gabardine is a warp-faced twill with a very distinct steep twill line. It has a 60° angle or greater and always has many more warp threads than filling.

Cotton gabardine is made with 11, 13, or 15 harnesses. Long floats (over 5 or more picks) which make the diagonal line are combined with short floats between the sharp ridges. Cotton gabardine is used for slacks and shorts, wind repellent jackets, and raincoats.

Rayon and wool gabardines are sometimes made with a 3-harness arrangement in which the warp yarns are crowded closely together, giving a steep twill.

Satin Weave

Satin is the third basic weave that can be made on a regular loom. Long floats, in either the warp (Figure 5:30) or filling direction (Figure 5:31), predominate on the surface of the fabric. Note, in the checkerboard designs, that no two interlacing points are adjacent to each other. In regular satin weave, the points

of interlacing progress two or more to the right or left with each filling that is inserted. Satin weave fabrics are often woven face down since fewer harnesses (less weight) need be lifted. Figure 5:32 shows a four up, one down five-harness pattern used in satin fabrics.

Long floats have more luster than short floats. An eight-harness weave has one inter-

Fig. 5:30. Satin weave—warp floats.

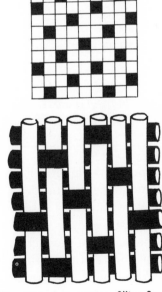

Fig. 5:31. Satin weave—filling floats.

Fig. 5:32(a). Satin-weave fabric. Low-count fabrics show a twill effect.

5 harness interlacing

Fig. 5:32(b). 4/1 satin weave.

lacing for every eight yarns (seven up, one down) and when used in damask is called *double* damask. Longer floats are less durable because of increased tendency to snag.

8 harness interlacing

Fig. 5:33. Satin weave, 8-harness interlacing.

Designs are usually achieved by a change in the direction of floats to make figures, stripes, or checks. (*See* page 153.) Satin fabrics are seldom printed; sateens often are.

Luster is the outstanding characteristic of satin weave fabrics. Fiber, yarn and long floats all contribute to the luster. Bright filament fibers of low twist give more luster. These are used in warp surface satins since filament fibers with low twist have adequate strength for use as warp yarns during weaving, whereas low twist spun yarns do not. Spun yarn floats are used in filling sateens since a lower twist spun yarn has enough strength for use in the filling. To increase the luster of spun yarn floats, a finish is usually needed. (*See* Schreinering on page 176.)

Few interlacings permit the yarns to be packed together to give a smooth, lustrous fabric with more softness and drape than the other basic weaves. No twill effect should be visible on the surface although in some low count fabrics a slight twill line is sometimes evident. Count is an important factor in quality.

Because of the few interlacings, the warp float fabrics have a high warp count and the filling float fabrics have a high filling count. These fabrics are unbalanced but the higher count compensates for the lack of balance. (*See* page 134.)

There is a definite *right* and *wrong* to the fabric. The long floats completely cover the surface, so crepe yarns can be used to give softness and drapability to satin fabrics, and inexpensive yarns can be used to reduce the cost.

Satin Weave Fabrics

Damask, a figured fabric made with satin warp and filling floats, is discussed on page 154.

SATIN

Fabric	Count	*Kind of Yarn* Warp	Filling
Crepe back satin	128 x 68	100 denier acetate	100 denier rayon crepe
Satin	200 x 64	100 denier rayon	100 denier rayon
Nylon satin	320 x 140		
Slipper satin	300 x 74	75 denier acetate	300 denier acetate

Satin is always made of filament yarns and is only made with warp floats. Most satins have a 4/1 interlacing but some slipper satins are made with longer floats, 7/1. Satin is made in many weights for use in dresses and linings. It is especially good for linings since a high count is possible which makes durable fabrics, and, because of the smoothness of the fabric, it slips on and off easily. Filling yarns may be crepe, regular or low twist to give differences in texture. Crepe filling yarns make a soft drapable fabric.

Quality in satin is important in linings particularly. The higher the count the better the quality and the more durable the fabric. Low count satins will pull out at the seams, rough up during wear, and the floats shift in position to make bubbly areas or wrinkled effects on the surface of the cloth.

Care should be directed toward maintenance of luster and prevention of distortion of floats. Wash or dry clean as determined by the fiber content and press on the wrong side or iron with the direction of the floats. Slippage of yarns occurs very easily in low count fabrics and the displaced yarns give the appearance of wrinkles in the fabric.

SATEEN

Fabric	Typical Thread Count	*Kind of Yarn* Warp	Filling
Filling sateen	60 x 104 carded	32s	38s
	84 x 136 carded	40s	50s
	96 x 180 combed	40s	60s
Warp sateen	84 x 64 carded	12s	11s
	160 x 96 carded	52s	44s

Filling sateen is a smooth, lustrous cotton fabric used for draperies and dress fabrics. It is usually made with carded yarns in a 1/4 interlacing. The warp count is always lower than the filling count. Yarns are similar in size to those used in print cloth but the filling yarns have a fairly low twist and are larger in size than the warp yarns. The luster is obtained by finish, since cotton fibers are low in luster and the satin floats alone will not give sufficient luster. Combed sateens are usually mercerized and Schreinered. Carded sateens are Schreinered only, because short fibers are used and the luster produced by mercerization would not justify the cost of the finish. Schreinering (*see* page 176) is a mechanical finish in which fine lines, visible only under a hand lens, are embossed on the fabric. Unless a resin is applied at the same time, the finish is only temporary.

Warp sateens are cotton fabrics made with warp floats in 4/1 interlacing. They usually have a "rounded" wale, twill effect. They are stronger and heavier than filling sateens because of the high warp count. They are less lustrous than filling sateen and are used where durability is more important than luster. Large amounts are used in tickings.

Chino is a lustrous warp sateen cotton fabric used for skirts, sportswear and home decoration.

Crepe Weave

Crepe weave (also called granite weave or momie weave) is made with floats of irregular lengths which give the cloth the appearance of being covered with minute spots or seeds.

Fabrics are as even sided as possible and the absence of long floats results in a firmer more tightly interlaced construction than either twill or satin.

Crepe weave fabrics are easier to press than true crepe because the fabric is not stretchy and the crinkled effect cannot be flattened out. They do not have the potential shrinkage of true crepes.

Crepe weave has been used with fabrics of acetate, nylon, or Dacron fiber content because these fibers do not lend themselves to true crepe techniques. Wool and cotton are also made with crepe weave construction because this gives the crepe effect with easier servicing, although cotton and wool can be made into true crepe.

Fig. 5:34. Yarn interlacing of crepe weave (momie or granite weave). Note the irregularity of the floats.

Rayon, which is very easily creped by true crepe techniques and which is less often used in the washable type crepe, is seldom used in crepe weave fabrics.

The names momie cloth, granite cloth, and sand crepe are applied to fabrics made with regular yarns and crepe weave.

Moss crepe is a combination of true crepe yarns and crepe weave. The fiber content is usually rayon and acetate. The yarns are ply yarns with one ply made of crepe-twist rayon. Regular yarns may be used in alternation with the ply yarns or they may be used in one direction while the ply yarns are used in the other direction. This fabric should be treated like a true crepe fabric.

CHARACTERISTICS OF CREPE FABRICS

*True Crepes Made of High Twist Yarns**	*Crepe Effects Made by Weave*
1. Permanent crinkle (will flatten during use)	Woven crinkle does not flatten
2. High potential shrinkage	Lower potential shrinkage
3. More drapability	
4. Resistant to raveling	Raveling is dependent on count and slipperiness of yarns
5. Resistant to wrinkling	Wrinkles do not show because of rougher surface
6. Resistant to seam slippage	
7. Stretchiness	
8. Dry cleaning preferable	Washable unless fiber requires dry cleaning

* See page 117.

Crepe Effect Fabrics

Cotton seersucker and cotton plissé are crepe effect fabrics which often are mistaken for each other.

Seersucker is made by slack-tension weave.

In slack-tension weaving, two warp beams are used. The yarns on one beam are held at regular tension while those on the other beam are at slack tension. As the reed beats the filling yarns in place, the slack yarns crinkle. The crinkle stripe may have slightly larger yarns or a different weave than the tight stripe. The fabric in Figure 5:35 has 2 x 1 basket weave in the crinkle stripe. The stripes are in the warp direction.

Seersucker can be identified by ravelling the warp yarns, which will be longer in the crinkle stripe than in the tight stripe. (*See* Fig. 5:35.)

Seersucker is usually heavier than plissé and is used for outer wear, while plissé is used mostly for lingerie.

Plissé is made by a mercerized finish.

Plissé is converted from lawn or print cloth by printing sodium hydroxide in the form of stripes or designs on the cloth. The caustic soda causes the fabric to shrink in the treated areas. Thus, there will be a difference in count in the crinkle stripe and the tight stripe. Notice in Figure 5:36 the defect which is due to an absence of caustic soda on the roller.

Plissé can be identified by pulling on the fabric. With little tension it becomes flat. In a printed or piece-dyed fabric the tight stripes will be darker in color because the caustic soda increases the dye absorbency of the cotton.

Plissé may sit out, but the crinkle is permanent and comes back after washing.

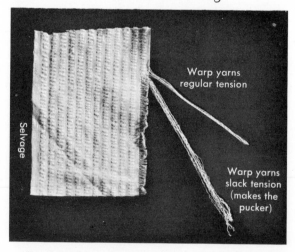

Fig. 5:35. Seersucker. Note difference in length of yarns in crinkled stripe.

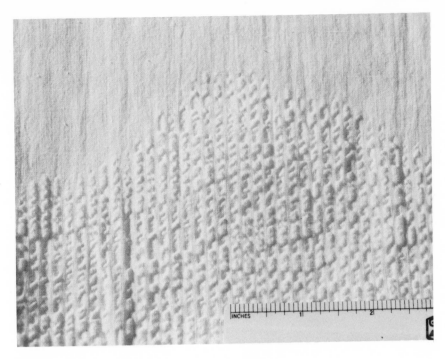

Fig. 5:36. Plissé.

Piqué or Cord Weave

This group of fabrics has a cord or wale produced by lengthwise woven areas held up as ridges by means of filling floats on the back of the fabric. The word *piqué* comes from the French word meaning "quilted," and the effect in this weave is similar to the raised effect in quilting.

The cords usually run in the warp direction. They vary in width from pinwale piqués (1/20 inch) to wide wale piqué (1/4 inch). The use of stuffer yarns laid under the ridge but not woven in with it emphasizes the quilted effect. Stuffer yarns are used in the better quality fabrics. Their presence or absence is one way of determining quality.

Piqués are made on a dobby loom. In wide wale piqué, 20 or more warp may be used in the face of the cord with two yarns woven in between each wale. In the six warp cord in Figure 5:37, two consecutive filling yarns float across the back of the odd numbered cords and are then woven in with the face of the even numbered cords. The next two consecutive filling yarns alternate with the first two by floating across the back of the even numbered cords and weaving into the face of the odd numbered cords.

Corded fabrics have a right and wrong side. These fabrics in general tear more easily in the lengthwise direction. If there are stuffer yarns, tearing the fabric crosswise is especially difficult. In wear, the floats holding the ridges and stuffer yarns wear out first.

Piqué fabrics tend to be more resistant to wrinkling than plain weave flat fabrics. They also have more body, and for this reason cotton piqués seldom need to be starched or resin

Fig. 5:37. Six-warp cord.

Fig. 5:38. Effect of wear on birdseye piqué. Wrong side of fabric at left, right side at right.

treated. Piqués should be ironed on the wrong side because the beauty of the fabric is in the cord or wale and pressing on the wrong side tends to flatten the wales less than top pressing.

Cord Fabric Descriptions

Fabrics in this group are Bedford cord, piqué, birdseye piqué, seersucker piqué, and novelty piqué.

Bedford cord is a heavy fabric with warp cords. It is used for upholstery, uniforms, riding habits, slacks. It is made with carded cotton yarns, woolen or worsted yarns, rayon or acetate, or combinations. The wales are wider than in piqué.

Piqué is lighter in weight than Bedford cord. Domestic piqués have warp wales. In cotton, the better quality fabrics are made with long staple combed mercerized yarns. Most of the piqué on the market today is made with carded yarns and without stuffer yarns. Piqués are unbalanced fabrics having more warp than filling yarns. Rayon piqués often have crepe filling yarns. These fabrics are true crepes in a piqué weave.

Birdseye piqué has a tiny diamond-shaped design formed by the wavy arrangement of the cords or wales. In this group of fabrics, birdseye piqué is the only one with filling cords. The birdseye design in diaper cloth looks similar, but it is made by satin type floats. Birdseye piqué has more body than warp piqué. Quality is determined by count of the cloth and fineness of yarns.

Some fabrics are called piqué but are not made with piqué or cord weave. These include: waffle piqué, embossed piqué, picolay, and dimity piqué. (*See* Glossary.)

Leno Weave

Leno comes from the French word *linon*, which means flax. At one time this weave was called gauze and derived its name from the French *Gazi*, meaning fine peculiar weave orig-

Fig. 5:39. Leno weave.

inating in Gaza, Asia. No doubt the lace-like fabric was originally made from linen yarns. Today, the term *gauze* refers to a low count plain weave fabric used for bandages, while *leno* refers to a particular weave.

Leno weave is used to make sheer, low count fabrics which have greater firmness and strength than other fabrics of the same low count. Each pair of warp yarns is crossed, one over the other, before the filling is inserted and this prevents slippage of the yarns.

Leno weave is made with a *doup attachment* which may be used on a plain or a dobby loom. This attachment consists of a doup needle, which is a thin hairpin-like element with an eye at its upper end. The doup needle is supported by two heddles. One of a pair of warp yarns, the doup end, is drawn through the doup needle and the other one of the pair, the ground end, is drawn between the heddles. Both yarns of a pair are drawn through the same dent in the reed.

During weaving, when one of the two heddles is raised, the doup end is drawn to the left. When the other heddle is raised, the doup end is drawn to the right. The ground end is always down.

Fabrics made in leno weave are *marquisette*, mosquito netting, bags for laundry, fruit and vegetables. Leno is combined with other weaves for novelty, open effects in dress goods and shirtings.

Marquisette is made of any fiber and is widely used for glass curtains. Dacron marquisette is one of the most popular fabrics for either tailored or ruffled curtains.

Thin, sheer marquisettes made of cellulose fibers are classed as flammable fabrics.

Care is determined by the fiber content.

Figured Fabrics

Figured fabrics are made by use of satin weave floats on any kind of background or extra yarns woven in as a design in the fabric.

Satin Weave Float Designs

Satin weave float designs are classified as small or large figures depending on the kind of loom used.

Small figures are made on a dobby loom which provides for 20 to 30 different arrangements of the warp yarns. This means that the figure must be complete with 20 to 30 filling yarns.

Small-figured fabrics can be called *madras*. It is one of the oldest staple cotton fabrics. Someone has said, "Textile terms are rooted in the history of the craft and wander in and out of common English usage in a disconcerting manner." Madras is one such term. Originating in Madras, India, the fabric was plain weave with stripes, cords, or small checks either white or colored. The imported *Indian madras*, today, is handwoven with white warp and colored filling "guaranteed to bleed." It is made with rather coarse yarns, about 12s. The patterns used are old traditional village patterns.

Madras gingham is a fine yarn gingham with stripes or small figures.

Shirting madras has a plain ground with cords, stripes, checks, and small figures made of satin floats.

Curtain madras is made with a leno weave and extra yarns which are woven in with long floats between designs. The floats are later sheared away.

Birdseye diaper has a characteristic diamond shaped pattern. This design was used originally in a costly white silk fabric for ecclesiastical vestments and later in France, made of linen, it was known as linge d'ypers from which the word diaper originated. Today the word diaper is used for the garment and birdseye refers to the weave.

Huckaback or *huck weave* gives a pebbly surface. The filling floats give absorbency. This weave is used primarily for towels.

Large figures are made on a Jacquard loom (*see* page 129) which controls each warp independently. For each arrangement of warp yarns, a card is punched. These cards are strung together and as they move over the loom the warp yarns are raised by rods. Those rods which go through the holes in the card raise the warp yarns attached to them and thus form the shed. Fabrics made on the Jacquard loom are damask, brocade and tapestry.

Damask is made with satin weave, of any kind of fiber and in many different weights. Linen damask is a variation of satin weave with filling floats in the design and warp floats in the background. Cotton damask is a variation of sateen with warp floats in the design and filling floats in the background. In single damask, floats cross over 4 yarns and in double damask floats cross over 7 yarns. Drapery or upholstery damask is usually made with colored yarns.

Damask is also used for dresses and suits. Low count damask is not durable because the long floats snag, rough-up or shift during use or care.

Brocade has satin floats on a plain or ribbed background. The floats are filling yarns of different colors than the background. Brocade is made of all fibers and in different weights. Unlike damask, it is not used for table linens.

Tapestry originally was an intricate hand-woven picture, usually a wall hanging which took years to complete.

The Jacquard tapestry which is mass produced today for upholstery use is a complicated structure consisting of two or more sets of warp and two or more sets of filling interlaced so that the face warp is never woven into the back of the cloth and the back filling does not show on the face. The back warp weaves into the back and when not on the face lies between the face and the back filling. This fabric is also called *brocatelle*.

Designs Made by Extra Yarns

Clipped spots, dots, or *designs* are made by using extra warp or filling yarns which interlace with some yarns and then float across the back of the fabric before interlacing with other yarns. When the fabric is finished the floats are cut and sheared off.

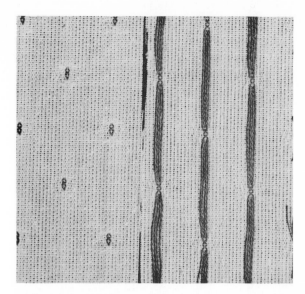

Fig. 5:40. Clipped-spot chambray made with extra warp yarns. From left to right: right side of fabric, fabric before clipping, and fabric after clipping.

Extra warp yarns are wound on a separate warp beam and threaded into separate heddles. Figure 5:40 is an unfinished fabric showing (1) fabric as it comes from the loom, (2) right side, (3) wrong side after clipping.

Extra filling yarns are inserted by different shuttles and are woven on a box loom which has a wire along the edge to hold the extra yarns so they need not be woven in the selvage. Figure 5:41 shows dotted swiss before and after clipping.

Fig. 5:41. Dotted swiss—extra filling yarns, before and after clipping.

Fig. 5:42. Dotted swiss, wrong side. Top to bottom: clipped dots, swivel dots, and paste dots.

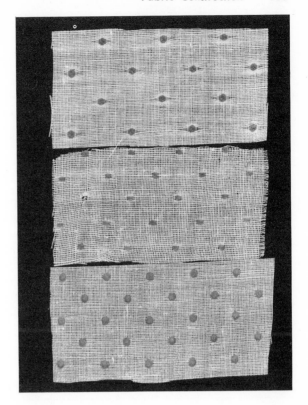

Fig. 5:43. Dotted swiss, right side. Top to bottom: clipped dots, swivel dots, and paste dots.

Swivel dots are made on a loom which has an attachment consisting of several shuttles. A spool of yarn is used for each shuttle. The fabric is woven face down to keep the shuttles and extra yarns above the ground fabric. Each extra yarn goes four times around the ground fabric and then the yarn is carried along the surface to the next spot where it is to be inserted. The yarn is sheared off between the dots. The cut ends are on the back of the fabric. These dots are often referred to as handtied but are really not tied—merely cut off.

Dotted swiss is made with either a clipped dot or a swivel dot on a sheer, crisp, cotton ground. The name is rather loosely used today to refer to any dotted fabric. Figures 5:42 and 5:43 show a clipped dot. Notice how the filling yarns are spread apart to provide room for the extra yarns. The same pictures show swivel loom dotted swiss, in which the extra threads are in the filling direction but do not spread

the ground yarns. Note also the paste dot, which is also called dotted swiss even though it is made by finish rather than by weave. Clipped spots pull out more readily than swivel dots; paste dots may stick to a hot iron. Paste dots or designs are often used on nylon or Dacron sheers which require little or no ironing.

Dotted fabric made on other backgrounds can be described by using the basic fabric name; i.e., dotted voile, clipped spot gingham or puff-dot marquisette.

Pile Fabrics

Pile fabrics are three-dimensional fabrics which have tufts or loops standing up from a basic cloth. The chart, page 156, lists five methods of making pile fabrics, characteristics, and uses.

Construction Technique	Uses	Characteristics	Identification
Knitted pile (Page 165)	Imitation furs Industrial polishing cloths	Fibers can make pile pliable Less expensive than weaving	On reverse side look for interlocking loops
Tufted or hooked pile	Rugs and carpets Bedspreads Chenille robes Blankets	Loosely twisted yarns punched into previously woven cloth High pile is possible Less expensive method of making carpeting	On reverse side look for straight rows of thick areas
Chenille yarns (Page 122)	Rugs and carpets Scatter rugs Upholstery fabrics Decorating yarns for fancy fabrics	Very deep, dense pile possible Luxury carpets, usually made to order Can be any size, shape, or color	Caterpillar-like yarn In fancy fabrics effect of pile clearer yarns is visible
Pile by finish (Page 187)	Flock designs on woven or knitted fabric	Short, compact; fabrics protruding from cloth	Fuzzy designs Rather stiff in design area
Woven pile	Dress weight and suiting weight fabrics Terry towels Rugs and carpets Ribbons Imitation furs	Very versatile	See discussion following

Pile Weave

Pile fabrics are three-dimensional fabrics made by weaving into the basic structure an extra set of warp or filling yarns to make loops or cut ends on the surface. (*See* Fig. 5:44.)

The cut-pile fabrics are brushed to untwist the yarns and loosen the fibers to give better cover to the fabric. Interesting designs are obtained by variation of pile height or by a combination of cut-pile and loop-pile.

Quality and durability are determined by thread count. The higher the count, the more dense the pile and the more durable the fabric. Wear comes on the pile yarns first, but a durable basic structure is necessary in order to have a satisfactory pile. Close weave increases the resistance of looped pile fabrics to snagging and of cut-pile fabrics to shedding and pulling out. A dense pile will stand erect, resist crushing, and give better cover. These characteristics are important in carpeting and sports fabric.

Pile fabrics are warmer than flat fabrics

Loop Pile

Cut Pile

Fig. 5:44. Pile fabrics.

because they entrap more body heat. If the pile is worn next to the body instead of on the outside, more heat is entrapped. Pile fabrics

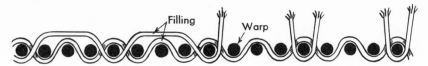
Fig. 5:46. Filling pile—floats are cut.

are absorbent when the proper fibers are used, because there is so much yarn on the surface. Terry toweling is made this way.

Care must be taken in washing and ironing to keep the pile erect. Cut-pile fabrics usually look better if dry cleaned, but they can be washed using techniques suited to the fiber content. All pile fabrics are softer and less wrinkled if tumble dried or line dried on a breezy day. Cut-pile fabrics should be pressed with a steam iron or with a damp cloth and dry iron, being careful not to put pressure on the iron. Flattening of the pile causes the fabric to appear lighter in color. A piece of pile fabric, such as crisp mohair upholstery, makes a good press cloth. Frequent brushing raises the pile of a fabric and also removes lint and dust.

Cutting and sewing pile fabrics require special consideration. Pile fabrics have an up and down. Garments should be cut so the pile is directed up. (See Fig. 5:45.) The fabric looks richer as one looks into the pile. However, it is not as important that the pile be directed up as that all pieces be cut with the pile going in the same direction. Otherwise, light is reflected differently, and it looks as if two differ-

ent colors were used in the garment. The direction of the pile can be determined by running the hand over the fabric.

Classification and Identification

Pile fabrics are classified by the set of yarns used to form the pile.

FILLING PILE FABRICS

Corduroy and velveteen are the only fabrics in this group. Filling pile fabrics are made with one set of warp and filling yarns and another set of filling yarns making the pile. Fabrics are woven with the extra yarns floating across the ground weave.

In corduroy the floats are arranged in lengthwise rows, while in velveteen they are scattered over the basic fabric.

Fig. 5:47. Corduroy gray goods, showing some of the floats cut.

The fabrics are cut by a separate machine consisting of guides which lift the individual floating yarns from the ground fabric and of

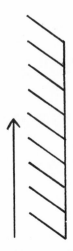
Fig. 5:45. Pile should be directed "up."

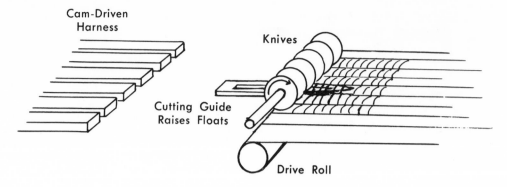

Fig. 5:48. Diagram of machine for cutting corduroy.

revolving knives which cut the floats. (*See* Fig. 5:48.) When the wales are wide enough, the guides and knives can be set to cut all floats in one operation. For pin-wale corduroy and velveteen, alternate rows are cut and the cloth must be run through the machine twice.

The fabrics are finished by scouring, brushing many times, singeing, and waxing. The back of both velveteen and corduroy is given a slight nap.

Both velveteen and corduroy are made with long staple combed, mercerized cotton used for the pile. In good quality fabrics, long staple cotton is used for the ground as well. The ground may be a twill or a plain weave. With a twill weave, it is possible to have a higher count and, therefore, a denser pile.

Corduroy can be recognized by lengthwise wales which vary from wide wale, 5-8 wales per inch, to pin wale, 16-21 wales per inch. Pin wale corduory has a shallower pile and is more pliable. It is warm, washable, durable, inexpensive, and requires no ironing.

Velveteen has more body and less drapability than velvet. The pile is not over ⅛ inch high.

WARP PILE FABRICS

Velvet	Fake fur
Velour	Terry cloth
Plush	Friezé

Warp pile fabrics are made with two sets of warp and one set of filling yarns, the extra set of warp yarns making the pile. Several techniques are used:

Double Cloth Method

Two fabrics are woven, one above the other, with the extra set of yarns interlacing with both fabrics. There are two sheds, one above the other, and two shuttles are thrown with each pick. The fabrics are cut apart while still on the loom by a traveling knife that passes back and forth across the breast beam. With this method of weaving, the depth of the pile is determined by the space between the two fabrics.

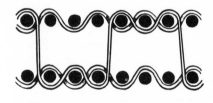

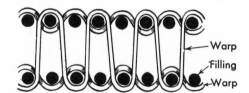

Fig. 5:49. Warp pile—double cloth method. W-interlacing above, V-interlacing below.

Slack Tension Method

The pile is formed by a special weaving arrangement in which three picks are put through and beaten up with one motion of

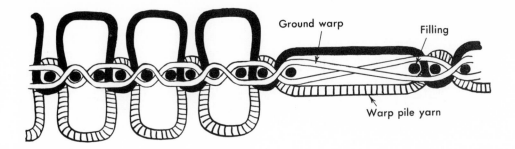

Fig. 5:50. Warp pile—slack tension method.

the reed. After the second pick in a set is inserted, there is a let-off motion which causes the threads on the warp-pile beam to slacken, while the threads on the ground pile beam are held at tension. The third pick is inserted and the reed moves forward all the way and all three picks are beaten up firmly into the fell of the cloth. (*See* Fig. 5:50.) These picks move along the ground warp and push the pile warp yarns into loops. The loops can be on one side only or on both sides. The height of the loops is determined by the distance the first two picks are left back from the fell of the cloth.

Terry cloth and some friezés are made by this method. Shag-bark gingham, which is a combination of plain weave with scattered loops, is also made like this.

Over Wires

A single cloth is woven with wires placed across the width of the loom over the ground warp and under the pile warp. Each wire has a knife edge which cuts all the yarns looped over it as it is withdrawn. Uncut pile can be made over wires without knives or over waste picks of filling yarns. The wires are removed before the cloth is off the loom, while the waste picks are removed after the fabric is off the loom. Frieze and mohair-pile plush are made in this way.

Fabrics

Velvet was originally made of silk and was a compact, heavy fabric. Today, velvet is made of rayon, nylon, or silk filaments with a pile ¹⁄₁₆

inch high or shorter. (*See* Glossary for types.)

Velvet is not wound on bolts as are other fabrics, but it is attached to hooks at the top and bottom of a special belt so there are no folds and creases in the fabric.

V*elour* is a cotton fabric used primarily for upholstery and draperies. It has a much deeper pile than velveteen and is heavier in weight.

Plush is a cut-pile fabric, may be cotton, wool, silk, or rayon. It has a deeper pile than velvet or velour, usually greater than ¼ inch. Plush is used for coats, capes, upholstery, and powder puffs.

Fur-like fabrics may be finished by curling, shearing, sculpturing, or printing to resemble different kinds of real fur.

Terry cloth is a highly absorbent cotton fabric used for bath towels, beach robes, and sports wear. Loops may be on both sides or on one side only. Fabric does not have an up and down.

Frieze, an uncut pile fabric, is an upholstery fabric usually made of mohair with a cotton back. Durability of frieze depends on the closeness of the weave.

WARP VS. FILLING

It is important to tell warp from filling when cutting out a garment, especially when the selvage has been removed from the fabric. Uncut pile has the extra or long loop yarns in the warp direction, so pulling one of the loop yarns will indicate warp direction.

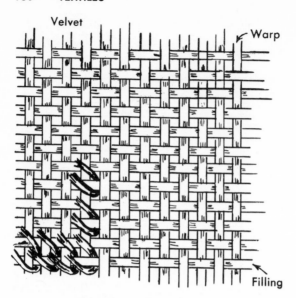

Fig. 5:51(a). Pile yarns in velvet.

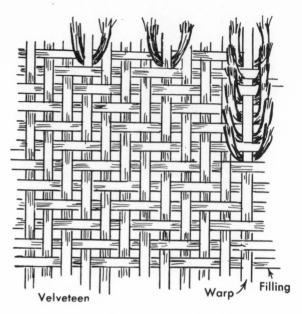

Fig. 5:51(b). Pile yarns in velveteen.

Velvet and velveteen, the hard-to-tell-apart fabrics, can be distinguished by fiber content, since velvet is usually made with filaments, and velveteen of cotton. To tell warp direction in these fabrics, ravel adjacent sides. In velvet the tufts will be interlaced with a filling yarn, in velveteen they will be interlaced with a warp yarn. (*See* Figs. 5:51a and b.)

Another way to tell warp direction is to bend the fabric. In velveteen the pile "breaks" into lengthwise rows, since the filling tufts are around the warp threads. In velvet the pile breaks in crosswise rows, since the warp tufts are around the ground filling yarns. This technique works best with medium to poor quality fabrics.

REFERENCES

1. Frishman, Daniel, "Pile Fabrics," *American Dyestuff Reporter*, 48:103 (Dec. 1959).
2. Herrnstadt, Gerald E., "New Trends in Pile Fabrics," *Modern Textiles Magazine*, 38:60 (Jan. 1957).

TUFTED FABRIC

Tufting is a process of making pile fabrics by punching extra yarns into an already woven fabric. The ground fabric ranges from thin cotton sheeting to heavy duck and the pile yarns can be of any fiber content. The weight of the ground fabric and the kind of yarns are determined by the end-use.

Tufting is a less costly method of making pile fabrics because it is an extremely fast process, does not require as much floor space for machinery and involves less labor and time to create new designs. One high speed tufting machine can insert the pile yarns in a fabric sixty times faster than a standard loom can weave a blanket. A tufted bed size blanket can be made in two minutes. A similar comparison can be made in carpeting. A tufting machine can produce approximately 645 square yards of carpeting per hour compared to an Axminster loom which can weave about 14 square yards per hour.

Tufting developed in the southeastern United States as a handcraft. It is said that the early settlers trimmed off wicks from their homemade candles and carefully worked them into bed spreads to create interesting textures and designs in otherwise drab covers. About 1900 a new interest in candlewick bedspreads developed and a needle was used to insert the thick yarn and to speed up the process. This grew into a cottage industry and many people depended on this handcraft for their income. Hooked rugs, made with yarn or rags, were also made by hand by the same process. In the 30's, machinery was developed to convert the hand technique to mass production using just a single needle and later multiple needle machines. Cotton rugs, bed spreads, and robes were produced in many patterns and colors at low cost. In 1950 the first room width carpeting was made; by 1960, 67% of the broadloom carpeting was made by tufting.

In 1960, Barwich Mills, Inc. started pilot plant operations on tufted blankets. This end-use combines pile construction with a napped finish. It has the advantage over traditional blanket fabric of maintaining a strong, firm ground fabric since the fibers are teasled from the pile yarns to create the nap. Also the thickness of the blanket is determined by the height of the pile rather than by the thickness of the yarn. If tufted blankets prove to be successful, there will be other end-uses explored, for example children's sleepers and coat linings.

Tufting is done by a series of needles, each carrying a yarn from a series of spools held in a creel. The backing fabric is held in a horizontal position, the needles all come down at once and go through the fabric a pre-determined distance much as a sewing machine needle goes through cloth. Under each needle is a hook which moves forward to hold the loop as the needle is retracted. For cut loop pile a knife is attached to the hook and it moves forward as the needles are retracted to cut the loop. The fabric moves forward at a pre-determined rate and the needles move downward again to form another row of tufts.

Variations in texture can be made by controlling the amount of yarn to each needle giving loops of different heights. Cut and uncut tufts can be combined. Tweedy textures are obtained by using two or more different colored plys in the tufting yarns. New techniques of dyeing have been developed to produce colored patterns or figures in which the color penetrates the tufts completely.

The tufts are held in place by the blooming (untwisting) of the yarn and by shrinkage of the ground fabric in finishing. In carpeting a latex coating is put on the back to help hold the tufts in place.

REFERENCES

1. "Tufting Gets a Blanket Order," *Textile Industries,* **125**:15 (Dec. 1961).
2. Ellis, Peter, "Machine Made Carpets," *CIBA Review* 1961/4.
3. American Carpet Institute, Inc., "Basic Facts About the Carpet and Rug Industry," New York: American Carpet Institute, 1961.

KNITTING

Knitting is a process by which needles are used to form one or more yarns into a series of interlocking loops. A knitting machine can make fabric two to five times as fast as a loom. Knit fabrics find wide use in hosiery, underwear, dress and blouse fabrics, sweaters, coatings, and gloves. Knit fabrics are very desirable because they do not wrinkle easily, shape to the body without binding, are elastic and porous, yet light and warm. Some garments can be knit into shape or "fashioned" and do not need to be cut and sewn.

Some of the advantages of knit fabrics may become disadvantages. The unstable shape of the knit stitches results in loss in shape and size in many cotton, wool, and rayon knit garments when they are laundered. Greater shrinkage occurs in knit garments dried in a dryer than occurs in air drying or in comparable woven fabrics dried in a dryer. Recent research has shown that shrinkage is due to the "geometry" of knit stitches rather than shortening of the yarns in the fabric. It has only been in the last few years that methods for controlling shrinkage in knit fabrics have been developed. (*See* page 192.)

Because knit fabrics shape to the body so easily, they sometimes tend to fit too snugly and it is difficult for large women to buy garments with adequate fullness.

Fig. 5:52. The two-bar high-speed warp knitting machine for tricot fabrics. (Courtesy of the Textile Machine Works.)

Knit fabrics are warm in still air, but must be covered by a wind-repellent outer layer to keep the body sufficiently warm on a windy day. On a warm, humid day knits may be too warm because they tend to fit snugly and keep warm air close to the body.

Knitted fabrics are in unprecedented demand today. In the last decade the output of knit fabrics and garments has increased more than 25 per cent. Knits are made from all fibers, including silk and linen. The synthetic fiber yarns, especially filament yarns, are easier to knit because they are more uniform. These knit fabrics can be heat-set to stabilize them. Knitting yarns have even less twist than filling yarns and must be very uniformly made in order to prevent the "rings" that cause thick and thin places in a knit fabric. Laminating knits to polyurethane foams has made it possible to use thin, and in same cases unevenly knit, jerseys for outerwear.

The two methods of knitting are warp-knitting and filling-knitting. These terms are borrowed from the weaving technique and refer to the way the loops are formed.

Warp Knits

Warp knits are machine knit from one or more sets of yarns placed side by side, as warp yarns are placed for weaving. Warp knit fabrics are usually knit flat. Warp knitting provides the fastest means of cloth fabrication. A modern warp knitting machine, knitting fabric 168 inches wide, can produce 1000 courses and 4,700,000 stitches per minute.

Warp knitting came into being about 1775 with the invention of the tricot machine or warp loom by Crane of England. This machine knitted fabrics 16 inches wide and was primarily used for silk stocking cloths. The development of this machine was unique in that there is no evidence that warp knitting was practiced as a hand technique. Figure 5:52 shows a modern tricot knitting machine. In 1880 Kayser established a warp knitting mill in the United States.

Warp knits are made on six different types of machines. Those most commonly used are Tricot, a machine employing a single needle bar with two guide bars for plain fabrics and two to four guide bars for patterned fabrics, and Raschel, a machine having one or two needle bars and up to 24 guide bars.

In warp knits the loops are all made simultaneously by interlooping individual warp yarns into the loops of adjacent warp yarns. The loops form vertical wales on the right side and horizontal wales or courses on the wrong side. (*See* Fig. 5:53.)

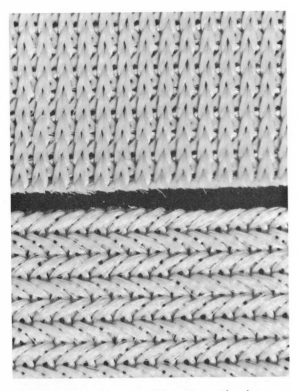

Fig. 5:53. Two-bar tricot fabric. Face side above, reverse side below.

Tricot (pronounced tree'ko) comes from the French word *tricoter* meaning to knit and is the name given to warp knit fabrics which are widely used in underwear, dress and blouse fabrics and in bed sheets. Tricot knits are stronger, less sheer and have less stretch than filling knits. They are either run or snag resistant or run proof.

Tricot jersey fabrics are knit 160 inches wide and cut into 40 inch widths for sale as yard goods or for use in ready-to-wear garments. Most tricot fabrics are made of filament yarns. Nylon jersey is heat-set to stabilize the fabric. If it is off-grain, it cannot be straightened because the yarns have been set and will not assume another position when they are wet.

Raschel knitting machines combine high productivity with extensive pattern designs. They knit anything from very fragile hair nets, tulles and veilings to coarse rugs and fur cloths. Elastic fabrics for foundation garments are made on Raschel machines.

One way in which warp knits are finished is by running the fabric through a Schreiner calender. The calender flattens the yarn bundles and reduces the openness of the stitches. Fabrics are smoother and look whiter. *Satinette* is one trade name for Schreinered nylon tricot. Nylon lace is also Schreinered to give better luster and appearance.

Filling Knits

Filling knits are made with only one yarn carried back and forth to make a flat fabric or are knit completely around to make a circular fabric. Filling knits are made both by hand and by machine, since only one yarn is used.

During the knitting process, stitches may be added or dropped to make a garment larger or smaller. This is called "fashioning." Openings may also be knit into the garment.

Filling knits can be made very sheer and they stretch and shape more easily than warp knits. If a stitch is broken they run or ladder.

There is no known date for the beginning of hand knitting but the first mechanical knitting frame was made in 1589. Queen Elizabeth I is supposed to have had the first pair of silk stockings knitted on this machine. See Figure 5:54 for a modern circular knitting frame.

Filling knit fabrics are usually plain knit or rib knit. A third stitch, or purl stitch, is used to make some imitations of hand knit gar-

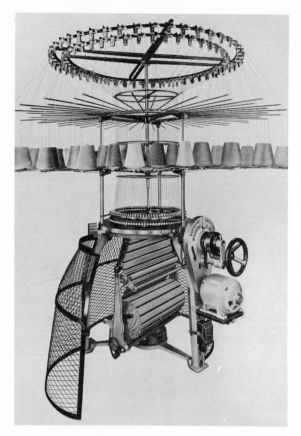

Fig. 5:54. Circular knitting machine for filling knits. (Courtesy of the Supreme Knitting Machine Co., Inc.)

ments for children and in combination with plain or rib knit in patterned fabrics.

Plain knit is one in which the loops are drawn to one side of the fabric. These knits have a definite right and wrong side with wales on the face side and courses on the reverse side. The face of the fabric has more sheen than the back. Plain knit is also called jersey stitch, named for the turtle neck sweaters originally worn by sailors from the Isle of Jersey. This stitch is used in knitting sweaters, yard goods in dress and suiting weights, sport shirts and hosiery.

Rib knit is made by drawing every other stitch to the face of the fabric. These fabrics look the same on the right and wrong side. Rib knits have more elasticity crosswise than plain knits and are therefore used as wrist and neck bands on sweaters. Rib stitch is also used in making bulky knits. It is seldom used in

yard goods for outer wear garments but is used in underwear fabrics. Rib stitch fabrics do not curl at the edges as do plain knits.

Purl stitch knits look the same on the face and the reverse side and look like the reverse side of jersey. This stitch is used to make sweaters, especially for infants and children, and booties. The fashion for bulky knits has increased the use of this stitch. Purl knits have excellent stretch both crosswise and lengthwise.

Fig. 5:55. Plain knit. Face side at left, reverse side at right.

Fig. 5:56. Rib knit.

Fig. 5:57. Purl knit.

Wool jersey is a circular filling knit fabric that does not run or ladder since the fuzziness of the wool yarns causes them to cling together. It may be slightly napped on one or both sides. It may be made with regular or novelty yarns. Wool jersey, which is made in tubular form, is seldom pressed at the factory with the wales parallel to the creases of the fabric, and the courses or crosswise ridges straight with the cut edge. Before cutting a garment from wool jersey, put a basting line or a line of pins along a wale to mark straight lengthwise grain, refold the cloth, and then straighten by steam pressing or wetting the fabric. A very small needle should be used in stitching.

Cotton jersey (stockinette) is a circular knit used for underwear, pajamas, T-shirts, and cotton sweaters.

Acrylic fiber jerseys are being used extensively in blends with wool or alone. The majority of the sweaters on the market are made from acrylic fibers. It is estimated that 50 per cent of American women own sweaters of Orlon and that 50 per cent of the men's and children's sweaters are made of Orlon.

High-Pile Knits. These fabrics are similar in appearance to woven pile fabrics. The knitted back makes the fabric more pliable with better draping characteristics. It has only been since 1955 that fabrics with a true fur-like appearance and texture have been available. They have the luxurious hand and dense face of the furs but are much lighter in weight and require no special storage. Until recently, special care in cleaning was necessary because the heat-sensitivity of the fibers caused shrinkage and fabric distortion when they were cleaned in the normal manner. By using a cold tumble dryer and combing the pile rather than steam pressing, the fabrics can be successfully dry cleaned.

High-pile knits are made from acrylic, modacrylic, or olefin fibers or blends or combinations of these fibers. The back is knit from fibers (Dynel) which will shrink during the finishing operation and make the pile surface more compact. There is a trend to use cotton for the back to reduce the cost of the fabric.

The background is knit with yarns but the pile is made from a *sliver*. Fibers from the sliver are picked up by the needles along with the ground yarn and are locked into place as the stitch is formed.

The steps used in finishing these fabrics are: (1) heat-setting, which shrinks the ground fabric and shrinks and expands the diameter of the individual face fibers, (2) tigaring—a brushing operation which removes surplus fiber from the face of the fabric, (3) shearing and (4) electrofying, a process which combs the fibers first in one direction and then in another by grooved heated cylinders which rotate at high speed. This process imparts high luster to the pile. The electrofying process may be repeated many times to develop the required finish.

Double knits are made with two sets of needles, creating firm fabrics that have more body and durability than single knits. They have the good characteristics of regular knits, and in addition do not "sit out," require no skirt lining, and can be hung on hangers. The most commonly used stitch is the double piqué stitch, which gives a subtle diamond-effect surface. The double piqué stitch is made on specially designed circular equipment and is most attractive in finer gauges. Other double-knit

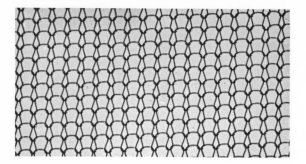

Fig. 5:58(a). Hosiery—60 gauge, 15 denier. (Courtesy of E. I. du Pont de Nemours & Company.)

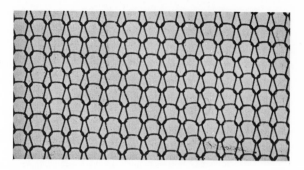

Fig. 5:58(b). Hosiery—51 gauge, 15 denier. (Courtesy of E. I. du Pont de Nemours & Company.)

stitches are used to make floral or geometric designs.

Hosiery

Hosiery is made with filling knit because it is very elastic, can be shaped, and can be made more sheer than warp knit. Two types of hose are full-fashioned and circular.

Full-fashioned hose are knit flat and are shaped by dropping stitches (fashion marks) so the hose is leg-shape. The foot is also shaped and there is always a true seam down the back and across the bottom of the foot. Full-fashioned hose also have a gap in the welt (double area at the top) because it is not possible to stitch the seam to the very end. This gap gives added stretch at the top of the stocking.

Circular knit hose are also called seamless or no-seam. To give shape to these hose, the ankle area is knit with smaller needles. It is possible to decrease the size of the knit stitch 100 times from the top to the ankle without changing the number of the stitches.

Prior to the use of nylon in hosiery, full-fashioned hose gave much better fit at the ankle and foot because the shape was knitted in. Nylon, which can be heat-set into a desired leg and foot shape, has made it possible to have good fit in circular knit hose. Many people prefer the circular knit because they are more comfortable in the foot and because one need not worry about keeping seams straight. Also the fashion for bare legs has had some influence. In 1958, 25 to 35 per cent of

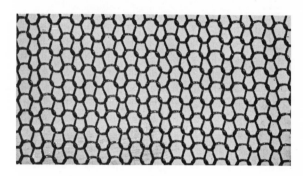

Fig. 5:58(c). Hosiery—45 gauge, 30 denier. (Courtesy of E. I. du Pont de Nemours & Company.)

women's fine quality hose were circular knit. For people with fleshy thighs, the full fashioned hose still are more comfortable because they tend to be larger at the top than do seamless hose of the same foot size.

The size of the knit stitch is referred to as *gauge*. It means the number of needles in 1½ inches of the needle bar across the machine.

The size of the stitch in circular knits is given as the number of needles in the circle of the knitting machine. The range is from 260 to 474. In 1949 the Federal Trade Commission permitted the use of the word *gauge* in descriptions of circular knit hose provided that the word is accompanied by the term *circular knit, seamless,* or *no-run.* Gauges range from 42 to 90. A 474 needle circular knit is comparable to 60 gauge. The higher the gauge number the smaller the knit stitch. (*See* Figs. 5:58a and b.) High-gauge gives more elasticity to the stocking and increases its resistance to snag-

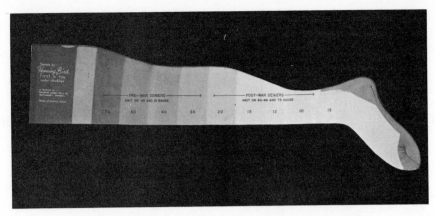

Fig. 5:59. Full-fashioned hose, showing different denier sizes.

ging. The most commonly used gauge is 51. (*See* Fig. 5:58b.)

Denier is the weight and thickness of the yarn. It ranges from 7 to 70. A 30-denier stocking is twice as durable as a 15-denier stocking. A 70-denier stocking is extremely heavy and durable while a 7-denier one is sheer and fragile. The nylon yarns used in hose are 7, 10, 12 and 15 denier monofilaments and 15, 20, 30, 40, 50 and 70 multifilaments.

In 1955 double and triple loop hose were introduced. These are not ply yarns but rather two or more monofilaments knitted as one. For example a 7-denier and a 10-denier yarn

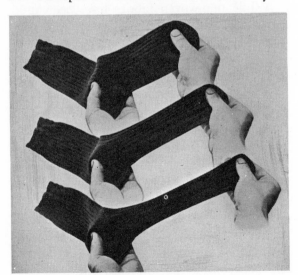

Fig. 5:60. Man's Helanca sock before and after stretching. (Courtesy of the Duplan Corporation.)

are knitted together on the same needle. The advantage of the multiple loop is that when snagged only one of the yarns may break.

Stretch yarns are widely used in hose as well as in men's and children's socks. Figure 5:60 shows a man's Helanca sock before and after stretching. Three sizes—small, medium and large—take the place of nine sizes needed with regular yarns.

No-run hosiery is made by two modified stitches, the "spiral-float stitch" and the "half-transfer stitch." These are complicated stitches based on the principle that when a thread is broken something in the stitch keeps a run from forming. Holes may develop, however.

REFERENCES

1. Peel, Robert, "The Warp Knitting Industry," *Canadian Textile Journal*, 78:47 (Jan. 1961).
2. Sands, George W., "The Drycleaning and Laundering of Textile Materials," *Canadian Textile Journal*, 78:47 (Jan. 1961).

FELT AND NON-WOVEN OR BONDED-FIBER FABRICS

Non-woven or bonded fabrics are any web or mat of fibers held together with a bonding material, or by the action of thermoplastic fibers mixed in with the fiber webs. Felts of

	Uses of Non-woven Fabrics		
Apparel	*Household*	*Surgical*	*Industrial*
Interfacings	Place mats	Masks	Food packaging
Shoe linings	Towels	Caps	Linings
Shoulder pads	Sheets	Aprons	Filters
Diaper linings	Pillow slips	Dental bibs	Laminated fabrics
Diapers	Mattress pads	Pads	
Falsies	Draperies	Sanitary napkins	
Petticoats			
Protective clothing			
Bibs			
Aprons			
Coveralls			
Smocks			

wool or part wool are non-woven, but they are not bonded. No yarns are used in either fabric.

True felt is a mat or web of wool or part wool fibers held together by the interlocking of the scales of the wool fibers. This interlocking process is known as felting and is explained in the section on wool properties, page 29. Felting is one of the oldest methods of making fabrics. Primitive peoples made felt by washing wool fleece, spreading it out while still wet, and beating it until it had matted and shrunk together in fabric-like form.

In the modern factory, layers of fiber webs are built up until the desired thickness is attained and then heat, soap, and vibration are used to mat the fibers together and to shrink or full the cloth, crowding the fibers into a smaller area. As the cloth shrinks, it becomes harder and stronger. The texture of the final product depends on the *fulling* or shrinkage time and the quality of the wool.

Finishing processes for felt resemble those for woven fabrics.

Felt has many industrial and some clothing uses. It is used industrially for padding, sound proofing, insulation, filtering, polishing, and wicking. The clothing uses are limited to loose-fitting garments, such as jackets and flared skirts because felt lacks the flexibility and elasticity of fabrics made from yarns. What would happen during wear to a tight-fitting felt skirt? Embroidered felt is currently being featured for dressy skirts and jackets. It is much more expensive than plain felt. Felt has wide use in such things as hats, house slippers, and clothing decorations. Felt does not fray so it needs no seam finish. This also makes it very desirable for decorations or pennants. Colored felt letters or decorations on white sports sweaters or other garments often fade in washing, so they should be removed or the garments should be sent to a dry cleaner who knows how to treat them.

While non-woven fabrics have been used primarily in disposable items, it is hoped that durable outer wear will be made which will be acceptable to the consumer.

Non-woven fabrics have a structure produced by the formation of permanent bonds where individual fibers touch each other.

Any kind of fiber can be used and the choice depends on the fiber properties, processing characteristics, cost, and end-use. Re-used and reprocessed fibers as well as new fibers of various lengths are used.

Fiber webs are made in two ways: oriented webs and random webs. Oriented webs are made on conventional carding equipment. The web comes from the card onto the conveyor apron. Several webs may be superimposed to obtain the desired thickness. They can have the fibers all going the same direction (lengthwise) or some webs may be laid at right angles to other webs. In the latter case, the fabric will have strength both lengthwise and crosswise, while in the former case, the strength will be lengthwise.

Random webs are made on special machines which operate by suspending the fibers in a rapidly moving airstream and carefully depositing them on a collecting screen. These webs have equal strength and elasticity in all directions.

Fibers in the web are held together in several ways:

1. Needle punching
2. Solvent bonding
3. Heating
4. Printing
5. Padding

Needle punching consists of passing a properly prepared web over a needle loom as many times as is necesary to produce the desired strength and texture. A needle loom consists of a board with barbed needles protruding two to three inches from the base. As the needle pushes through the web, the barbs catch a few fibers and cause them to interlock mechanically. Fabrics are finished as woven fabrics are —pressed, steamed, calendered, dyed or printed, brushed, napped or embossed. Fabrics made in this way are used mostly for outer wear and household fabrics.

Solvent bonding is done by applying a suitable solvent to gelatinize the fibers which are then bonded together by pressure.

Heat setting of thermoplastic fibers is done by passing the web through heated rollers. Du Pont has developed synthetic fibrous particles which they call "fibrids." These fibrids are $\frac{1}{16}$ to $\frac{1}{36}$ of an inch long and have twig-like projections, which hold the fibers in the web in place until they are fused together by heat. The name "textryl" has been given to interfacing fabric made in this way. A Dacron textryl has been used since 1959 in one line of men's wash-and-wear suit. In 1961, two blouse manufacturers started using textryl interfacings.

Printing a bonding substance on the web in the form of crosswise stripes, bars, or diamonds forms a discontinuous bonded web. These non-wovens have good drape and a fabric-like hand, but often have poor strength properties.

Padding is done by running the web through an impregnating bath and then through a padder to remove excess bonding emulsion to form a continuous bonded web. This technique is used primarily on thin or moderately thick webs. Flexibility of the fabric depends on the bonding agent used.

Over 200 products are used as bonding agents, ranging from starch, glue, and casein to thermoplastic and thermosetting resins.

Non-woven fabrics are cheaper than woven fabrics but lack their launderability, durability, and draping qualities. They are not as cheap as paper, but are competing with it in some uses since non-wovens have the advantage of more cloth-like appearance, higher wet strength, better drape, and less tendency to lint. Many non-wovens can be washed several times. Non-woven fabrics can be made in varying thicknesses and with different degrees of stiffness.

Fig. 5:61. Non-woven napkins and guest towel, bonded by printing crosswise stripes.

Sprayed Fibers

An interesting new development which is being investigated by the American Viscose Corporation is that of making fibers with a spray gun. They have tried many fiber solutions and have been most successful in forming lightweight webs from polystyrene. The solution is forced through the gun. It solidifies in an air stream in the form of fine fibers. The air stream floats the fibers to a collecting belt. The fibers vary in length and diameter due to pressure from the solution pump and the velocity of the compressed air. The force with which they are thrown on the collecting belt causes them to adhere together mechanically in a random web. These fabrics have good drapability and sufficient strength and resistance to abrasion. It is predicted that this technique might by-pass all conventional processes of making garments—spinning, weaving, sewing—and that a one-piece garment can be sprayed onto a rotating form.

REFERENCES

1. Nicely, D. C., "New Interest in Production of Needle Punched Fabrics," *Canadian Textile Journal*, **77**:46 (Sept. 1960).
2. Till, Derek E., "Sprayed Fibers," *Modern Textiles Magazine*, **40**:36 (Oct. 1959).
3. Howden, J. W., "Non-Wovens," *Textile Industries*, **125**:53 (Oct. 1961).
4. *Ibid.*, **125**:74 (Dec. 1961).
5. *Ibid.*, **126**:87 (Mar. 1962).

PLASTIC "FABRICS"

A fabric is a planar structure produced by interlacing yarns, fibers, or filaments. Technically, anything that is not made from fibers is *not* considered a fabric. We have materials on the market that are used for clothing and household purposes which are not made from fibers but are used as fabrics. They are the *plastic* films and they are sometimes spoken of as plastic fabrics.

Plastic "fabrics" are of two types: unsupported film and supported film. The supported film has a woven, bonded, or knit fabric backing. It is more expensive than the unsupported film but it has greater sewability and is less apt to tear along seams or where it is tacked to furniture.

Large quantities of unsupported film are used for draperies, place mats, and table coverings. Gift sets of plastic table cloths with matching rayon napkins are now on the market. Table coverings of plastic film have the disadvantage of shrinkage with heat. This usually occurs in areas where hot dishes have been placed. The result is a bumpy, unattractive cloth. Some clothing uses other than raincoats are plastic-coated fabric for baby panties and bibs. These may have either a woven or knit fabric base. The vinyl jackets shown in Figure 5:62 cost much less than leather and are very similar in appearance.

The use of plastic film for textiles has increased tremendously in recent years. It was recently reported that three out of five raincoats are plastic. The newest development is a plastic film that is perforated with thousands of tiny, almost microscopic holes. These holes

Fig. 5:62. Vinyl jackets. (Courtesy of the United States Rubber Company.)

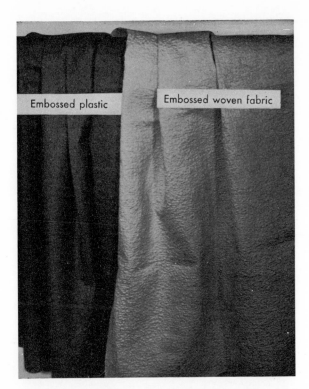

Fig. 5:63. Comparison of embossed plastic fabric and embossed woven fabric.

are too small to let the rain in but permit air to circulate. This eliminates the clamminess that comes from high humidity and lack of ventilation. Seat covers for chairs are also made with tiny holes to let the air escape as one sits down on the chair. This permeability will eliminate one of the chief drawbacks to clothing uses.

Another reason for increased use of plastic is improvement in the "hand" and appearance of the "fabrics." Notice in Figure 5:63 how much alike the two fabrics are. Not only are plastics becoming more like fabrics, but the glazed and embossed fabrics look and feel more like plastic.

Mylar film, a polyester of the Dacron family, has been used as a coating on leather shoes to give luster and greatly increased durability.

Most plastics are made of vinyl compounds, polyethylene, or Mylar, as mentioned above. Cellophane has some use as film cut into strips to make yarns for hats or decorative fabrics.

Plastics are made by the following methods:

a. Extruding a solution through wide, very narrow slits into warm air or a liquid hardening bath. This is very similar to the methods of making fibers.
b. Casting a solution on a large revolving drum where it dries and is then stripped off.
c. Calendering or pressing a moulding powder between hot rolls which exert tons of pressure and transform it into film.

The advantages of plastics are ease of maintenance, resistance to soil, good wrinkle recovery, high durability, waterproofness, and low cost. They can vary in thickness from very thin, transparent film to heavy leatherette.

In the following list are given some of the properties of plastics that have been or are being improved.

a. Flexibility—this is shown in the draping qualities of the plastic in the picture.
b. Permeability or porosity.
c. Texture and appearance—plastics are softer and more pleasant to the touch. Embossed surfaces give not only interesting design but a more fabric-like feel. Embossed design and use of color can simulate the appearance of any woven design.

The disadvantages that still require research are the unpleasant odor present in some of the vinyl plastics, stiffening at low temperatures, shrinking at high temperature, and cracking as a result of volatilization of the plasticizer. Many of the advances that have been made in the plastic field have come through research by food industries to improve food packaging films.

Lack of standards has previously been a problem in the plastic industries. New standards have been proposed to cover such things as thickness, shrinkage, defects, cracking, strength, volatility of plasticizer, and flammability. When these standards are put into use by the industry, buying plastics will be a much simpler problem for the consumer.

Plastic foam laminates are a new development in apparel interlinings. They were developed from the principle that insulating efficiency depends on dead air cells in linings, rather than on an inherent fiber property. The advantages of the foams are light weight, resiliency, resistance to matting or bunching in laundry or dry cleaning. A ⅜₂-inch, 3 oz. per square yard sheet of urethane foam has the same insulating value as a 14–16 oz. per square yard sheet of wool batting. Foams can be made to adhere to a lining fabric, to a coat or jacket shell, or they can be used as an interlining in the traditional manner. Three generalizations which will help people achieve professional results in sewing with foam laminated fabrics are:

1. Pick a simple pattern. Sewing is more difficult with foam laminates and the less detail in the pattern the better the results will be.
2. Sew with paper or seam tape between the presser foot and the foam. This is the best way to get an even seam.
3. Trim and flatten darts and facings to get smooth bulk-free results. Since the fabric won't ravel, it can be trimmed quite close. Flatten with pressing, stitching or gluing.

REFERENCE

Pinault, R. W., "Foam Laminates," *Textile World*, **111**:44 (Aug. 1961).

VI. FINISHES
AND FINISHING MATERIALS

A *finish* is defined as anything that is done to fiber, yarn or fabric either before or after weaving or knitting to change the appearance (what you see), the hand (what you feel), and the performance (what the fabric does).

The properties of a fiber can be completely changed by a finish and pieces of the same cloth can be finished so they bear little resemblance to each other.

Fabrics have always been finished. Early finishing was done to improve the appearance and hand only. Natural dyes applied by laborious hand processes were used to color fabrics. To make sleazy fabric into salable merchandise, china clay and starch were added to fill up the spaces between the yarns. Various mechanical finishes were applied to make fabrics smoother, more lustrous and better looking. These finishes were temporary and were lost during the first washing.

Two important durable finishes, which have been used for over 50 years are *mercerization* and *tin weighting* of silk. The uses of mercerization have increased while weighting of silk has almost ceased.

The arts and techniques of finishing have developed to the extent that the finish is as important and in some cases more important that the fiber content.

The consumer needs to recognize visible finishes and to recognize the *need* for non-visible finishes. She needs to know how good the finish is in terms of serviceability. Is the finish permanent, durable, temporary, and if temporary is it renewable?

A *permanent* or *durable finish* is one which lasts the life of the garment.

Durable also refers to a finish that lasts longer than a temporary finish but while still present in the fabric may be unsatisfactory in appearance. A *temporary* finish lasts until the garment is washed or drycleaned.

A *renewable* finish is one which can be applied by the homemaker with no special equipment, or it may be applied by the drycleaner.

Finishing may be done in the mill where the fabric is constructed or it may be done in a separate establishment by a highly specialized group called *converters*. Most mills, especially cotton weaving mills, are not equipped to do finishing. Converters operate in two ways: they perform a service for a mill by finishing goods to order, in which case they are paid for their services and never own the fabric; or they buy the fabric from a mill, finish it according to their own needs, and sell it to the cutting trade or as yard goods under their own trade name.

In 1960 there were over 1800 finishing plants, 50 per cent of these were located in the Southeastern U.S. Seventy-eight per cent of the fabric finished was of cotton.

All fabric finishing adds to the cost of the fabric. Since it is relatively easy to prepare man-made fiber fabrics for finishing, these plants have lower costs.

When a finish is new and in demand the converter can realize a greater profit. The wash-and-wear finish is an illustration of this.

The chart gives a price comparison of an 80 square percale from gray goods to retail store.

80 Square Percale Type Fabric

Gray goods	$0.22
Plain finish converter	.29
Plain finish retail	.50 +
Wash-and-wear converter	.35
Wash-and-wear	1.50 + (retail 1955)
Wash-and-wear	.75 + (retail 1960)

Many factory finishing processes are similar to operations done in the home. In the study of this unit, observe these similarities.

Gray goods (grey, greige, or loom state)
are fabrics, regardless of color, which have been woven on a loom and have received no wet or dry finishing operations. Gray goods fabrics have gray goods names such as print cloth, soft-filled sheeting, and so forth, which are used only for the gray goods. Other gray goods names such as lawn, broadcloth, and sateen, are also used for the finished cloth.

Mill finished fabrics are those which can be sold and used without converting although they may be sized or Sanforized before they are sold.

Converted or finished goods are those which have received wet or dry finishing treatments such as bleaching, dyeing, or embossing. Some converted goods retain the gray goods name while others, such as madras gingham, are named for the place of origin, and still others, such as silence cloth, are named for the end-use. See Figure 6:1 for some of the fabrics that can be converted from a single gray goods.

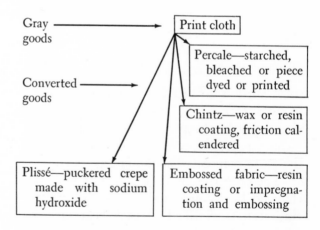

Fig. 6:1. Fabrics converted from print cloth gray goods.

All gray goods must be cleaned and made ready for the acceptance of the finish. Gray goods contain a warp sizing which makes the fabric stiff and interferes with the absorption of liquids. This must be removed before further finishing can be done. Also, fabrics are often soiled during weaving and must be cleaned for that reason.

Initial Fabric Cleaning

DESIZING

Desizing is the process of removing the sizing on the warp yarns. A desizing substance, sulfuric acid or an enzyme, solubilizes the starch which is then completely removed by washing.

Degumming or boil-off are terms used to describe the desizing of silk. Silk is woven "in the gum" with the sericin forming the protective covering for the silk filaments. Boiling-off consists of washing in a caustic solution. Boil-off is also used as a desizing operation for the man-made fibers.

WASHING

Washing removes the sizing, dirt and oil spots.

Kier boiling of cotton in an alkaline solution, sometimes combined with bleaching is done in a pressure kier which resembles a large pressure cooker. (*See* Fig. 6:2.) The boil is

Fig. 6:2. Cotton fabric being placed in pressure kier. (Courtesy of Coats & Clark, Inc., New York, N.Y.)

done from 2 to 14 hours depending on the type of goods, results desired, and the strength of the alkaline solution. After boiling, cold water is pumped in and the goods are rinsed until cool.

Scouring of wool fabric is necessary to remove warp sizing, oils used in spinning, and dirt or grease acquired in weaving. Heavy and medium weight woolens are washed as a continuous rope of cloth in a continuous piece washer. Lightweight fabrics and clear finished worsteds (those in which the weave shows clearly) are washed full width in a broad washer. These fabrics are liable to crease when washed in rope form.

SINGEING

Singeing is the burning of free projecting fiber ends from the surface of the cloth. These protruding ends cause roughness, dullness, pilling, and interfere with finishing.

Singeing is the first finishing operation for all smooth finished cotton fabrics and for clear finished wool fabrics.

Fabrics containing heat-sensitive fibers such as Dacron/cotton blends are often singed after dyeing because the little melted balls on the ends of the fibers may cause unevenness in the color. Singeing is one of the best remedies for the problem of pilling.

Singeing is usually done by a gas-flame singer. The fabric is first run open width over a heated roll to dry it and is then run at high speed through a gas flame and into a water bath to extinguish any sparks. The water bath may contain the desizing agent.

Finishing Operations

When the fabrics are cleaned and ready for further finishing, the order of application and the kind of finish applied varies with the fiber content of the fabric.

In the discussion that follows, finishes are grouped together as

Mechanical: finishes which cause a physical change only.

Additive: finishes in which a compound or substance is held mechanically on the fiber or fabric.

Chemical: finishes in which a chemical reaction causes a permanent change in the fiber.

MECHANICAL FINISHES

Calendering

Calendering is a mechanical finishing operation performed by a "stack" of rollers through which the cloth passes. There are several types: namely, the simple calender, the friction calender, the moiré calender, the Schreiner calender and the embossing calender. Each produces a different finish.

Most calender machines have three rollers. (Others have 2, 5, or 7.) Hard metal rollers alternate with softer cloth wrapped rollers or with solid paper rollers. Two metal rollers never run against each other. The different calender machines and the finishes they produce are discussed below.

The *simple calender* corresponds to the household ironer and gives a smooth ironed finish to the fabric. The cloth is slightly damp before it enters the calender. The metal roll is heated. The cloth travels through the calender at the surface speed of the rollers so the rollers simply exert pressure to smooth out the wrinkles and give a slight sheen.

The *friction calender* is used to give a highly glazed surface to the cloth. If the fabric is first saturated with starch and waxes, the finish is only temporary, but if the resin finishes are used, the glaze will be durable.

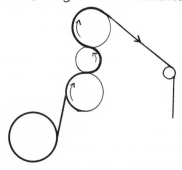

Fig. 6:3. Calender machine.

The cloth is first passed through the finishing solution and then dried to a certain degree of dryness. It is then threaded into the calender. The speed of the metal roller is greater than the speed of the cloth and the roller polishes the surface just as the sliding motion of the hand iron polishes fabric. If the metal roll is hot, a higher glaze is obtained.

The *moiré calender* has been used for more than 200 years to produce a "water-marked" design on ribbed silk and wool fabrics. When acetate came on the market it was possible to have a permanent moiré pattern.

True moiré is applied to ribbed fabrics such as taffeta and faille. The rib is essential in producing the pattern since the rolls of the calender are smooth. An embossed moiré design is made on a calender with an engraved roll.

True moiré is made by placing two layers of ribbed fabric, one on top of the other, so the ribs of the top layer are slightly "off-grain" in relation to the under layer. The two layers are stitched or held together along the selvage and are then fed into the smooth, heated, metal roll calender. Pressure of 8 to 10 tons causes the rib pattern of the top layer to be pressed into the bottom layer and vice-versa. Flattened areas in the ribs reflect more light and create a contrast to unflattened areas. This procedure can be modified to produce patterned moiré designs other than the water-marked one.

The *Schreiner calender* has a metal roller engraved with 200 to 300 fine diagonal lines which are visible only under a hand lens. (The lines should not be confused with yarn twist.) Until the advent of the resins and the thermoplastic fibers, this finish was a temporary one and was removed by the first washing. The primary purpose of this finish is to produce a *deep-seated luster*, rather than a shine, by breaking up reflectance of light rays. It also *flattens* the yarns to reduce the openness between them, and give *smoothness* and *cover*.

It can upgrade a sleazy material. This finish was originally used with cotton sateen and

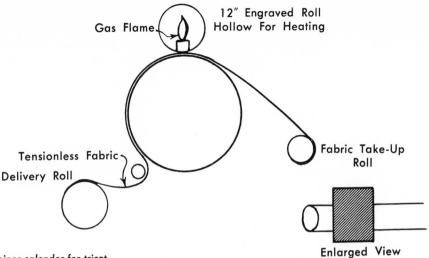

Fig. 6:4. Schreiner calender for tricot.

table damask to make them more lustrous and more saleable. It was later used on polished resinated cottons and sateens as a durable finish. In 1957 it was first used to produce the *Satinette* finish on nylon and Dacron tricot jersey. It has upgraded tricot and aroused increased interest in its use for the following reasons: the Satinette finish is permanent in laundry, thin fabrics are more opaque, smoothness gives a better base for printing color on the fabric. There is less tendency for tricot garments to sag at the hemline.

The diagram in Figure 6:4 shows a Schreiner calender for tricot fabrics. In order to avoid stretching the knit construction, the fabric is delivered to the calender in a tensionless state.

The *embossing calender* produces either flat or raised designs on the fabric. Embossing became a much more important finish after the heat-sensitive fibers were developed because it was possible to produce a durable, washable, embossed pattern. Nylon, Orlon, acetate, polyesters and fabrics made of nylon and metallic yarns are used. If the fabrics are made of solution dyed fibers, they can be embossed directly off the loom and are then ready for sale. Embossed satins are used in high style garments and can be sold for a much higher price than the unembossed fabric.

The embossing calender consists of two rolls, one of which is a hollow engraved metal roll heated from the inside by a gas flame. The other is a solid paper roll exactly twice the size of the engraved roll.

The process differs for the production of flat and raised designs.

Flat designs are the simplest to produce. A copper roll, engraved in deep relief, revolves against a smooth paper roll. (*See* Fig. 6:5.) The hot engraved areas of the roll produce a glazed pattern on the fabric. Embossed brocades are an example of this type of design.

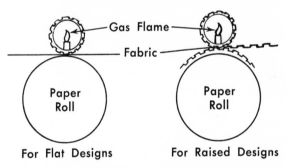

Fig. 6:5. Embossing rolls.

Raised or *relief* designs require a more complicated routine. The paper roll is soaked in water and then revolved against the steel engraved roll (without fabric) until the pattern of engraving is pressed into the paper roll. (*See* Fig. 6:5.) The temperature is adjusted to suit the fabric which is then passed between the rolls.

Pleating

Pleating is really a variation of embossing. It is an ancient art which dates back to the Egyptians who used hot stones to make the pleats. Colonial women in the United States used heavy pleating irons to press in fancy pleats and fluting.

Today, pleating methods are highly specialized operations done by either the paper pattern technique or by the machine process.

The *paper pattern method* is a hand process and therefore more costly but it produces a wider variety of pleated designs. Garments in partly completed condition, such as hemmed skirt panels, are placed in a pleated paper pattern mold. The fabric is placed in the paper mold by hand and another pattern mold is placed on top so the fabric is pleated in between the two pleating papers. The whole thing is rolled into a cone shape, sealed and put in a large curing oven for heat-setting.

The *machine pleating method* is less expensive. The machine has two heated rolls. The fabric is inserted between the rolls as high precision blades put the pleats in place. A paper backing is used under the pleated fabric and the pleats are held in place by paper tape. After leaving the heated roll machine the pleats are *set* in an aging unit.

Durability of pleats differs in the eyes of the producer and the consumer. If the pleat line is still evident after wear or washing, the producer considers this permanent and satisfactory. The consumer, however, is interested in having the pleats hang perfectly flat as if they had just been pressed.

The heat-sensitive fibers, especially nylon, take permanent pleats. Chemicals can be added to cotton and wool to make them hold durable pleats. Figure 6:6 shows a wash-and-wear Orlon/wool pleated skirt during and after washing with no ironing.

Individuals who perspire freely or have moist skin will find it difficult to keep pleats in a sharply-pressed condition.

REFERENCES

1. Richardson, Graham M., "Schreiner Calendering of Nylon Tricot," *Modern Textiles Magazine*, **38**:72 (Mar. 1957).
2. "How Newburg Produces Moiré Finishes," *Textile World*, **107**:131 (Sept. 1957).
3. "Embossing Upgrades Thermoplastic Fabrics," *Textile World*, **108**:76 (Aug. 1958).

Beetling

Beetling is a finish that is used on linen and a few fabrics resembling linen. As the cloth revolves slowly over a huge wooden drum, it is pounded with wooden block hammers. This pounding may continue for a period of 30 to 60 hours. It flattens the yarns and makes the weave appear less open than it really is. The increased surface area gives more luster, greater absorbency, and smoothness to the fabric. Beetled fabrics are softer than unbeetled fabrics. The effect of beetling disappears somewhat in laundering but is usually restored by ironing. Not all linen fabrics are beetled. Table linens and dress linens of the typical linen-look are always beetled.

Decatizing (Decating)

Decatizing produces a smooth, wrinkle free and lofty hand on woolen and worsted fabrics and on blends of wool and man-made fibers. The process is comparable to steam ironing.

The dry cloth is wound under tension on a perforated cylinder. Steam is forced through

Fig. 6:6. Washing Orlon/wool blend skirt.

the fabric. The moisture and heat cause the wool to become plastic and tensions relax and wrinkles are removed. The yarns become set in the shape of the weave and are fixed in this position by the cooling-off which is done with cold air. For a more permanent set, dry decating is done in a pressure boiler.

Wet decating often precedes napping or other face finishes to remove wrinkles that have been acquired in scouring. Wet decating as a final finish gives a more permanent set to the yarns than does dry decating.

A high degree of luster can be developed by the decating process because of the smoothness of the surface.

Tentering

Tentering, one of the final finishing operations, performs the double process of *straightening* and *drying* fabrics. If the fabric is started into the tenter frame in a crooked position it will be dried in an "off-grain" shape. This means that the crosswise grain or threads are on the diagonal or pulled into a curved shape rather than being at right angles to the yarns in the lengthwise direction. If the finish has been starch or gelatin, this "off-grain" condition is a temporary one because the consumer can straighten the fabric. If, however, the finish was a wash-and-wear or a heat-set one, the fabric is *set* in this crooked condition and cannot be straightened.

The use of a variable speed-drive mechanism on the tenter frame will control the speed of the two sides of the tenter and keep the filling yarns at right angles to the lengthwise yarns. This device may be a hand controlled one or it may be one controlled by an electronic eye. These straightening devices are called "weft straighteners."

Tenter machines are similar to a curtain stretcher in principle. They are of two types; the pin tenter and the clip tenter. The diagram, Figure 6:7, shows a pin tenter and dryer. The pin device on the sides moves around like a caterpillar tractor wheel. The clip tenter operates in the same way except that the fabric is gripped by a series of clips. More tension can be exerted by the clip tenter but it may also damage some fabrics, in which case the pin tenter is used.

The marks of the pins or the clips are often evident along the selvage. Thin fabrics are often made with heavy selvages to strengthen them for tentering and other finishing operations.

Loop Dryer

Fabrics with a soft finish, towels, and stretchy fabrics such as knits are not dried on the tenter frame but are dried on a loop dryer, where the drying can be done without tension. Many rayon fabrics are dried on loop dryers.

Napping and Napped Fabrics (A Face Finish)

Napping was originally a hand operation in which the napper tied together several teasels (dried thistle-like vegetable burs, Figure 6:11) and swept them, with a plucking motion, across the surface of the cloth to raise the fibers from the ground weave. The teasels had a gentle action and the barbs broke off before causing any damage to the cloth.

The raised fibers formed a *nap* on the surface that completely changed the appearance and texture. *Thus napped fabrics are literally "made" by the finishing process.* Figure 6:8 shows a fabric as it looks before and after napping.

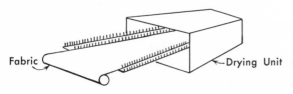

Fig. 6:7. Tenter.

Fig. 6:8. Napped fabric before and after napping.

Teasels are still used in the machine finishing of fine wool fabrics such as duvetyn. For machine processing (gigging) they are mounted on rollers and as the barbs wear off or break off, the worn teasels are replaced by new ones. The fabric may be either wet or dry.

Most napping is now done by rollers covered by a heavy fabric in which bent wires are embedded. (See Fig. 6:9.)

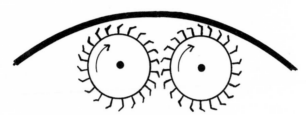

Fig. 6:9. Napping rolls. Counter-pile roll on left, pile roll on the right.

Napping machines may be either single action or double action.

Fewer rollers are used in the single action machine. They are all alike and travel at the same speed. They are called pile-rolls and the bent ends of the wires point in the direction in which the cloth travels but the rollers rotate in the opposite direction. These rollers are all mounted on a large drum or cylinder which rotates in the same direction as the cloth. The pile-rolls must travel faster than the cloth in order to do any napping.

In the double action napping machine every other roll is a counter-pile roll. This roll has wires which point in the direction opposite to those of the pile-roll. The counter-pile roll must travel slower than the cloth in order to produce a nap. When the speed of the rolls is reversed (pile-rolls at slower speed and counter-pile rolls at faster speed) a "tucking" action occurs. Tucking pushes the raised fibers back into the cloth and makes a smooth surface. Reasons for napping:

1. *Warmth*. A napped surface and the soft twist of the filling yarns increase the dead air space. Still air is one of the best insulators.

2. *Softness*. This characteristic is especially important in baby clothes.
3. *Beauty*. Napping adds much to fabric attractiveness.
4. *Water and stain repellence*. Fiber ends on the surface cut down on the rapidity with which the fabric gets wet.

Quality, Characteristics, and Care

The amount of nap does not indicate the quality of the fabric. The amount may vary from the slight fuzz of Viyella flannel to the very thick nap of imitation fur. Short compact nap on a fabric with firm yarns and a closely woven ground will give the best wear. Stick a pin in the nap and lift the fabric. A good durable nap will hold the weight of the fabric. Hold the fabric up to the light and examine it. Press the nap aside and examine the ground weave. A napped surface may be used to cover defects or a sleazy construction. Rub the fabric between the fingers and then shake it to see if short fibers drop out. Thick nap may contain flock (very short wool fibers). Rub the surface of the nap to see if it is loose and will rub up in little balls (pilling). Notice the extreme pilling on the sweater in Figure 6:10.

Fig. 6:10. Pilling on a wool sweater.

Some napped fabrics have an up and down. To test this, brush the surface of the fabric. Brushing against the nap roughs it up and causes it to look darker because more light is absorbed. This is the "up" direction of the fabric. When the nap is smoothed down, the reflection of light from the surface gives a lighter shade of color. Napped fabrics should be made with the nap "down" so garments will be easier to brush. However, the direction of the nap is not as important as the fact that the same direction of nap is used in all parts of a garment.

Low count fabrics usually have low twist yarns and when strain is applied the fibers slip past one another and do not return to their original position. Thus garments tend to "bag" in the seat and elbow areas. Tightly twisted yarns are more resistant to bagging. It is best to line low count napped fabrics or to make the garment with gored or flared skirts.

Wear on the edges of sleeves, collars, buttonholes, and so forth, causes an unsightly contrast to unworn areas. Very little can be done to it except that a vigorous brushing will give a fuzzier appearance. *Price is no indication of resistance to wear*, since the more expensive wool fibers are finer and less resistant to abrasion. Wear will flatten the nap but if nap is still present on the fabric it can be raised by brushing or steaming. Loosely napped fabrics will shed short fibers on other garments or surfaces. They also shed lint in the wash water so should be washed separately or after other articles are washed. Napped fabrics are fluffier if dried on a breezy day or dried in a dryer.

Construction

Napped fabrics must be made from especially constructed gray goods in which the filling yarns are made of *low twist* staple (not filament) fibers. Turn back to page 115 and reread the information about yarn twist. The difference in yarn structure makes it easy to identify the lengthwise and crosswise grain of the fabric. Figure 6:11 shows the warp and filling yarns from a camel's hair coat fabric, before and after napping.

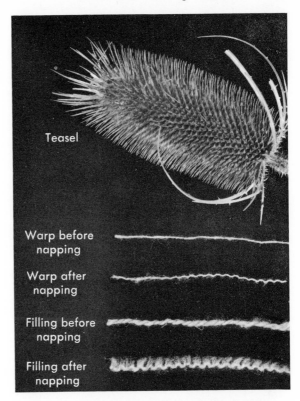

Fig. 6:11. A teasel; yarns before and after napping.

Fabrics can be napped on either or both sides. The nap may have an upright position or it may be "laid down" or "brushed." When a heavy nap is raised on the surface, the yarns are sometimes weakened. Wool fabrics are fulled or shrunk to bring the yarns closer together and increase fabric strength.

Yarns of either long or short staple fibers may be used in napped fabrics. Worsted flannels, for example, are made of long staple wool. The short staple fiber yarns used in woolen flannels have more fiber ends per inch, and thus can have a heavier nap. In blankets, which are heavily napped for maximum fluffiness, a fine cotton (core) ply is sometimes used in the yarn to give strength.

Although napped fabrics can be made of any staple fiber, they are most frequently made of cotton, rayon, wool, or the acrylic fibers. Pilling and attraction of lint due to electrostatic properties are problems with the nylons and polyesters.

Napped fabrics may be plain weave, twill weave, or knit. More filling yarn is exposed on the surface in a 2/2 twill or a filling faced twill, therefore a heavier nap can be raised on twill fabrics. The knit construction in napped fabrics is often used for articles for the baby. Some brands of coats are always made of napped knit fabrics.

Napping is less expensive than pile weave as a way of producing a three-dimensional fabric.

Napped Fabrics

Wool		Rayon	Cotton
Flannel	Suede*	Rayon	Flannelette
Fleece	Duvetyn*	flannel	Duvetyn*
Broadcloth*	Kasha *	Brushed	Suede*
Melton*	Chinchilla*	rayon*	Outing
Kersey*	Zibiline*	Suede*	flannel
			Canton
			flannel*

* See Glossary for fabric descriptions.

The name flannel is almost synonymous with the word napped. When the name is used alone it implies wool fiber content. If the fabric is made of fiber other than wool, a descriptive adjective is used with the word *flannel*—for example, *cotton* flannel.

Flannel is an all-wool napped fabric made in dress, suit, or coat weights. It may be made with either worsted or woolen yarns. They may be yarn-dyed.

Worsted flannels are important in men's suits and coats and are used to a lesser extent in women's suits and coats. They are firmly woven and have a very short nap. They wear well, are easy to press, and hold a press well.

Woolen flannels are fuzzier, less firmly woven fabrics. Many have been given a shrinkage control treatment which alters the scale structure of the fiber. Because this causes some weakening of the fabric, 15 to 20 per cent nylon is blended with the wool to improve the strength. These fabrics do not take or hold sharp creases so are best when used in less tailored garments.

Fleece is a coat-weight fabric with long brushed nap or a short clipped nap. Quality is very difficult to determine.

Cotton flannels flatten under pressure and give less insulating value than wool because cotton fibers are less resilient. The fibers are also shorter, thus there is more shedding of lint from cotton flannels. The direction of nap (up and down) is relatively unimportant in these fabrics because in many, the nap is very short, and also because their chief uses are robes, nightwear, baby clothes, and sweat shirts.

Flannelette is a plain-weave fabric which is converted from a gray-goods fabric called soft-filled sheeting. It is napped on one side only, has a short nap and a printed design, unless it is white. The nap will form small pills and is subject to abrasion. Suede and duvetyn are also converted from the same gray-goods but are sheared close to the ground to make a smooth, flat surface. Duvetyn is the lighter weight of the two.

Outing flannel is a yarn-dyed fabric (or white) which is similar in fabric weight and length of nap to flannelette but is napped on both sides.

As the warp yarns in both fabrics are standard weaving yarns, it is easy to identify the grain of the fabric.

Rayon flannel is widely used in dresses and suits. It is similar in appearance to worsted flannel but is much less expensive. It is usually a blend of rayon and acetate.

NAPPED FABRICS—BLANKETS
(Tufted Blankets Page 161)

Blankets are a specialized end-use group of fabrics which are used primarily for warmth. The maximum amount of nap is desired since the effectiveness of the blanket depends on the amount of dead air space it has.

With the modern heated house and the electric blanket now in use, fewer blankets are needed than were needed years ago. There is also a trend toward the use of the thinner "sheet" blanket.

Fiber content is an important factor in the selection of the blanket because fibers differ in their ability to maintain dead air spaces. Other fiber properties are also important considerations.

Wool has been widely used because of its excellent springiness. Mohair is even fluffier but is more expensive and seldom on the market in this country. Wool is the most expensive of the commonly used fibers. Its nonflammability is of value since many fires are started by people who fall asleep while smoking in bed. Its drawbacks, other than price, are: it shrinks easily and becomes boardy when shrunk, and it is also subject to moth damage and must be stored in sealed containers with a sprinkling of moth crystals.

Cotton and rayon are low cost but lack the resiliency necessary to keep the blanket fluffy. Cotton, however, is very washable so is a good choice if frequent washing or sterilization is necessary.

Acrylics and modacrylics excel in softness, light weight and bulk. They are washable, and not subject to moth damage. The acrylics, however, burn like cotton. Good quality acrylic blankets are comparable to wool in price.

Blends containing wool are just as subject to moth damage as are 100 per cent wool blankets.

Olefins are the lightest weight and low in cost.

Construction

The warp yarn twist is usually low in blanket fabrics and some of the nap comes from the warp yarn. See the chart for a typical Orlon blanket construction.[1]

Loom count 36 ends 41 picks
3 x 1 double woven
Warp Z-twist, 12.5 t.p.i.
   Type 42 2½-inch staple
Filling Z-twist, 7 t.p.i.
   Type 39 Orlon

[1] Houser, K. D., and Bidgood, L., Jr., "How to Finish Orlon Blankets," *Modern Textiles Magazine*, **38**:50 (Nov. 1957).

Fig. 6:12. Double-faced blanket construction.

Fig. 6:13. Blanket of single-cloth construction in twill weave.

The Type 39 Orlon filling yarn is a blend of staple lengths ranging from 1¼ to 3 inches and with deniers of 2 to 6.

A double woven blanket construction is shown in Figure 6:12. Single-cloth construction in either a plain or twill weave is shown in Figure 6:13. As mentioned previously, yarns in highly napped fabrics may be made with a cotton core for strength.

Care

Most blankets can be washed. Wool blankets must be washed in warm water with as little agitation as possible to prevent shrinkage.

Electric blankets should not be dry cleaned because of damage to the insulation of the

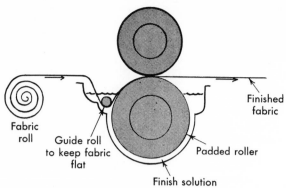

Fig. 6:14. Padding machine.

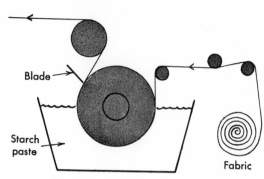

Fig. 6:15. Backfilling machine.

wiring. Be sure to read the directions that come with the blanket.

In order to reduce the frequency with which a blanket must be cleaned, protect it by turning down a length of the end of the sheet over the upper part of the blanket.

Shearing

Shearing is a finishing process done by a machine similar to a lawn mower. Gray-goods fabrics are sheared to remove loose fiber or yarn ends, knots, etc.

Napped and pile fabrics are sheared to control the length of the pile or nap surface and to create design or smooth surface. *Sculptured* effects are made by flattening portions of the pile with an engraved roller and then shearing off the areas that are still erect. Steaming the fabric raises the flattened portions.

Straightline designs in either the warp or filling direction or diagonally on the cloth are made by lifting the cutter blade at regular predetermined intervals.

Brushing

Brushing follows shearing to clean the surface of clear face fabrics. For pile and napped fabrics, when combined with steaming, it will lay the nap or pile in one direction and fix it in that position thus giving the "up-and-down" direction of pile and nap fabrics.

Inspecting

Fabrics are inspected by pulling or running them over an inverted frame in good light.

Broken threads are clipped off, snagged threads are worked back into the cloth, and defects are marked so adjustment can be made when fabrics are sold. The fabric is then wound on bolts or cylinders ready for shipment.

ADDITIVE FINISHES

The pad machine, often called the "work horse" of the textile industry, is used to apply both chemical and additive finishes. It will apply them in either liquid or paste form, on one or both sides, by immersion or by transfer from a roller which revolves in the finishing solution. A simple pad machine is shown in Figure 6:14.

Padding is done by passing the fabric through the finishing solution, under a guide roll and between two padding rolls. The rolls are of metal or rubber depending on the finish to be applied. The rolls exert tons of pressure on the fabric to squeeze the finish into the fiber or fabric in order to assure good penetration. Excess liquid is squeezed off. The fabric then travels on into the steaming and/or washing and/or drying machine.

The backfilling machine is a variation of the pad machine. It applies the finish to one side only, usually to the wrong side of the fabric. The fabric is held tightly against the large roll which revolves in the finishing paste and a blade scrapes off the excess. This finish is used to make inexpensive fabrics look more expensive and is only as permanent as the type of finish and process permit.

ADDITIVE FINISHING MATERIALS

Additive finishes are applied to give texture (body, stiffness, softness), luster, embossed designs, abrasion resistance, etc. to the fabric. They are held on the surface mechanically and their permanence depends on the efficiency of the finish and the type of finish itself.

Sizings

Sizings (also called dressings) are used to give body, stiffness, strength, weight, and/or smoothness to the fabric. Warp yarn sizing is discussed on page 174.

The chart lists the commonly used sizings.

Sizings

Starch (temporary)
Gelatin (temporary)
Softeners (temporary)

Resins (durable)
Cellulose solutions (durable)

Starching at the mill is similar to starching at home except that the starch mixture contains waxes, oils, glycerine and similar compounds which act as softeners. For added weight, talc, clay, and chalk are used. Starches come from wheat, corn, potatoes, sago, and other plants. Each starch has individual properties which determine its use.

Gelatin is used on the rayons because it is a clear substance that does not detract from the natural luster of the fibers. Instead, it enhances it. Many rayon fabrics are sold in the loom state and the gelatin is removed by washing. It can be restored by a home process:

Dissolve 2 tablespoons of gelatin in 1 gallon of water. Rinse the garment in the solution and remove excess liquid to prevent its draining to the lower edge and stiffening it.

Cellulose solutions are dissolved cellulose similar to the solution from which rayon fibers are spun; carboxy methyl cellulose is one that is commonly used. They have in the past been used for a durable finish on table linens. They are also used for warp sizings.

Rubber (latex) has been used for years as a waterproof coating on rainwear and more recently as a warp yarn coating for denim fabrics to increase their abrasion resistance. It is also used as a coating for the back of tufted carpets and rugs to hold the tufts in place and for non-slip purposes, and as a binder to hold flock or pigment colors to a fabric surface.

The thermoplastic resins are used as durable coatings and sizings for man-made yarns and fabrics. They give abrasion resistance, slippage control, body, snag resistance and are also used as adhesives and water-proofings. They are available at the store as *plastic starches*.[2]

The thermosetting resins, urea and melamine formaldehyde, were first used as surface coatings in 1940, when a process was developed for polymerizing them on the surface of the fabric. The fabric is kept under tension to cause the solution to migrate to the surface where it is dried, polished, embossed, and cured. (*See* Fig. 6:16.) These resins are held to the surface by a *chemico-mechanical* action.

Glazed effects produced by this means are of two kinds: Glazed chintz is often a plain color but may be printed. It has a heavy, rubbery layer of resin on the surface. Polished cotton is similar but has a much thinner layer of resin on the surface and is much more apt to wrinkle during washing.

Embossed designs are similar to the glazed fabrics except that an engraved roller presses a raised pattern into the cloth.

Resin on the surface   Resin on the surface only
and on the yarns

Fig. 6:16 (Left). Continuous resin coating.
Fig. 6:17 (Right). Discontinuous resin coating.

If these fabrics have the resin applied as a continuous coating, they are uncomfortable for summer wear because they prevent the passage of moisture vapor. (*See* Fig. 6:16.) If

[2] Trade names, Permastarch and Plastastarch.

Thermoplastic Resins	*Thermosetting Resins*
Also used as raw materials for fibers	Never used to make fibers
Soften when heated	Set or shaped by heat
Rubbery in texture	Less rubbery; stiffen fabric more
Chemically reacted to make the polymer before application	Applied as monometers and polymers on the fabric as the finish is cured
Simple process (similar to applying nail polish)	More complex process; chemical reaction occurs during heating

Thermoplastic process:

Resin dissolved in solvent
↓
Padded on fabric
↓
Solvent evaporates

Thermosetting process:

Water solution of monometer resin
↓
Padded on fabric
↓
Dried, polished, embossed, etc.
↓
Cured in hot oven

Kinds:
  Latex rubber
  Cellulose acetate
  Nylons
  Polyesters
  Polyvinyls
  Acrylic esters
  Polyolefins

Kinds:
  Urea formaldehyde polymers
  Melamine formaldehyde polymers (monometers used for the cross-linked crease resistant finishes)

they are applied as a discontinuous coating the fabric can "breathe" and is more comfortable. (*See* Fig. 6:17.)

Resins are large molecules (polymers) which cannot penetrate the fiber except in monomer form. The accompanying chart lists the resins and gives a comparison of the two groups. There is no hard and fast line between these two groups, as illustrated by the fact that rubber, a natural thermoplastic resin, can be changed into a thermosetting resin by the process of vulcanization. Because the thermosetting resins are monomers when they are applied, they can be made to penetrate the fiber. This is discussed with wash-and-wear finishes on page 189.

Some of the glazed chintz finishes have been very satisfactory. The embossed finishes and the thermoplastic coatings (nylon stiff petticoats, for example) have varied with the quality of the finish and its application. The use of the commercial "plastic starches" is

Fig. 6:18. Laundry wrinkles in an embossed cotton shirt.

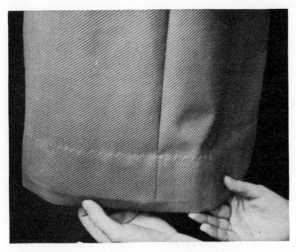

Fig. 6:19. Hemline crease that would not press out.

helpful in some cases in restoring the appearance. These fabrics are difficult to press so that seams are flat and creases come out. Pressing while quite moist gives best results. The pictures illustrate some of the problems. (*See* Figs. 6:18 and 6:19.)

Flocking

Flock are very short fibers which are attached to the surface of the fabric by an adhesive to make a pile-like design or fabric.

Flock may be made of cotton, rayon, or wool fibers. Rayon is best because it is cheaper, and the fibers are straight and can be cut to uniform lengths. Also, because there is no crimp in the rayon fiber, it can be cut square at the ends and will anchor more firmly in the adhesive. (*See* Fig. 6:20.) The adhesive is a latex that is dissolved in a solvent which evaporates.

There are two basic methods of applying the flock—vibration and electrostatic forces. In both methods the adhesive is applied first as a coating or by an engraved roller or by screen printing.

The vibration method can be used to apply to one or both sides of the cloth. The flock is sifted down and the vibration of the cloth causes a static charge to build up. This static orients the flock vertically. (*See* Fig. 6:21.)

For flock on both sides, the fabric enters a flocking chamber where flock is showered on it, top and bottom. The fabric is vibrated, and static orients the flock vertically.

The electrostatic method is similar except that the cloth is passed through an electrostatic field to orient the flock on the fabric.

This method is superior as it gives a thicker flock. Rayon fiber also gives thicker flock than wool or cotton.

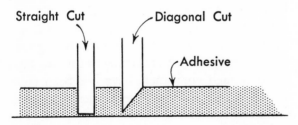

Fig. 6:20. Flock with square-cut ends anchored more firmly.

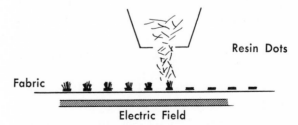

Fig. 6:21. Flock is oriented vertically by electric charge.

SPECIAL FINISHES

Wash-and-Wear and Easy-Care Finishes

The National Cotton Council has adopted the name "Easy-Care" for fabrics that are crease resistant during wear and for fabrics that are crease resistant during wear, washing, and drying.

"A wash-and-wear fabric is one that can be made into a garment that will satisfactorily retain its original neat appearance after repeated washings and wear with occasional or no ironing." [3]

Although wash-and-wear has a narrower meaning, in the following discussion the two terms are used interchangeably.

Easy-care of apparel and household textiles is extremely important for several reasons:

(1)   Larger families with more young children mean many clothes to be cared for.

(2)   Informal living means more sports wear and casual type clothing.

(3)   Efficient laundry equipment is in most homes.

Textile people are still telling consumers to "hand wash and drip dry" most treated cottons and synthetics, but this is not realistic. Most consumers pay little attention to the labels. In fact, unless the label is sewed in, most consumers forget which label goes with which garment. Everything goes into the automatic washer and dryer!

Dr. Genevieve Smith of Sears Testing Laboratory reported that from 1500 questionnaires sent to homemakers, 38 per cent of the housewives put cotton and synthetics in the same wash load and only 50 per cent laundered fine fabrics by hand; 88 per cent used liquid bleach, 41 per cent of whom used it regularly.

(4)   More women work outside the home.

(5)   More homemakers do all their own work.

These factors do not seem to be temporary, but to be setting the pattern for the future, so there should be more, rather than less, demand for "easy-care" clothing.

Easy-care fabrics can be produced by: use of 100 per cent synthetic fibers, proper fabric and yarn construction, chemical finishes, or combinations of the above.

History

The first finishes were developed in Great Britain in the late 1930's. Urea formaldehyde was used on linen and rayon to give resistance to wear wrinkles. Rayon has low washability, and the resin finishes gave poor wet abrasion resistance, so their use on rayons was limited to dry cleanable fabrics.

In 1940, melamine formaldehyde was used on cottons, and crease resistant cottons developed in volume and importance.

Nylon was the first wash-and-wear fiber. The acrylics appeared in 1950, Dacron in 1953.

By 1954, Dacron/cotton blends were being used. Washable durable pleats, washable men's suits—all were promoted from the "easy-care" angle (even men could wash out their own underwear and shirts).

This concept had such an effect that consumers today want wash-and-wear in all fabric including cotton. Wash-and-wear cottons are possible with improved finishes. In 1950, cyclic ureas were used; in 1958, cellulose reactants were found to have performance superior to the older finishes. In 1960, derivatives of divinyl sulfone were developed.

At first, the manufacturers of cotton fabric were skeptical of the new finishes and wanted to iron out all of the problems before they attempted large scale production. They found that untreated fabrics did not sell. Wash-and-wear cottons were first introduced in 1955, and by 1960 two thirds of all broad-woven goods (4 billion yards) were being resin finished. Even though consumers have not been completely satisfied with these fabrics, they continue to buy them.

Finishing Materials (Resins and Finishes)

Fabrics wrinkle if they have crisp finishes, if there are many interlacings per square inch,

[3] Press, J. J., ed., *Man-Made Textiles Encyclopedia*, New York: Textile Book Publishers, 1959.

Resin and Reactant	Advantages	Disadvantages
Urea formaldehyde	Good light fastness Fair wash fastness Low cost	High chlorine retention High chlorine damage Moderate fishy odor Not satisfactory for cotton
Melamine formaldehyde	Good wash fastness Fair light fastness	Chlorine retention high to low Tendency to yellow
Cyclic urea	Soft hand Very good wash fastness Chlorine resistant Does not yellow Good to poor light fastness	Finish "loosened up" during laundry Sour or repeated washing
Aldehydes	Excellent wash fastness Fair light fastness No fishy odor No chlorine retention	Reduces strength

if the yarns are fine and of medium to high twist, and if the molecules can be deformed readily. More wrinkling occurs when fabrics are moist or wet than when dry.

Fibers vary in wet and dry wrinkle resistance. Synthetic fibers are hydrophobic. The polyesters have molecular chains that resist deformation; other synthetics have fair to good resistance to deformation.

The protein fibers have good resiliency when dry, but they wrinkle when wet, and therefore have good crease resistance, but poor wash-and-wear properties.

The cellulose fibers have poor resistance either wet or dry. The principle of crease resistant finishes for cellulose and of "wash-and-wear" finishes for cellulose and protein fibers is based on prevention of the swelling of the fibers and/or prevention of intermolecular slippage.

The finishing agents vary, but in all cases, the molecules must be small enough to penetrate the fiber. There are two theories on how the chemicals work:

(1) The deposition theory is that the monomers form polymers inside the fiber. This exerts slippage-hindering effects through hydrogen bonding with the hydroxyl groups of the cellulose. These resins formed inside the fiber also reduce the absorbency of the fiber.

(2) The cross-linking theory, which is the commonly accepted one today, is that the treating agent forms cross-links between the adjacent cellulose chains and, thus, decreases intermolecular slippage.

Because the deposition theory assumed that a substance was polymerized in the fabric, the finish was called a resin finish, as were the surface coatings described earlier. For this reason, the term "resin finish" will, no doubt, be used in the literature to cover resins, resin formers, and reactants, until some generic name is agreed upon.

The accompanying table lists some of the resins used, with their advantages and disadvantages.

Fig. 6:22 (Left). Resin located near the fiber surface.
Fig. 6:23 (Right). Thorough penetration of fiber.

A wash-and-wear finish usually contains more than the resin former or reactant. Some of the following substances are mixed with the thermosetting resin or reactant: a catalyst, a thermoplastic polymer, polyvinyl alcohol, silicone emulsion softener, optical bleach, and other substances to give a better hand.

Application of Finish

The finishing solution is forced into the fabric by the pad machine. The fabric is dried ½ inch wider than the final cloth width, and is then cured at high temperature, at which time the reactant cross-links with the cellulose. It is then washed, dried, tentered, and Sanforized.

The *location* of the resin in the fiber can be controlled just as the location of dye in a fiber can be controlled. Figure 6:22 shows the resin located near the outer surface of the fiber, and Figure 6:23 shows thorough penetration. Difference in penetration gives a difference in properties. Thorough penetration of a fiber would make it more crease resistant than incomplete penetration.

The *amount* of resin used should be enough to give satisfactory performance, but not too much to change the hand of the fabric. The fabric will have 4 to 5 per cent increase in weight.

Durability of the finish is somewhat dependent on the conditions it must undergo in cleaning. Alkaline washing, chlorine bleaching, and acid souring are factors in commercial laundering that weaken the finish. Durability also depends on the finish itself. A good finish costs 5½ to 6 cents per yard, while a poor finish costs 2½ cents per yard.

The finish can be applied by the dry cleaner. There are about 34,000 drycleaning plants in the country, all of them equipped with boilers, presses, hot boxes, and other equipment suited to the application of wash-and-wear finishes.

Problems Arising from Easy-Care Finishes

Some of the factors related to the serviceability of resin treated fabrics are discussed below.

Durability of the resin is important, no matter what the end-use. In general the aldehydes have the best wash fastness. The cyclic ureas are better than the older urea and melamine formaldehyde resins, but some of them are affected by the acid sours used in commercial laundries. Resins which form many cross-linkages are better. Usually, the more resin used the more durable the finish.

Strength loss is one of the most important aspects of resin finishes. A reduction in strength of 25 per cent is an inherent part of the process. If the fabric is stiffened, there is even greater loss in tear strength. The marked improvement in creaseproofing, however, may make it worth while.

Decrease in strength is *not* due to chemical tendering of the cloth since stripping of the resin will restore the tensile strength to its original value.

Strength loss is due to change in the mechanical properties of the fibers. If the finish forms many short rigid cross-links, the fiber will lose elasticity and will break more readily when stretched. If there is a surface deposit, strength will be low because fibers and yarns have lost elasticity.

When an acid catalyst is used with the finish, tendering results. Fabric construction can be adjusted somewhat to compensate for this loss. Research has shown that strength is better in weaves with *long floats* such as sateens, or with *basket weaves* such as Oxford. Slightly coarser filling yarns improve the tear strength of broadcloth. Balancing the weave-crimp in warp and filling yarns is helpful.

Wear resulting from lack of abrasion resistance is usually shown first in the edges of cuffs, pockets and in the roll of the collar.

Chlorine Damage

Chlorine bleaches will cause yellowing and tendering of the cellulose. The nitrogen groups (NH) pick up the chlorine and hang on to it during rinsing and dry storage. The heat of ironing releases the chlorine in the form of hydrochloric acid (HCL) and the acid weakens the fabric causing strength loss. If there is no hot ironing there is no damage. Rinsing with an antichlor, such as sodium thiosulfate, will remove the chlorine. The amount of chlorine retained need not be high to cause damage. More chlorine is retained with urea formaldehyde than with melamine. In the cyclic ureas, the amine groups are not free to pick up chlorine (*see* chart on page 189), and the aldehydes do not contain nitrogen, thus they are non-chlorine retentive.

Odors

The fishy amine odor is produced during the curing step and is held in the fabric as an amine salt. When articles are stored or when clothing is worn during hot, humid weather, the amines combine with the moisture and a fish odor results. The odor is due to the formation of free formaldehyde.

Sewing Problems

Resin treated fabrics create problems for the home sewer. Fabrics can seldom be straightened if they are "off-grain." In plaid gingham, this makes matching impossible. It is difficult to ease-in excess fabric. Creases will not lie flat. Collars and cuffs must be edge stitched if a flat effect is desired. Pin marks show, and if machine stitching must be ripped, the needle holes show and the fabric may tear easily.

Summary of Wash-and-Wear Fabrics

Satisfactory wash-and-wear garments depend upon:
  (1) fiber content,
  (2) yarn and fabric construction,
  (3) finishes, including fast dyes,
  (4) garment construction.

Fibers must be resilient to both wet and dry deformation. Of the commonly used fibers, the polyesters, the acrylics, and the tri-acetates are excellent in this respect. Rayon and cotton, when treated with resin impregnations, are good. For colored goods, blends of resins are used to give performance plus low cost. In some cases, urea formaldehyde is used alone because of its low cost and good light fastness. Colored goods are not often bleached and, if no ironing is done, the urea formaldehyde should be satisfactory. Glyoxal is not used because it does not have very good crease resistance and it is expensive.

Yarns should be constructed so there are few strains which relax in laundering.

Resins are durable finishes, but if the resin comes out, shrinkage may occur. For this reason, the resin blends that are used contain a resin which is resistant to acid sours and a resin which has good recovery properties.

Besides the resins, the finishes of most importance are fast color dyes. Directions for care relate, very often, to the color performance as well as to the wash-and-wear performance.

Garment construction should include thread, linings, interfacings, and trimmings that do not shrink, fade, or wrinkle. Enough ease should be allowed so there is no apparent shrinkage. Wash-and-wear garments relax somewhat and, in the parts of the garment where there is no tension during wear, some apparent shrinkage takes place. For example, in trousers, there is tension around the waist, but nothing to hold the legs down. Ordinarily, pressing the trousers would flatten the yarns enough so they would resume their original length. If the trousers are not pressed, they appear to have shrunk in the legs.

Resin finishes are not all equally good, but, if the converter chooses the correct resin, applies and cures it correctly, and if the consumer cares for the fabric properly, the fabric will behave much better than a similar untreated fabric.

Some trade names for "easy-care" or wash-and-wear finishes are:

Belfast, Deering-Milliken process licensed to many finishers. It involves basic molecular modification of cotton fibers with limited use of resin. The fabric can be washed and dried in any manner.

Bancare, Everglaze, Minicare, Tutored and *Bancroft.*

Sanforized Plus. (*See* page 194.)

Super-Kwik-Kare and *Reevallure* (Reeves Brothers trade marks).

Dextraset (Dexter Chemical trade mark).

REFERENCES

1. "Wash and Wear Review," *Textile Industries,* **123**:114 (Oct. 1959).
2. J. J. Press, ed., *Man-Made Textiles Encyclopedia,* New York: Textile Book Publishers, 1959.
3. National Cotton Council, "Easy-Care Cottons," Memphis, Tenn.: National Cotton Council, no date.
4. Flynn, P. J., "Wash-and-Wear Problems in Merchandising," *Modern Textiles Magazine,* **39**:55 (July 1958).
5. Stravakas *et al.,* "How Fabric Structure Affects Wash-Wear," *Textile Industries,* **124**:141 (Oct. 1960).
6. Munro, W. P., "Cellulose Reactant Symposium," *American Dyestuff Reporter,* **51**:30 (Feb. 1962).

Stabilization

A fabric is stabilized when it retains its original size and shape during use and care. Unstable fabrics shrink or stretch. Of these two, shrinkage is the most serious problem.

A washable fabric should not shrink more than 2 per cent. Shrinkage of 5 per cent in a size 15 shirt will make a change of ¾ inch in sleeve length and 2 to 3 inches around the chest. This would reduce it to a size 14.

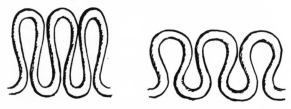

Fig. 6:24. Redmanizing reorients knit stitches—left, before Redmanizing; right, after Redmanizing.

There are two types of shrinkage, relaxation or fabric shrinkage and progressive or fiber shrinkage. The chart lists the finishes used to control shrinkage.

SHRINKAGE CONTROL FINISHES

Relaxation Shrinkage Control <u>*Relaxes Fibers*</u>	*Progressive Shrinkage Control* <u>*Stabilizes Fibers*</u>
Redmanized for cotton knits	Chlorination
Sanforized for cotton, linen, and cross-linked rayon weaves	Resin impregnations for wool
	Surface resins
	Resin impregnations for rayon
London shrunk for woolens and worsteds	
Heat-set for thermoplastics	

RELAXATION SHRINKAGE—METHODS OF CONTROL

Cotton knits are stretched 10 to 35 per cent lengthwise as they come from the knitting machine and also during wet processing, making the fabric longer and narrower than before.

The *Redmanized* process is a relaxation shrinkage control for *knit* fabrics. The fabric is run through the Redmanizing "range" which dampens and stretches it widthwise to reorient the stitches. Following this, it is dried in a *tensionless* state on a conveyor type dryer which consists of a series of small wire baskets. The fabric is fed into the baskets faster than the conveyer runs forward. A blast of air places the fabric in the baskets so that it is in small loops, each loop supported by the basket.

Cotton and linen woven fabrics show relaxation shrinkage when the strains of weaving tensions, warp yarn sizing, dyeing, and so forth are released as the fabric becomes wet in laundering. If the fabric contains starch, not all relaxation shrinkage occurs until the starch is removed. This may take three or more washings. Shrinkage that occurs during this period is called *delayed relaxation shrinkage.*

During weaving, tension keeps the warp yarns straight. (*See* Fig. 6:25.) The filling is inserted in a straight line, but is beaten back into the cloth and then takes on crimp while the warp yarns stay straight. When the fabric is thoroughly wet and allowed to relax, the yarns readjust themselves and the warp yarns move from a straight position to one of crimp. (*See* Fig. 6:25.) This change from straight to crimp position *shortens* the fabric in the warp direction. Less change occurs in the filling direction. Mechanical treatments are used to control relaxation shrinkage.

Fig. 6:25. Position of the warp on the loom (left) and after the fabric relaxes when it becomes wet (right).

Before the 1930's, washable garments were often purchased a size too large and then shrunk down to fit. Then the Cluett Peabody Company developed the first shrinkage control method for cotton and linen fabrics. Garments bearing the Sanforized label can now be purchased in the proper size without danger of shrinkage beyond one per cent. Sanforizing was unsatisfactory on rayon until the new high wet-modulus type was developed.

Sanforize and Rigmel are trade names for compressive shrinkage processes used on woven cloth. The principles involved can be demonstrated by placing a piece of fabric over the clenched fist, then placing a rubber band over the cloth. When the fist is opened and the band is released, the cloth will be squeezed or compressed.

In the factory process, a woolen felt blanket is the medium that shrinks the cloth. A thick blanket will shrink the cloth more than a thin one. The blanket with the moist cloth adhering to its surface, is passed around a feed-in roll. In this curved position, the stretched outer surface, A in Figure 6:26, is longer than the inner surface, B. The blanket then reverses its direction and curves around a heated drum. The outer curve becomes the shorter inner surface and the fabric adhering to it is compressed. The fabric which is now against the drum is dried and set with a smooth finish. The number of yarns per square inch will increase, and the cloth will actually be improved after compressing.

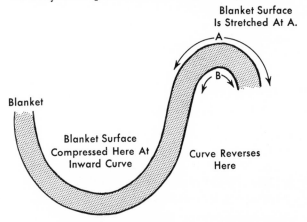

Fig. 6:26. Reversal of curves can cause change in size that compresses the fabric.

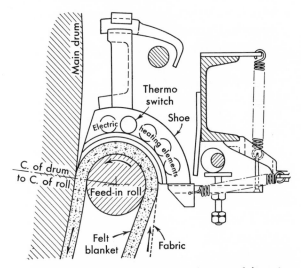

Fig. 6:27. Enlarged cross-sectional diagram of the point in the compressive shrinking process where length shrinkage is obtained. The electrically heated shoe holds the fabric firmly on the outside of the blanket so that when the blanket collapses in straightening out, the fabric is shrunk accordingly. (Courtesy "Sanforized" Division of Cluett, Peabody & Co., Inc.)

Research has shown that faulty laundering will cause compressively shrunk fabrics to shrink. Tumble drying may also compress the yarns beyond their normal shrinkage.

The trade name *Sanforized Plus* may be used on wash-and-wear fabrics which meet specified standards: shrinkage control, wrinkle resistance, smoothness after washing, tensile strength and tear strength.

Wool Fabrics

London shrunk is a 200-year-old finish which removes strains caused by spinning, weaving, and finishing. (*See* Fig. 6:28.)

At first, the wool was laid out in the fields of the city of London and the dew soothed away the stresses and improved the hand of the fabric. While techniques have been modernized, there is still much hand labor involved. A wet blanket, wool or cotton, is placed on a long platform, a layer of cloth is then spread on it, and alternate layers of blankets and cloth built up. Sufficient weight is placed on top to force the moisture from the blankets into the wool. The cloth is left in the pile for about twelve hours. The cloth is then dried in natural room air by hanging it over sticks. When dry, the cloth is subjected to hydraulic pressing by building up layers of cloth and specially made press boards with a preheated metal plate inserted at intervals. A preheated plate is also placed on the top and bottom. This set-up of cloth, boards, and plates is kept under 3000 lbs. pressure for 10 to 12 hours. London shrinking is done for men's wear fine worsteds—not for woolens or women's wear.

Today, the right to use the label "Genuine London Process" or something similar is licensed by the Parrott group of companies, Clothworkers of London, Leeds, and Haddersfield to garment makers all over the world.

A similar method for home use is that of rolling wool in a wet sheet, allowing it to stand for six hours, and then placing it flat on a table or floor to dry. If it is straightened while wet, pressing may be unnecessary. This is the best means for straightening wool which has been

Fig. 6:28. "London shrunk" label.

tentered or decated "off grain." It should not be used on wool crepe. Fabrics which have a flat surface, such as wool broadcloth or some wool flannels, may be changed in appearance.

Wool should always be tested for shrinkage prior to cutting. A simple method is to draw a right angle on the ironing board, place the warp edge along one side and the filling edge along the other side, and hold the steam iron over the fabric. If either edge shrinks away from the pencil line, the wool will shrink during steam pressing and it should be shrunk.

PROGRESSIVE SHRINKAGE—METHODS OF CONTROL

Wool Fabrics. Washable wool is important in children's clothing, in skin contact clothing, and in blends with washable fibers. If wool fabrics continue to maintain their position in the competitive market with fabrics made from wool-like fibers which have easy-care characteristics, they must be finished to keep their original size and surface texture with home cleaning techniques. It might be assumed that people who can afford professional care will not be interested in washable wools. One other assumption might be that washable wools (those given a felting shrinkage control treatment) are the poor-to-medium quality wools.

Whether or not these assumptions are true, felting shrinkage control is important today, as evidenced by the fact that 250 patents for felt proofing wool were issued prior to 1957.

Wool felts because of its surface structure, its ability to stretch, and its ability to recover from stretching. Wool is unique in that the fiber has a broken outer surface with the scales overlapping in one direction. (Wool fibers have an "up and down.") When wool is wet, the fibers tend to move toward the root end; since they are not spun into yarns with the root ends in the same direction, they move in all directions.

To prevent felting shrinkage, the finish must *alter the surface of the fiber* or *alter its elastic properties.*

The differential friction effect can be reduced by removing the scales, modifying the surface, or masking the scales with a surface coating. The most widely used processes are *halogenation* treatments, primarily with chlorine. These are low in cost, can be applied to large batches of small items, do not require padding or curing equipment, and are fairly effective. The processes are fairly delicate and, if not carefully done, are apt to damage the fibers. The scales are more resistant to damage than the interior of the fiber, and, if they are completely removed, there is considerable reduction in wearing properties, loss of weight, and change in hand. The fabrics sometimes feel harsh and rough.

Masking the scales by a *surface coating* is done with acrylic, vinyl, polyamide, or silicone resins. These finishes change the hand of the fabric, making it feel heavier and less wool-like. Surface finishes tend to minimize pilling and fuzzing (one of the greatest problems in wash-and-wear wools), give fabrics better wash-and-wear properties, and increase resistance to abrasion.

To alter the elastic properties, finishes which cross-link with the fibers are used. These *impregnated* finishes (usually called resins) give the same good and poor characteristics as the surface coatings, but they may be more durable.

The effectiveness of felting shrinkage treatments depends on the kind and amount of finish used, and on the yarn and fabric construction. Worsteds need less finish than woolens. Low count fabrics and low twist yarns need more finish to give good washability.

Treated wools are usually considered machine washable, but care should be taken to use warm, not hot, water and a short agitation period. Hand washing is preferable since soil is easy to remove from wool and the hand process insures a lower temperature and less agitation. Machine washing may cause more loosening of fibers, which results in a fuzzy or slightly pilled surface.

Wash-and-wear wools are possible by spraying a reducing agent on a previously shrunk fabric and then steaming. This process, called "Si-ro-set," was developed by the Scientific and Industrial Research Organization in Australia, and is available to manufacturers throughout the world.

Rayon Fabrics. The shrinkage of rayon is an uncontrolled type of shrinkage which varies depending on the handling of the fabric when wet. When it is wet, it can be stretched and it is difficult to keep from overstretching it during processing. If dried in this stretched position, it will have high potential shrinkage and it will shrink when wet again and dried without tension. Unfortunately, it is difficult to dry it without tension because the moisture in the fabric adds enough weight to stretch it.

Rayon shrinkage control treatments reduce the swelling property of the fiber and make it resistant to distortion. Resin impregnation forms cross-links or chains which keep the fiber from stretching. The resin also fills up spaces in the amorphous areas of the fiber, making it less absorbent. The non-nitrogenous resins (the aldehydes) are superior to the other resins because they do not weaken the fabric and are non-chlorine retentive and have excellent wash fastness. Treated rayons are machine washable, but the wash cycle should be short.

Thermoplastic fibers are stabilized by heat-setting.

CHEMICAL FINISHES

Chemical finishes are some of the oldest finishes used. Natural dyes, iron rust dyeing, caustic from ashes and urine, and bleaching by sunlight are examples.

Some of the chemicals now used in large quantities by the textile industry are listed below.[4]

Chemical	Tons, 1959
Caustic soda (alkali)	255,000
Sodium phosphate	70,000
Soda ash	75,000
Chlorine	30,000
Sulfuric acid	30,000
Sodium sulfate	45,000
Hydrogen peroxide	12,000

Chemical finishes are usually permanent and unlike the additive finishes do not add to the weight of the fabric.

Bleaching

The principles involved in bleaching are the same whether the bleaching is done as a fabric finish, as a preparation for further finishing, or in the home during laundering.

Bleaching cleans and whitens gray-goods. The natural fibers are an off-white color because of the impurities they contain. Since these impurities are easily removed from cotton, most cotton gray-goods are bleached. Wool is, however, very difficult to bleach without damage, and the bleaching step is often omitted since wool has good affinity for dyes and other finishes even if not bleached.

Bleaching is also used to strip dye from fabrics which have been imperfectly dyed or need to be redyed.

The consumer uses bleaches to remove stains,[5] and off-white "tattle-tale" gray colors that develop in washing. "Tattle-tale" gray is caused by the soil and soap curds from wash-

[4] Compiled from current literature.

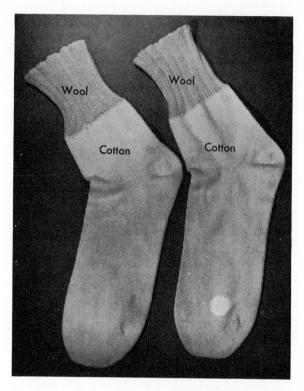

Fig. 6:29. White anklets of cotton and wool after bleaching in chlorine bleach.

water and should be removed by reconditioning treatments rather than by a bleach. Better still, wash often and use correct washing procedures from the start. Reconditioning is done by soaking the article in a solution made with a non-precipitating water softener[6] and then washing it in hot, sudsy, *softened* water. This must be repeated several times.

Mild bleaches may be used on fabric to remove stains without damage to the original color of the fabric. Garments which have a resin finish should not be bleached with chlorine since yellowing will result.

[5] A good reference is "Stain Removal from Fabrics— Home Methods," *Farmers Bulletin* #1474, U.S. Department of Agriculture.

[6] Calgon, Phosphotex, and Noctil are trade names.

CHARACTERISTICS OF BLEACHES

Most bleaches are oxidizing agents. This means that the actual bleaching is done by *active oxygen*. A few bleaches are reducing agents. These are used to strip color from dyed fabrics.

Bleaches may be either acid or alkaline in nature. They are usually unstable, especially in the presence of moisture. This means that bleaches which are old or have been improperly stored will lose their oxidizing power.

Any bleach will cause some damage, and since damage occurs more rapidly at higher temperatures and concentrations, these factors should be carefully controlled.

The same bleach is not suitable to all kinds of fibers. Fibers vary in their chemical reaction and bleaches must be chosen with regard to fiber content. The anklets in Figure 6:29 had been all white, but when bleached with a chlorine bleach the wool-ribbed cuff section became discolored while the cotton feet remained white.

KINDS OF BLEACHES

For many years the common household bleaches were *liquid* chlorine bleaches. Liquid bleaches are now packaged in plastic containers which have replaced the glass containers formerly used. Liquid bleaches are cheap and efficient bleaches for cotton and rayon. However, the weekly wash now contains the new fibers and many of them are either damaged or unaffected by the household chlorine bleaches. The weekly wash also contains many fabrics with crease-recovery and embossed finishes which should *not* be bleached with chlorine. All of these factors have led to the development of milder, more convenient *powder* bleaches.

Chlorine bleaches are efficient bleaches for cellulose fibers but should *not* be used in concentrated solutions or at high temperatures. The bleaching is done by the hypochlorous acid liberated during the bleaching process. Acid *tenders* cellulose fibers. Therefore, chlo-

rine bleaches must be thoroughly rinsed out or an antichlor (sodium thiosulfate) should be used. Chlorine bleaches, other than sodium chlorite, are of no value on the protein and thermoplastic fibers and if used will cause yellowing. A new chlorine bleach with a name so long it is called DDH (dichlorodimethylhydantion) has many of the properties desired in the other chlorine bleaches. It also bleaches by the action of hypochlorous acid but its difference lies in the fact that hypochlorous acid is released only as that present is used up. Therefore fabric damage is less apt to occur. It is also easily stored. Chlorine bleaches are efficient bactericidal agents, and as such can be used for sterilizing fabrics.

Peroxide bleaches are common factory bleaches for cellulose and protein fibers and fabrics.

Hydrogen peroxide is an oxidizing bleach. A 3 per cent solution is relatively stable at room temperature and is safe to use. Peroxide will bleach best at a temperature of 180–200°F. in an alkaline solution. These bleaching conditions make it possible to do peroxide bleaching of cellulose gray-goods as the final step in the kier boil. Figure 6:2 shows cotton yarn in a kier ready for bleaching. The continuous peroxide bleaching process is economical and gives good uniform results. It requires only two and one half hours to accomplish.

In the peroxide *cold bleach* procedure, the fabric is soaked overnight or for a period of 8 hours. This is often done on cotton knit goods and wool to preserve a soft hand. Peroxide is good for removing light scorch stains.

Sodium perborate is a powder bleach [7] which becomes hydrogen peroxide when it combines with water. It is a safe bleach for home use with all kinds of fibers. Satisfactory results have also been obtained with the thermoplastic fibers by use of the cold bleach process. Powder bleaches are recommended for regular use in the wash water to maintain the original whiteness of the fabric rather than as a whitener for discolored fabrics.

[7] Trade names: Dexol, Snowy, Vans, Safety, etc.

Acid bleaches such as oxalic acid and potassium permanganate have limited use. Citric acid and lemon juice are also acid bleaches which are good rust spot removers.

Reducing bleaches are good for stripping color from dyed fabrics. Sodium hydrosulfite is available at the drug store.

Optical bleaches are also used to whiten off-white fabrics. These bleaches are fluorescent white compounds, not true bleaches. The fluorescent white compounds are absorbed into the fiber and emit a bluish fluorescence that covers up yellowish tinges. At the mill, optical bleaches give best results when used in combination with the bleach rather than as a substitute for it. A recent process was developed for treating fabric with the fluorescent white before bleaching with hydrogen peroxide. This gives excellent whiteness. These new fluorescent whites are often incorporated in soaps and detergents as "whiter than new" ingredients.

Acid Finishes

A crisp, highly transparent or parchment effect in cotton cloth, produced by treatment with strong sulfuric acid, is one of the oldest finishes. It is a Swiss or organdy finish produced by the Heberlein process. Since acid damages cotton, the process must be very carefully controlled, and "split-second" (five to six seconds) timing is necessary to prevent *tendering* or weakening of the fabric.

Three effects are possible: all-over parchmentization, localized parchmentization, and a plissé effect on either of the first two.

Since all-over parchmentizing is for the purpose of producing a transparent effect, a sheer fabric of combed lawn is used. The goods are singed, desized, bleached, and mercerized. Mercerization is such an important part of the process that the fabric is mercerized again after the acid treatment in order to improve the transparency.

The fabric is then dyed or printed with colors that will resist acid damage. The cloth is immersed in the acid solution and partial

solution of the surface of the cellulose takes place. Upon drying, this surface rehardens as a cellulose film and gives permanent crispness and transparency. After the acid treatment, the cloth is neutralized in weak alkali, washed, and then calendered to give more gloss to the surface. This all-over treatment produces *organdy* fabric.

In localized parchmentizing, if the design is a small figure with a large transparent area, an acid-resist substance is printed on the figures and the fabric is run through the acid bath. The acid resistant areas retain their original opacity and contrast sharply with the transparent background. (*See* Fig. 6:30.)

Fig. 6:30. Localized parchmentizing gives transparent background.

If a small transparent design is desired, the acid is printed on and then quickly washed off.

The three-dimensional plissé effect is achieved by printing caustic soda on the parchmentized fabric. The untreated areas pucker as the caustic soda causes the printed areas to shrink. The plissé effect can also be made on fabric with local parchmentization.

Burnt-out or etched effects are produced by printing sulfuric acid on a fabric made of fibers from different fiber groups, rayon and silk, for

Fig. 6:31. Burnt-out effect—acid has eaten away pile, leaving transparent background.

Fig. 6:32. Mercerization of warp yarn. (Courtesy of Coats & Clark, Inc., New York, N.Y.)

example. (*See* Fig. 6:31.) The rayon will be "eaten" away leaving sheer silk areas.

Carbonizing, which is the treatment of wool yarns or fabrics with sulfuric acid, destroys vegetable matter in the fabric and more level dyeing can be obtained. Carbonizing is also done on re-used and reprocessed wool to remove any cellulose that may have been used in the original fabric. Carbonizing gives better texture to all-wool fabrics.

The principle of partial solution of the surface of a fabric is used also in making nylon plissé, sculptured nylon, and nylon damasque. Phenol is printed on nylon fabric which partially dissolves and shrinks as it dries, thus creating a puckered surface.

Mercerization

Mercerization is the action of an alkali (caustic soda) on a fabric. Cross-linked rayon and high wet-modulus rayon can be mercerized, while regular rayon can not.

Mercerizing was a revolutionary development discovered in 1853 by John Mercer, a calico printer. He noticed that his cotton filter cloth shrank, became stronger, more lustrous,

and more absorbent after filtering the caustic soda used in the dye process.

Little use was made of mercerization at that time because the shrinkage caused a 20 to 25 per cent yardage loss, and the increased durability caused mill men to fear that less fabric would be used. In 1897, Lowe discovered that if the fabric were held under tension, it did not shrink but became very lustrous and silk-like.

Mercerization is used on cotton and linen for many different reasons. It increases the luster and softness, gives greater strength, and improves the affinity for dyes and water-borne finishes. Plissé effects can be achieved in cotton fabrics. (*See* page 150.)

"Mercerized cotton" on a label is associated with luster. Cotton is mercerized for luster in both yarn and fabric form.

Yarn mercerization is a continuous process in which the yarn under tension passes from a warp beam through a series of boxes with guide rolls and squeeze rolls, through a boil-out wash, and a final wash. (*See* Fig. 6:32.)

Fabric mercerization is done on a frame which contains mangles for saturating the cloth, a tenter frame for stretching the fabric both crosswise and lengthwise while wet, and boxes for washing, neutralizing with dilute sulfuric acid, scouring, and rinsing. Turn to page 39 for a discussion of the changes that occur in the cotton fiber. The amount of improvement in luster corresponds to the difference in luster between dull and bright spun rayon.

Although all mercerized cotton is more lustrous than unmercerized cotton, when mercerization is done under tension, the luster is greatly increased. This increased luster is greatest when done on sheer fabrics containing good quality, long staple cotton fiber. The mercerizing of short staple cotton for luster is not practical.

Greater absorbency results from mercerization because the caustic soda causes a rearrangement of the molecules, thus making the hydroxyl groups available to absorb more water and water-borne substances. Thus dyes can enter the fiber more readily, and when they can be fixed inside the fiber, they are more fast. Caustic soda is also used in vat dyeing to keep the vat dye soluble until it penetrates the fiber. Mercerized cotton and linen take resin finishes better for the same reason.

Increased strength might be considered an important plus value from mercerization. Mercerized cotton fibers are stronger because in the swollen fiber the molecules are more nearly parallel to the fiber axis. When stress is applied, the attraction, which is an end to end molecular attraction, is harder to rupture than in the more spiral fibril arrangement.

COLOR

Color is one of the most important aspects in fabric. In many cases it is the primary reason for purchase. In all cases (except, perhaps, blue jeans or bleeding madras) one wants to keep the original color for the life of the textile.

COLOR PROBLEMS

Many color problems occur with fabrics.

Color loss occurs through bleeding, crocking, and migration, if dye is not combined chemically with the fiber or if pigments are not firmly attached to the surface of the fiber. (*See* pigment printed blouse, page 79.) *Bleeding* is color loss in water. *Crocking* is color loss from rubbing or abrasion while wearing the garment. *Migration* is shifting of color in printed fabric.

If the color is not fast in the fabric as purchased, it may not be possible to make it fast. Salt and vinegar are used as exhausting agents for household dyes, but there is no available research to support the theory that they will "set" color.

Change of color from fume fading (discussed on page 68), perspiration, and light result when a chemical change occurs in the dye. Perspiration may cause either acid or alkaline damage. Light fading is caused by oxidation of the color. Color damage of this type is sometimes accompanied by fabric damage. The dye itself tenders cotton (Fig. 6:33) and rayon fabrics. Sulfur in a dye will combine with moisture in the air to form sulfuric acid, which is harmful to the cellulose.

Fig. 6:33. Tendering of cotton draperies caused by sulfur dye, atmospheric moisture, and heat.

Today this problem is quite critical in draperies, because so many people have picture windows and have invested considerable money to dress their windows. So much fabric is necessary to cover the window that it no longer is possible to care for the draperies in the home. The added cost of care has in many cases meant that the draperies are not cleaned as often as they should be. The problem results when the draperies are apparently in good shape when sent to the cleaner but come back with color changes and splits. Research has shown that all fibers with the exception of Fiberglas are subject to degradation by sunlight and also from acidic gases present in homes using central heating. The fibers listed are in the order of sunlight resistance:

1—Fiberglas	4—Linen	7—Acetate
2—Acrylics	5—Cotton	8—Fortisan
3—Polyester	6—Rayon	9—Nylon
		10—Silk

Lining draperies will increase their resistance to degradation and to color change. Frequent cleaning to remove the acidic condition of the draperies should lengthen their life. It has been estimated that draperies should be cleaned every nine months.

Discharge prints often wear out first in the white or colored areas because the bleached areas of the dark background are weakened by the discharging paste. (*See* Fig. 6:34.)

Wear may remove the surface color of heavy fabrics. Movement of yarns in bending causes undyed fibers to work out to the surface. Color streaks may result from uneven removal of warp sizing before the dye is applied. These fabrics may be labeled "fast color" and no doubt they are, but the portions of the fabric which did not come in contact with the dye were not even dyed! Some resin treated fabrics show this sort of color change because the dye either was applied with the resin and did not penetrate sufficiently, or the fabric was dyed after being resin treated, in which case there were not enough places for the dye to be anchored.

Fig. 6:34. Effect of wear on discharge-printed bandana handkerchief.

Perhaps the best way to predict color performance in heavy fabrics is to examine the fabric. In yard goods, ravel off a yarn to see if it is the same color throughout. In ready-to-wear, look at the edge of seams. In heavy

Fig. 6:35. Denim jeans—loss of surface color.

prints, look at the reverse side. The more color on the wrong side, the better the dye penetration.

The problem for the producer is to select a dye or pigment suited to the fiber and the end-use of the fabric, to apply the color so it will be fast, and to inform the purchaser (garment manufacturer or retailer) of the fastness properties. Problems are encountered because, in some cases, the desired hue is not available with the satisfactory fastness properties at the price the purchaser is willing to pay, or the technique for application is too costly if the fabric is to be competitive in price.

The problem for the consumer is to know what he expects from the textile, to read labels for guarantees of fastness and for suggested care and to report to the retailer if fabric has not given satisfactory performance.

No one dye is fast to everything, and the dyes within a group are not equally fast. A complete range of shades is not available in each of the dye groups. The dyer chooses a dye which is suited to the fiber content and the end-use of the fabric. Occasionally the garment manufacturer or the consumer select fabrics for uses which are different than the fabric manufacturer intended. For example, a lining fabric used for draperies may not be fast to sunlight.

One cannot tell by looking at a fabric the kind of dye that has been used or how fast the color is. It is very important, therefore, to look for labels which guarantee fastness of color and suggest how to care for the fabric.

KINDS OF COLOR

Color has always been important in textiles. Until 1856 natural dyes and pigments were used as coloring agents. These dyes and pigments were obtained from plants and insects. When Perkin, a young chemist, discovered mauve, the first synthetic dye, a whole new industry came into being. All over Europe chemists started to develop synthetic dyes. Germany became the foremost center for syn-

thetic dyes and it was not until World War I, when our trade with Germany was cut off, that a dye industry was developed in the United States. Since that time many dyes and pigments have been developed so that today there are hundreds of colors from which to choose.

There are two kinds of color: dyes and pigments. (*See* Fig. 6:36.) The chart shows the differences between these two coloring substances.

Dyes	*Pigments*
1. Soluble substances	1. Insoluble
2. Penetrate into the fiber and are fixed by chemical action, heat, or other treatment	2. Held mechanically on the surface by resins

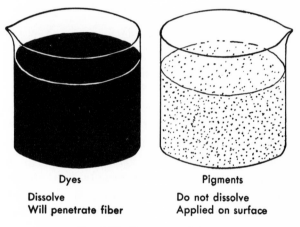

Dyes — Dissolve — Will penetrate fiber

Pigments — Do not dissolve — Applied on surface

Fig. 6:36. Pigments and dyes.

Pigments are insoluble color particles which are held on the surface of a fabric by a binding agent. Their application is quick, simple, and economical. Any color can be used on any fiber, since the pigments are held on mechanically. Stiffening of the fabrics, crocking, and fading are some of the problems encountered. Pigments are also mixed with the spinning solution for man-made fibers. Fluorescent colors are pigments that glow when exposed to ultraviolet light. They have been increasingly useful in safety clothing and furnishings.

Dye must be in small particles which can be thoroughly dissolved in water or some other

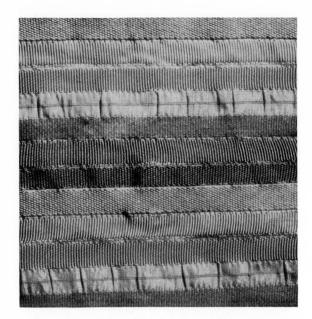

Fig. 6:37. Six-fiber test cloth showing difference in color absorbed from Texchrome, a mixture of several dyes.

carrier in order to penetrate the fiber. Undissolved particles stay on the outside and the colors then have poor fastness to crocking and bleeding.

Fibers have affinity for certain dyes but will not absorb others. The thermoplastic fibers have been difficult to dye because they are low in absorbency. The 6-fiber cloth in Figure 6:37 was piece dyed with Texchrome, a mixture of several dyes. The wool is deep yellow, cotton is blue, rayon is lavender, nylon and acetate are light yellow.

All of the fibers in a fiber group have an affinity for the same dyes but they do not dye in the same way. For example, rayon, which is 100 per cent cellulose, swells greatly and dyes much more readily than cotton or linen which contain less cellulose.

APPLICATION OF COLOR

Dyes are fixed in the fiber in various ways. Some are absorbed directly by the fiber; some require a mordant or assistant which has an affinity for both the dye and the fiber; some are developed in the fiber by chemical treatments.

Dyes are classified according to the method of application and their characteristics. (*See* chart, page 204.)

STAGES OF APPLYING COLOR

Color is applied at various stages of production of fabrics. This has little to do with fastness, but has a great deal to do with dye penetration. Some color problems are due to poor dye penetration. A knowledge of equipment and methods used may give the consumer a better understanding of these problems.

Dyed Before Yarn Spinning

Solution (spun or dope) dying consists of adding colored pigments to the spinning solution; thus each fiber is colored as it is spun.

Stock or fiber dye is used when mottled or heather effects are desired. Dye is added to loose fibers before yarn spinning. Good dye penetration is obtained but the process is fairly expensive.

Top dyeing gives results similar to stock dye and is more commonly used. Tops, the loose ropes of wool from the combing machine, are wound into balls, placed on perforated spindles and enclosed in a tank. The dye is pumped back and forth through the wool.

Yarn Dye After Spinning; Before Weaving or Knitting

Yarns are dyed in skeins or packages. Packages contain 1 to 2 pounds of yarn wound on perforated spools or tubes. Some warp yarns are dyed on large perforated beams. Rayon is usually dyed in the cakes in which it is laid after spinning. It is difficult to wind the rayon in packages and have the correct tension to allow for the swelling of the fibers when they become wet. The packages are placed on carriers, put in the dyeing machine and fastened in place. A lid is clamped on and the dye is circulated around the packages in a two-way motion. Yarn dyeing is less costly than raw stock dyeing.

CLASSIFICATION OF DYES

Dye	Characteristics	Fiber
1. Acid dyes (dye liquor is acidic).	Vary in fastness to light and washing. Bright colors.	Wool, silk, nylon, Orlon, Acrilan, Creslan.
2. Basic dyes (contain amino dyes).	Brilliant colors. Many are not fast in washing, light, or rubbing.	Wool, silk, nylon, modacrylic.
3. Direct cotton dyes.	Wide color range. No brilliant colors. Used where fastness is not necessary.	Protein, cellulose.
4. Azoic dyes, also called napthol (developed on fiber). Insoluble color precipitates made by adding a solution of diazo compound to an alkaline solution of naphthol.	Good fastness surpassed only by vat dyes. Have tendency to crock.	Widely used on cotton prints. Polyester, Creslan, Nytril, Acrilan.
5. Developed direct dyes (similar to direct cotton dyes, but must be developed on the fiber).	Good wash fastness. Fair light fastness.	Cotton, rayon, silk, linen.
6. Mordant and chrome dyes (can be made to combine with metallic salts).	Excellent fastness to wet processing and dyes.	Wool, Acrilan.
7. Sulfur dyes (made by reaction of sulfur with organic compounds). Not water soluble, put into solution with alkali.	Wide range of rather dull colors. Fast to washing. Fair fastness to light.	Wool, Creslan, cellulose, Zefran.
8. Vat dyes: a. anthraquinone, b. indigoid, c. sulfide (insoluble in water). Pigments reduced to leuco compounds which are soluble in alkali. Pigments are re-oxidized by air or oxidizing agent.	Most satisfactory of all dyestuffs.	Cellulose, Zefran, Creslan.
9. Acetate dyes (dispersed dyes) which include insoluble azo or anthraquinone dyes kept in colloidal suspension by sulfonated oils.	Good fastness to light, washing, and perspiration. Subject to fume fading.	Acetate, nylon, Orlon, Acrilan, Creslan, modacrylic.

Piece Dying After Weaving or Knitting

Piece dyeing usually produces solid color fabrics.

Cross dyeing is piece dyeing of fabrics made of fibers from different groups such as protein and cellulose or cellulose and acetate. These fabrics which are dyed after weaving have heather effects, checks, stripes, or plaids because the fibers have affinities for specific dyes.

Piece dyeing is done with various kinds of equipment.

Jig dyeing, Figure 6:38, consists of a stationary dye bath with two rolls above the bath. The cloth is wrapped around the rolls in open width and is rolled back and forth through the dye until the desired shade is obtained. Since the cloth is run through the dye bath once every 20 minutes or so and is on the rollers the remaining time, there are some problems

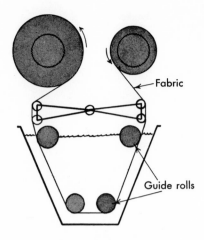

Fig. 6:38. Jig dyeing.

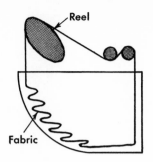

Fig. 6:39. Winch dyeing.

of level dyeing. Acetate, rayon and nylon are usually jig dyed.

Pad dyeing is a method in which the fabric is run through the dye bath in open width and then between squeeze rollers which force the dye into the fabric. Notice in the Figure 6:14, that the pad box holds only a very small amount of dye liquor, making this an economical method of piece dyeing. The cloth runs through the machine at a rapid rate, 30 to 300 yards a minute.

Winch, reel or beck dyeing is the oldest type of piece dyeing. (*See* Fig. 6:39.) The fabric, in a loose rope sewed together at the ends, is lifted in and out of the dye bath by a reel. The fabric is kept immersed in the dye bath except for the few yards around the reel. Penetration of dye is obtained by continued immersion in a slack condition rather than by pressure on the wet goods under tension. This method is used on lightweight fabrics which cannot withstand the tension of the other methods and on heavy goods, especially woolens. Reels are of various shapes—oval, round, octagonal.

Continuous machines called ranges are used for large lots of goods. They consist of compartments for wetting-out, dyeing, after treatments, washing, and rinsing.

High temperature dyeing is necessary to get good dye penetration on the thermoplastic fibers (except acetate and Dynel). The following methods have given satisfactory results.

Hot-Oil Process. The cloth after being padded with vat or sulfur dyes passes into the hot-oil bath at 220–250°F. When the wet cloth comes into contact with the hot oil a violent reaction occurs. A steam-oil emulsion is formed. The dye and chemicals are quickly exposed to heat-energy required for the reduction of the pigments and the soluble dye is rapidly absorbed by the fiber. The oil is removed, dye is oxidized to develop insoluble pigments, rinsed, soaped, and then rinsed once more.

Thermosol Process. Fabrics are dyed at normal temperatures on regular equipment, dried and then heat-set for 30 seconds to 1 minute at 350°F. Colors are fast to machine washing. Dacron responds best to this treatment.

The Baroter. This is a new machine developed to dye small batches of fabric under pressure with little tension on the fabric. Dyeing is done at 15 pounds pressure at 250°F. Using the copper-ion technique with the Baroter has produced heavy shades on Orlon. Satisfactory dyeings without carriers have been done on Dacron.

Molten-Metal Process. Fabrics are dyed with vat colors, dried and then passed through a U-shaped tank in which a molten metal alloy is maintained at 200–250°F. As the cloth passes through the molten metal, the dye is reduced under pressure. The metal is rinsed out and the fabric oxidized, scoured, and rinsed. This method is used to obtain level dyeings in dense fabrics, in slubby yarn type constructions, and for embroidered fabrics in which it is difficult to obtain the same shade on the ground and embroidery.

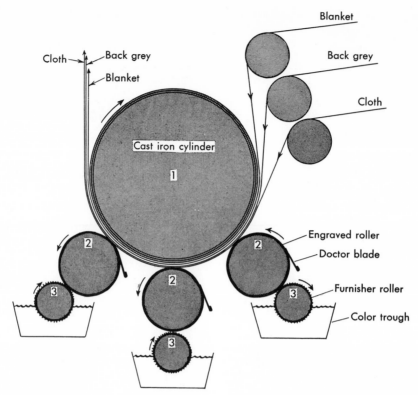

Fig. 6:40. Roller printing machine.

Printing After Weaving or Knitting

Printing is the application of color in the form of a design on a fabric.

Discharge printing is usually done on dark backgrounds. The fabric is first piece dyed in any of the usual methods. A discharging paste which contains chemicals to remove the color is then printed on the fabric. Dyes which are not harmed by the discharging materials can be mixed with printing solution if color is desired in the discharge areas. The fabric is then steamed to develop the design either as a white or colored area. Better dye penetration is obtained with piece dyeing than with printing and it is hard to get good dark colors except by piece dyeing. Discharge prints can be detected by looking at the wrong side of the fabric. In the design area the color is often not completely removed and one can see evidences of the background colors especially round the edges of the design. Background colors must be colors that can be removed by

strong alkali. Discharge prints are usually satisfactory.

Resist printing is just the opposite of discharge printing. A resist paste is printed on a white fabric which is then piece dyed. This method is only used with dyes which cannot be discharged, such as aniline black.

Batik is a hand process in which hot wax is poured on a fabric in the form of a design. When the wax is set, the fabric is piece dyed. The wax prevents penetration of color into the wax covered portions. Colors are built up by piece dyeing, light colors first, covering portions and redyeing until the design is complete. The wax is later removed by a solvent.

Tie and dye is a hand process in which yarn or fabric is wrapped in certain areas with fine thread or string. The yarn or fabric is then piece dyed and the string is removed, leaving undyed areas.

Warp printing is done on the warp yarns prior to weaving. This technique gives an interesting rather hazy pattern, softer than other prints. Warp prints are usually ribbed fabrics.

Direct roller printing was developed in 1785 about the time all textile operations were becoming mechanized. Figure 6:40 shows the essential parts of the printing machine.

A cast iron cylinder (1 in the Figure) is the roller around which the cloth is drawn as it is printed. The copper printing roller (2 in the diagram) is etched with the design. There are as many different rollers as there are colors in the fabric. In the diagram, three engraved rollers are used. Furnisher rollers are covered with hard rubber or brushes made of nylon, Orlon, or hard rubber bristles. They revolve in a small color trough, pick up the color and deposit it on the copper rollers. A doctor blade scrapes off excess color so that only the engraved portions of the copper roller are filled with dye when it comes in contact with the cloth. The cloth to be printed, a rubberized blanket, and a back gray cloth pass between the cylinder and the engraved rollers. The blanket gives a good surface for sharp printing, the gray goods protect the blanket and absorb excess dye.

Rayon and knitted fabrics are usually lightly coated with a gum sizing on the back to keep them from stretching or swelling as they go through the printing machine.

After printing, the cloth is dried, steamed, or treated to set the dye.

Duplex printing is roller printing which prints on both sides of the fabric with the same or different patterns. It is used primarily for unlined draperies.

Printed fabrics are often printed off-grain. In an all-over design this is not important, but in large checks and plaids or designs with crosswise lines, matching at seam lines is impossible and slanting lines across the fabric are seldom desirable. The reason for off-grain prints is that the fabric is started into the machine crooked or the mechanism for moving the fabric does not work properly. It is a problem which can easily be corrected at the mill and if consumers *will refuse* to buy off-grain prints and let retailers know why they are not

buying them, better prints will be on the market.

Block printing is a hand process which is seldom done commercially because it is costly and slow. A design is carved on linoleum blocks, the blocks are dipped in a shallow pan of dye and stamped on the fabric. Uniform pressure is needed to transfer the color to the fabric.

Stencil Printing. Flock printing (page 187) has more depth or texture than other prints. The roller used is a hollow copper cylinder which is perforated in the form of a design. The printing paste is in a trough inside the cylinder and flows through the perforations on to the cloth as it is pressed against the roller. As the material leaves the cylinder, it is dusted with rayon flock. *Lacquer printing* is done as is flock printing except that colored enamel or opaque ink is used.

Screen printing is done commercially for small yardages, 500 to 5000 yards. The cloth to be printed is pinned or pasted to a long flat table which has been covered with a thick wool felt pad, an oil cloth which protects the felt, and a cotton cloth which must be

Fig. 6:41. Screen printing—machine can be operated by one man. (Courtesy of *Textile World*.)

changed quite often as it takes up color from the dyed fabric. The screens consist of wooden or metal frames over which silk, nylon, or Vinyon gauze has been stretched. The design is applied to the screen by a photographic method in which the screen is covered with sensitized gelatin film and a plate of the original design is reproduced on the film. All but the design is painted out with caustic-resistant paint and the unpainted gelatin is washed out in warm water. A special screen is prepared for each color in the design. Along the sides of the table a metal straight edge with adjustable stops makes it easy to set each screen correctly. After the screen is set, the color in paste form is poured on the screen and is forced through the screen by moving a squeegee across the screen. A screen printing machine that can be operated by one man is shown in Figure 6:41. Screen printing is used extensively for designs larger than the circumference of the rolls used for roller printing.

REFERENCES

1. Marnon, D. E., "The Hot-Oil Process," *Modern Textiles Magazine*, 33:57 (July 1952).
2. Gibson, J. W., Knapp, P., and Andres, R. J., "'Thermosol' Method of Dyeing," *American Dyestuff Reporter*, 42:1 (Jan. 1953).
3. Cole, Paul M., "Revolution in Batch Dyeing," *Modern Textiles Magazine*, 33:76 (Sept. 1952).
4. Goldberg, J. P., "Developments in Dyeing and Finishing," *Canadian Textile Journal*, 70:47 (July 1953).
5. Sands, George W., "The Dry Cleaning and Laundering of Textile Materials," *Canadian Textile Journal*, 78:52–53 (Jan. 1961).
6. "Textiles Printed from Paper Transfers," *Textile Industries*, 126:145 (May 1962).

Waterproof and Water-Repellent Fabrics

A *waterproof* fabric is one which no water can penetrate. A *water-repellent* fabric is resistant to wetting, but if the water comes with enough force, it will penetrate the fabric.

The Federal Trade Commision has suggested the use of the terms "durable" and "renewable" in describing water-repellent fabrics.

It is more difficult to select a water-repellent coat than a water-proof coat because the finish is not obvious and one must depend on the label for information. However, there are some guides for buying which the consumer can recognize. *The cloth construction is far more important than the finish.* The closer the weave, the greater the resistance to water penetration. The kind of finish used is important in selection because it influences the cost of upkeep. The use of two layers of fabric across the shoulders gives increased protection but the inner layer must also have a water-repellent finish, otherwise it will act as a blotter and cause more water to penetrate.

Care is important in water-repellent fabrics. The greater the soil on the coat, the less water-repellent it is.

Waterproof Fabrics	*Water-Repellent Fabrics*
Fabrics are plastic films or low-count fabrics with a film coating.	High-count fabrics with a finish which coats the yarn but does not fill up the interstices of the fabric.
Characteristics	
No water can penetrate.	Heavy rain will penetrate.
Most plastic fabrics stiffen in cold weather.	Fabric is pliable, and is no different than untreated fabric.
Cheaper to produce.	Fabric can "breathe"—is comfortable for raincoats.
Permanent.	Durable or renewable finish.

Water repellency is dependent on surface tension and fabric penetrability and is achieved by (1) finish and (2) cloth construction.

Finishes that can be applied to a fabric to make it repellent are wax emulsions, metallic soaps, and surface active agents. They are applied to fabrics such as tackle twill, poplin, and rayon and cotton satin, all of which have a very high warp count and are made with fine yarns.

Wax emulsions and metallic soaps coat the yarns but do not fill the interstices between the yarns. These finishes are not permanent but tend to come out when the fabric is washed or dry cleaned. They can be renewed.

Surface active agents [8] have molecules with one end that is water-repellent and one end that will react with the hydoxyl (OH) groups of cellulose. After they are applied, heat is used to seal the finish to the fabric. This finish is permanent to washing and drycleaning.

Cloth construction can be water-repellent without a finish. *Shirley cloth*, developed at the Shirley Institute in England is similar in construction to the canvas bags found in Egyptian tombs. They were plain weave with two warp threads woven as one. They were always made of flax. Studies showed that cotton and flax swell about the same amount, so it was decided that twist made the difference between cotton and the flax. Shirley cloth is made of long, fine cotton fibers, 3-ply yarns of very low twist, and oxford weave. It is a nearly waterproof fabric. It is cool and porous when dry, but moisture causes the yarns to swell and close the interstices between them.

Flammability and Fire-Retardant Finishing

The Flammable Fabrics Act became effective on July 1, 1954.

The terms *flammable* and *inflammable* both mean "will burn." *Non-*flammable means "will not burn." Fire retardant means "burns slowly."

The mineral fibers are *flame proof*. The protein and some of the thermoplastic fibers are *fire retardant*. The thermoplastic fibers melt as they burn and may stick to the skin resulting in an even deeper burn.

Cellulose fibers burn easily and completely but leave an afterglow, a continued slow burning, that can be as dangerous as the flame itself.

The construction of the fabric determines the degree to which oxygen is made available to the fiber. Thick heavy fabrics burn slowly;

[8] Zelan is one example.

thin open fabrics burn very rapidly. Fabrics with a fuzzy surface burn along the surface before the base fabric catches fire.

Fabrics are divided into three groups according to their flammability.

Borderline fabrics that should be tested for flammability are sheer fabrics such as organdy, lawn and voile, and napped fabrics with short nap.

Dangerously flammable fabrics are very sheer fabrics and nets, long and/or irregular napped and pile fabrics with loose base construction, and fabrics with certain flammable finishes.

Brushed rayons are easier to ignite than other napped fabrics and burn with greater speed and intensity.

Blending fire-resistant fibers with cellulose fibers will lower the flammability of cellulose fabrics.

According to existing theories, fire-retardant compounds either cut off the supply of oxygen to the fabric by forming a coating or by producing a non-combustible gas, or chemically alter the fiber so it forms a non-volatile charred residue rather than the usual flammable tarry products.

Moth Proofing

It has been estimated that there is an annual loss of $100,000,000 due to damage of textiles by moths and carpet beetles. Most of this damage occurs where storehouses store raw wool, manufacturers store fabrics, and stores carry over suits and coats from one season to another. Moth damage is an equally serious problem for consumers.

Both moths and carpet beetles attack not only 100 per cent wool, but also blends of wool and other fibers. While they can digest only the wool, they eat through the other fibers. The damage is done by the larvae and not the adult moth. Clothes moths are about ¼ inch long; they are not the large moths that we may occasionally see about the house. Larvae shun bright sunlight and do their work in the dark. For this reason it is necessary to clean often under sofas, under sofa cushions, in creases of chairs and garments, and dark closets. Larvae are supposed to be killed by direct sunlight so it is a good practice to hang garments in the sun occasionally.

Means of controlling moth damage are as follows:

1. Cold storage.
2. Odors that repel. Paradichlorobenzene and naphthalene (moth balls) used during storage.
3. Stomach poisons. Fluorides and silicofluorides are used as a finish on wool fabrics. They are fast to dry cleaning but not fast to washing.
4. Contact poisons. DDT is very effective but requires frequent application.
5. Chemically changing the fiber to make it unpalatable to the larvae. Chemicals causing these changes are added during the dyeing process and are fast to both washing and dry cleaning.

Molds and Mildew

Molds and mildew will grow on and damage both cellulose and protein textiles. They will grow on but not damage the thermoplastic fibers. Losses are estimated in the millions of dollars.

Prevention is the best solution to the problem since cures are often impossible. To prevent mold or mildew, keep textiles clean and dry. Soiled clothes should be kept dry and washed as soon as possible. Sunning and airing should be done frequently during periods of high humidity. An electric light can be used in dark humid storage places. Dehumidifiers in homes are very helpful.

If mildew occurs, wash the article immediately. Mild stains can be removed by bleaching.

Antiseptic finishes are used to inhibit the growth of bacteria and other odor-causing germs and to prevent decay and damage from perspiration. These finishes are important in skin-contact clothing, shoe linings, and especially hospital linens. The chemicals used are surface reactants, mostly quarternary ammonia compounds. These substances can be added to the spinning solution of rayon and acetate fibers. Most diaper service establishments add the finish during each laundering. Eversan and Sanitized are two trade names.

Soil-retardant finishes are not very widely used, but there is need for them on cellulosic fabrics which cannot be laundered easily. The first attempt was made on rayon carpeting. Upholstery fabrics of cotton and rayon soil readily and need this kind of finish. Mixes containing colloidal silica or alumina have given good results. Polyester lattices have also been used. Water-repellent finishes render fabrics spot and stain resistant. Some of the finishes are resistant to water-borne stains, some are resistant to oil-borne stains, and some to both. Durable water-repellent finishes often hold greasy stains more tenaciously than untreated fabrics. Unisec and Scotchgard are trade names for finishes which give resistance to both oily and water-borne stains. Hydro-Pruf and Syl-mer are silicone finishes which give resistance to water-borne stains.

Fabric Glossary

Alpaca is a flat, dull fabric with the appearance of wool. It contains two-ply yarns, one ply a crepe viscose and the other ply a larger, regular twist acetate (grenai yarns). Crepiness is obtained from the viscose ply and body is obtained from the acetate ply. (Alpaca is also a specialty hair fiber used to make pile weave coating fabric.)

Balbriggan is a plain knit cotton fabric used for lingerie.

Balloon cloth is a fine yarn cotton fabric in balanced plain weave. It is used for dresses, blouses, coverings for balloon gas cells, airplane coverings, and typewriter ribbons.

Barathea is a ribbed fabric with a broken-surface effect due to weave. It has filament yarn in the warp and filament or staple in the filling. It may be silk, rayon, or acetate.

Batiste, wool, is a smooth, balanced fabric which is white or light in color. It is not as sheer as wool voile, but is very light weight for a wool fabric.

Broadcloth is a lustrous woolen fabric which is highly napped and then pressed flat. The weave is not visible. Broadcloth has an up and down, and will reflect light differently if all pieces of a pattern are not cut going in the same direction.

Buckram is similar to crinoline except that it has a stiffer finish. Often two layers of crinoline are glued together to make a very heavy and stiff fabric. It is converted from cheesecloth gray goods.

Burlap is a coarse, heavy plain weave fabric made of jute. It is used primarily as carpet backing and furniture webbing, but can also be used for decorative textiles.

Butcher rayon is a crash-like fabric that is made in various weights. All kinds of names are given to this fabric. In heavier weights it looks like linen suiting. Butcher rayon may be an acetate and rayon blend or it may be 100 per cent rayon. It is often given a crease resistant finish. A Federal Trade Commission ruling prohibits the use of the word "linen" in this type of fabric.

Cambric is a fine, firm, plain weave balanced fabric finished with starch and has a slight luster on one side. It is difficult to distinguish from percale, nainsook, or longcloth.

Canvas is a heavy, firm, rather stiff fabric made

of cotton or linen and is used for awnings, slipcovers, shoes, etc.

Hair canvas is a woven interfacing material in various weights. Coarse goat hair combined with wool, cotton, or rayon is used in the filling direction. Armo and Hymo are trade names.

Casement cloth is any light weight, plain weave fabric used for glass curtains.

Cavalry twill is a smooth surfaced twill with a pronounced double twill line.

Challis (pronounced shal'i) is a lightweight, plain weave balanced fabric with a soft finish. Originally of wool, it is now made of any staple fiber or blend of fibers. Cotton challis has a slight nap to achieve softness. Challis has been used for lingerie, blouses, and dresses and is usually printed.

China silk is a soft, sheer, plain weave fabric used in sheath linings and scarves.

Chinchilla is a heavy, twill-weave wool coating which has a napped surface that is rolled into little balls. It is one of the most durable coating fabrics.

Covert was first made in England, where there was a demand for a fabric which would not catch on brambles or branches during fox hunts. To make this tightly woven fabric, a two-ply yarn, one cotton and one wool, was used. Because the cotton and wool did not take the same dye, the fabric had a mottled appearance.

Cotton covert is always mottled and it may be made with ply yarns, one ply white and the other colored, or it may be fiber dyed white and a color. It is a 2 x 1 twill of the same weight as denim and is used primarily for work pants, overalls, and service coats.

Rayon covert looks like wool covert. It is made with a blend of rayon and acetate in dress weight.

Wool covert is made from woolen or worsted yarns. It may be mottled or solid color and may be suit or coat weight. It may be napped slightly or have a clear finish. The mottled effect is obtained by using two different colored plys or by blending different colored fibers.

Crepe refers to any fabric made with crepe yarns (true crepe) or with a puckered surface (crepe effects).

Canton crepe is a filling crepe made with coarse yarns of alternate S and Z twist (2S and 2Z); (4S and 4Z); (6S and 6Z). It has a low count and is rough looking. There is much crosswise stretch in the fabric. It is used for dresses and suit dresses. Dry cleaning is preferable.

Chiffon is a smooth, plain weave, balanced fabric. It is a soft, filmy fabric with fine yarns.

Crepe backed satin is a satin weave with crepe filling yarns.

Crepe de Chine was originally a washable silk crepe woven in the gum. Now it refers to a lightweight flat crepe.

Crepe Romaines, triple sheer and semi-sheer, are heavier fabrics than georgette and not as transparent. It is a 2/1 basket weave.

Crepon and bark crepe are heavy crepes with a rough appearance. Bark crepe has the appearance of tree bark. Crepon has wavy lines in the warp direction caused by high twist filling yarns. Dry cleaning is preferable.

Georgette has a duller texture than chiffon, with a texture similar to voile.

Dimity is a Greek word which means "double thread." Dimity cord has warp-wise cords made by weaving two or more yarns as one and separating them by areas of plain weave. Dimity is sheer with a crisp finish.

Barred dimity has cords in both warp and filling.

Duvetyn is similar to suede, but is lighter in weight and is more drapable. It has a soft, velvet-like surface made by napping, shearing and brushing.

Flannel refers to any napped fabric.

Canton flannel is a twill weave cotton fabric napped on one side. It has a long nap. It is used for work mittens and pocket linings.

Tarnish-resistant flannel is a solid-color cotton fabric which is impregnated with chemicals to absorb sulfur fumes. It is used for silverware cases and chest linings.

Viyella flannel is part wool, part cotton flannel similar to outing flannel, but with a twill weave. The cotton content makes it more washable than an all-wool flannel. It is used for shirts and baby clothes. The fabric is imported from England.

Foulard is a printed lightweight twill weave fabric of silk, cotton, rayon, or wool. Silk surah is a similar fabric.

Gauze is a low count, plain weave balanced fabric used for bandages.

Theatrical gauze is made from linen fiber which has more body and luster than cotton. It may be yarn dyed or plain color. Its chief use is for curtains.

Gingham is a yarn dyed, plain weave fabric which varies in weight from tissue to suiting. It may be balanced or ribbed. Usually it is made of cotton, but silk, rayon, and blends are called ginghams.

Shagbark gingham has slack tension loops scattered over the surface.

Herringbone fabrics have warp stripes which are made by changing the direction of the twill line. The chevron-like stripes may be of equal prominence, or one may be prominent and the other subdued. These fabrics are made in all weights, of all fiber contents, and in many types of interlacings.

Homespun is a coarse, balanced, plain weave fabric with a hand woven look. It is used for coats, suits, and dresses.

Hopsacking is a suiting weight fabric made with a basket weave.

Interfacing is a woven or non-woven fabric used to give body to a garment. Any fabric may be used. Choice depends upon weight of fabric and proper cleaning method. Specially prepared interfacings are:

Non-woven: Pellon, Keybak, Textryl, Pelonite
Woven: hair-canvas, Armo, Hymo, Siri, Wigan, Lamical

Jaspé cloth is a plain weave suiting weight cloth made with multi-colored warp yarns and plain filling yarns. It is used for slip covers and draperies.

Kasha is a type of flannel which has black and colored fibers in the filling yarns.

Kersey is a very heavy, thick, boardy wool coating fabric which has been fulled and felted.

Lamé is a fabric containing metallic yarns.

Linen [1] is the only fabric which can be called by the fiber name. Linen usually means a plain weave, suiting weight fabric.

Crebasi linen refers to a dress weight, plain weave linen fabric.

Handkerchief linen is similar in luster and count to batiste and like batiste it wrinkles badly. Linen yarns are more uneven than cotton yarns. This helps in identifying the fabric. Cotton and rayon yarns are sometimes made to resemble linen yarns by being purposely spun with irregularities.

Lining refers to any fabric used on the back of a shell.

Metal coated or reflective linings are lining fabrics that have a finish of metallic particles sprayed on the inner side. Aluminum is used because it is economical and lightweight, but any metal that flakes could be used. The metal can be applied to any type of fiber.

Sheath lining is a rayon fabric which resembles China silk.

Longcloth is a plain weave, balanced white cotton fabric used for handkerchiefs, lingerie, and blouses.

Melton is similar to kersey, but is heavier in weight.

[1] *Linen* and *flax* are terms which are used interchangeably.

Mousseline de soie is French for "silk muslin." It is a plain weave, balanced sheer fabric with a crisp finish.

Nainsook is a soft-finished and sometimes mercerized, plain weave, balanced cotton fabric. It may be white, pastel colored, or printed. Nainsook is similar to batiste, but it is less transparent. It is used for lingerie, handkerchiefs, interfacings, and infant's wear.

Ninon is a plain weave, sheer fabric made of acetate filaments and used for glass curtains.

Organza is rayon or silk organdy.

Osnaburg is a coarse, suiting-weight cotton fabric characterized by uneven yarns which have bits of cellulosic waste. It is used for slipcovers, draperies, and sports-wear.

Ottoman is a ribbed fabric with alternate large and small ribs made by adjacent filling yarns of different sizes.

Pajama check is similar to dimity in construction, but it is made with carded yarns and is not as sheer. It has a soft finish and grouped yarns in both directions.

Peau de soie is French for "skin of silk." It is a very smooth semi-dull satin construction which has satin floats on both sides of the fabric. It is a fairly heavy fabric made in silk, acetate, Orlon Cantrece, or in mixtures.

Piqué. (*See* page 151.)

Dimity piqué is neither like piqué nor like dimity. It has the sheerness of dimity, but not the double thread. It has the appearance of a piqué cord, but is not a cord weave. Dimity piqué is made with combed, cotton yarns and spaces are left at regular intervals between the warp threads (skipped dents).

Embossed piqué is a plain weave, balanced fabric which is treated with a resin, and then embossed in a piqué stripe. The resin finish is cured to make it durable.

Novelty piqué is any fabric which has a combination of piqué weave with another weave. Often the piqué stripe does not go the entire length of the fabric.

Picolay (trade name) is an embossed fabric which resembles birdseye piqué. Proper care must be given if the design is to last satisfactorily.

Seersucker piqué is made with slack tension weaving in which the tight stripe is a piqué weave. Wales and crinkle stripes are in the warp directions. Like all piqué, and unlike seersucker, the fabrics have a right and wrong side.

Waffle cloth is sometimes incorrectly called waffle piqué. Waffle cloth has a honeycomb or waffle design which is woven in. A dobby loom is used. It looks the same on the right and wrong sides. Waffle cloth is made in the same weight as pinwale piqué with carded or combed cotton, and is made in a heavier drapery fabric which has large waffle squares. Baby blankets with wool yarns are sometimes made with this weave.

Pongee is a wild-silk, plain weave fabric. It is also the name of a ribbed fabric comparable to broadcloth in weight which is made with acetate filament warp and cotton filling yarns.

Sailcloth is a suiting-weight cotton fabric in a 2/1 basket weave.

Sharkskin is a woolen or worsted 2/2 twill made with yarns of two different colors and having a smooth, flat appearance. The twill line, unlike most of the wool twill fabrics, goes up to the left. Acetate or Arnel sharkskin is a plain weave, solid color fabric, but it has the smooth, flat appearance of the wool fabric. It is used primarily for women's summer suits.

Suede is a plain weave or twill weave fabric which is napped and then sheared to resemble leather. Suedes for jackets and ski wear are often napped on both sides. Any suitable fiber can be used.

Taffeta refers to any plain weave, balanced or ribbed fabric made with filament yarns.

Faille taffeta has a crosswise rib made by using many more warp yarns than filling yarns. All ribbed taffetas have crispness.

Paper taffeta is a very lightweight, stiff, transparent fabric.

Pigment taffeta is woven with delustered rayon filaments with little or no twist, into a plain weave, balanced fabric. It is not crisp.

Tarlatan is a low count, plain weave, cotton cheesecloth with a starched finish.

Ticking is made in plain, twill, satin, or figure weave of cotton. Fabrics are used for mattress covers, slip covers, and upholstery. A lighter weight fabric is used for sports wear.

Tricotine is a clear-finish twill weave fabric in cotton, wool, or man-made fibers. It has a double twill line.

Tufted fabric is one in which the pile is made by inserting the extra yarns into an already woven backing fabric. The yarns are punched through the fabric by needles and are locked in the fabric by the blooming or untwisting action of the yarn plus the shrinkage of the backing fabric. They are not held in by weaving as are the pile yarns in other pile fabrics. In carpeting, the back is given a coat of lastex to give stiffness and skid resistance to the carpet. Chenille bedspreads and robes are made with cotton yarns on a heavy muslin background. All kinds of fibers are used in carpeting on a canvas-base fabric.

Velvet comes from the Latin "vellus" meaning a fleece or tufted hair. It is not known where or when it originated, but it was made the official fabric for both the court and the church during the Middle Ages. In France, blue velvet was reserved exclusively for the King's family. As people attained wealth and power, the use of velvet became more widespread.

Brocade velvet has a pile of different heights cut to form a design.

Chiffon velvet is very durable, lightweight, and is made with a rayon pile and a silk back. Faconné velvet is patterned by burnt out designs.

Embossed velvet has certain areas pressed flat.

Lyons velvet is a closely woven fabric with a deep pile which sometimes has a cotton pile and a silk back. It is used for coat collars, suits and coats, and for millinery.

Nacré velvet is a changeable fabric with the back of one color and the pile of another.

Panne velvet has the pile pressed flat and is a smooth, lustrous fabric.

Wool plaids and checks are often made with a 2/2 twill weave. They may be made with woolen or worsted yarns; they may be napped or smooth; they are always yarn dyed. They are named according to the arrangement of the colored yarns; for example, shepherd's check, hound's tooth check, Glen plaid.

Zibilene is a heavy coating fabric with a long, shaggy nap laid in one direction. The fabrics sometimes have crosswise ridges caused by a longer nap in those areas.

Index